574
Am35lt

teacher's guide

BSCS GREEN VERSION

AMERICAN INSTITUTE OF BIOLOGICAL SCIENCES
BIOLOGICAL SCIENCES CURRICULUM STUDY · *University of Colorado, Boulder*

RAND McNALLY & COMPANY · *Chicago*

65179

High WITHDRAWN

School

Biology

LIBRARY ST. MARY'S COLLEGE

Copyright © 1964 by AIBS.
All rights reserved. Prepared by BSCS.

Printed and published by Rand McNally & Company.
For permissions and other rights under
this copyright, please contact the publisher.

Made in U.S.A.

THE BSCS WRITERS

Marston Bates, University of Michigan, Ann Arbor: *Supervisor*, 1960–61
C. Haven Kolb, Overlea Senior High School, Baltimore County, Maryland: *Supervisor*, 1961———
Norman B. Abraham, Yuba City Union High School, California
Dean A. Anderson, Los Angeles State College, California
Richard P. Anderson, West High School, Salt Lake City, Utah
Ted Andrews, Kansas State Teachers College, Emporia
Walter Auffenberg, Biological Sciences Curriculum Study, Boulder, Colorado
Richard P. Aulie, Evanston Township High School, Illinois
John Behnke, Ronald Press, New York City
Marjorie Behringer, Alamo Heights High School, San Antonio, Texas
John Bodel, The Hotchkiss School, Lakeville, Connecticut
Rodney Bolin, Wheatridge High School, Colorado
Charles R. Botticelli, Harvard University, Cambridge, Massachusetts
John W. Breukelman, Kansas State Teachers College, Emporia
Donald H. Bucklin, University of Wisconsin, Madison
Peter Buri, San Francisco State College, California
C. Francis Byers, Elmira College, New York
Archie Carr, University of Florida, Gainesville
John Carroll, Pattengill Junior High School, Lansing, Michigan
Edwin H. Colbert, American Museum of Natural History and Columbia University, New York City
John W. Crenshaw, University of Maryland, College Park
Robert A. Daspit, St. Martinville High School, Louisiana
J. Maxwell Davis, William Henry Harrison High School, Evansville, Indiana
Eduardo Del Ponte, University of Buenos Aires, Argentina
Ingrith Deyrup, Barnard College, New York City
Judith Dobkin, Miami Senior High School, Florida
Robert H. Dunk, Berkeley High School, California
Harold Durst, Southeast High School, Wichita, Kansas
Gerald Einem, Melbourne High School, Florida
Frank C. Erk, State University of New York, Long Island Center, Oyster Bay
Chinaka Esiaba, Nigeria
Doris Falk, Fresno State College, California
John G. Farrow, Scarsdale High School, New York
Jack Fishleder, West High School, Phoenix, Arizona
Elena Martínez Fontes, Instituto Nacional del Profesorado Secundario, Buenos Aires, Argentina
Phillip R. Fordyce, Oak Park & River Forest High School, Oak Park, Illinois
Jack Friedman, Syosset High School, New York
O. Frota-Pessoa, UNESCO, Instituto Brasileiro de Educação, Ciencia e Cultura, São Paulo, Brazil
Thomas Furman, U.S. Office of Education, Washington, D.C.
Roberto Galán, Universidad de Los Andes, Bogotá, Colombia
Eugene Gennaro, Wisconsin High School, Madison
Ralph Gerard, University of Michigan, Ann Arbor
Byron Gibbs, Arizona State University, Tempe
Ronald K. Gibbs, Alexander Ramsey High School, St. Paul, Minnesota
Bentley Glass, Johns Hopkins University, Baltimore, Maryland
Donald Glittenberg, Lakewood High School, Colorado
Humberto Gómez, Universidad del Valle, Cali, Colombia
John Gundlach, Neenah High School, Wisconsin
Wesley Hall, Fairview High School, Boulder, Colorado
Robert S. Hamilton, Boulder High School, Colorado
Philip Handler, Duke University, Durham, North Carolina

PAUL DEH. HURD, Stanford University, California
ROJANEE JARUPRAKORN, Bangkok, Thailand
JEWEL JORDAN, Commerce High School, Georgia
PANEE KAOCHARERN (CHIOWANICH), Chulalongkorn University, Bangkok, Thailand
WILSON KISPERT, Cass Technical High School, Detroit, Michigan
EVELYN KLINCKMANN, San Francisco College for Women, California
MYRIAM KRASILCHIK, UNESCO, Instituto Brasileiro de Educação, Ciencia e
    Cultura, C. P. 2921, São Paulo, Brazil
VICTOR LARSEN, JR., Adelphi College, Garden City, New York
M. C. LICHTENWALTER, Wells High School, Chicago, Illinois
MARGARET J. McKIBBEN (LAWLER), Formerly of National Science Teachers
    Association, Washington, D.C.
WILLIAM V. MAYER, Wayne State University, Detroit, Michigan
DE WOLF MERRIAM, Highland Park High School, New Jersey
LORUS J. MILNE, University of New Hampshire, Durham
MARGERY MILNE, Durham, New Hampshire
WILLIAM MILSTEAD, University of Kansas City, Missouri
JOHN A. MOORE, Columbia University, New York City
HUGH MOZINGO, University of Nevada, Reno
ALFRED NOVAK, Stephens College, Columbia, Missouri
RUSSELL C. OAKES, Huntington High School, New York
ELRA M. PALMER, Baltimore City Public Schools, Maryland
ARTHUR PAPENFUS, Golden High School, Colorado
S. M. PATTEE, Jefferson Senior High School, Cedar Rapids, Iowa
PAUL G. PEARSON, Rutgers University, New Brunswick, New Jersey
GLEN E. PETERSON, University of Houston, Texas
GORDON E. PETERSON, San Marino High School, California
DAVIDA PHILLIPS, Hale High School, Tulsa, Oklahoma
EDWIN A. PHILLIPS, Pomona College, Claremont, California
JAMES F. RAGIN, Jack Yates Senior High School, Houston, Texas
FREDERICK A. RASMUSSEN, Chadsey High School, Detroit, Michigan
CLARENCE W. RICE, Eastern High School, Detroit, Michigan
LEON RINTEL, Forest Hills High School, New York City
L. M. ROHRBAUGH, University of Oklahoma, Norman
IMOGENE RUSSELL, Sandia High School, Albuquerque, New Mexico
JOSEPH J. SCHWAB, University of Chicago, Illinois
GEORGE SCHWARTZ, Forest Hills High School, New York City
DALE SMITH, University of Illinois, Urbana
FRANCIS W. SMITH, JR., Los Altos High School, Mountain View, California
RICHARD S. SMITH, Haverford Senior High School, Havertown, Pennsylvania
G. LEDYARD STEBBINS, University of California, Davis
WILSON STEWART, University of Illinois, Urbana
DENNIS STRAWBRIDGE, Michigan State University, East Lansing
ZACHARIAH SUBARSKY, Bronx High School of Science, New York City
GERALD D. TAGUE, Wichita High School East, Kansas
JOYCE B. THOMPSON, San Jacinto College, Pasadena, Texas
JANET TWENTE, University of Utah, Salt Lake City
JOHN TWENTE, University of Utah, Salt Lake City
R. W. VAN NORMAN, University of Utah, Salt Lake City
PAUL A. VESTAL, Rollins College, Winter Park, Florida
HENRY M. WALLBRUNN, University of Florida, Gainesville
ARTHUR C. WALTON, Knox College, Galesburg, Illinois
EDGAR WARREN, South High School, Denver, Colorado
CLAUDE WELCH, Michigan State University, East Lansing
F. W. WENT, Missouri Botanical Gardens, St. Louis

Jonathan Westfall, University of Georgia, Athens
Betty Wislinsky, West High School, Madison, Wisconsin
Robert L. Wistort, High Point High School, Beltsville, Maryland
Harry K. Wong, Menlo-Atherton High School, Atherton, California
J. D. Woolever, Riverview Senior High School, Sarasota, Florida
Delaphine G. R. Wyckoff, Wellesley College, Massachusetts

THE BSCS ARTISTS

Jane Larson, *Illustration Supervisor*
James E. Bramlett
Eugene J. Diodato, Jr.
Clarence W. Gardephe
Margery A. Gardephe
Robert G. Haynes
Orra Irwin
Robert T. Kusserow
William Lewis
Rita Linn
Robert N. Nesby, Jr.

Ross Norris
Barbara Nygren
Raymond S. Orosz
Kent Pendleton
Harry H. Platt
Gardner J. Ryan
T. W. Sielaff
Lawrence Strand
Roy M. Udo
Sarah B. Whitman
Robert F. Wilson

THE BSCS STAFF

Arnold B. Grobman, *Director*
William V. Mayer, Associate Director
Norman B. Abraham, Consultant
Walter Auffenberg, Associate Director (1960–1963)
Nathan Cohen, Photography Editor
Donald D. Cox, Consultant
J. Maxwell Davis, Consultant
Harold Durst, Consultant
Margaret Grant, Editor (1961)
Hulda Grobman, Consultant

Francis C. Harwood, Consultant
Paul DeH. Hurd, Consultant
Evelyn Klinckmann, Consultant
James Koevenig, Consultant
Lorenzo Lisonbee, Consultant
Alfred Novak, Consultant
Gordon E. Peterson, Consultant
John R. Schaefer, Consultant
Joseph J. Schwab, Editor (1960)
George I. Schwartz, Consultant
Margaret Sterling, Business Manager

THE AIBS

James Ebert, *President*
Hiden T. Cox, Executive Director
Gairdner Moment, Chairman, Education Committee
Bentley Glass, Chairman, BSCS

RAND McNALLY

William B. Miller, *Editor, 1962——*
Roberta McAllister, Copy Editor
Gordon Hartshorne, Designer
Ruth N. Coleman, Production Editor
Janice Johnson, Photography Editor
Marcel Godfriaux, Cartographer

COMMITTEES REVIEWING BSCS TEXTS

American Academy of Microbiology: Dr. Perry Wilson (Chairman), University of Wisconsin; Dr. Raymond Doetsch, University of Maryland; Dr. Neal Groman, University of Washington; Dr. Michael J. Pelczar, University of Maryland; Dr. Wayne W. Umbreit, Rutgers University

American Genetic Association: Dr. Ralph Singleton (Chairman), University of Virginia; Dr. F. B. Hutt, Cornell University; Dr. D. T. Morgan, University of Maryland; Dr. Marcus Rhoades, Indiana University

American Physiological Society: Dr. J. R. Brobeck (Chairman), University of Pennsylvania; Dr. Arthur W. Martin, University of Washington; Dr. R. R. Ronkin, University of Delaware

American Phytopathological Society: Dr. C. W. Boothroyd (Chairman), Cornell University; Dr. D. F. Crossan, University of Delaware; Dr. J. Dale, University of Arkansas; Dr. I. W. Deep, Oregon State College; Dr. C. W. Ellett, Ohio State University; Dr. W. .H. English, University of California; Dr. D. W. French, University of Minnesota; Dr. Arthur Kelman, North Carolina State College of Agriculture and Engineering; Dr. J. E. Mitchell, University of Wisconsin; Dr. J. H. Owen, University of Florida; Dr. G. K. Parris, Mississippi State College; Dr. D. W. Rosberg, Agricultural and Mechanical College of Texas; Dr. L. F. Roth, Oregon State College; Dr. Thomas Sproston, University of Vermont; Dr. R. B. Stevens, George Washington University; Dr. R. A. Zabel, Syracuse University

American Psychological Association: Dr. Donald Meyer, Ohio State University; Dr. Carl Pfaffman, Brown University; Dr. Stanley C. Ratner, Michigan State University

American Society for Horticultural Sciences: Dr. O. W. Davidson (Chairman), Rutgers University; Prof. A. F. DeWirth, Agricultural and Mechanical College of Texas; Dr. Russell Eggert, University of New Hampshire

American Society of Human Genetics: Dr. Arthur Steinberg (Chairman), Western Reserve University

American Society for Microbiology: Dr. H. J. Blumenthal (Chairman), University of Michigan Medical School; Mr. Byron Bernard, La Porte High School, La Porte, Indiana; Dr. Arthur R. Colmer, Louisiana State University; Dr. Arnold L. Demain, Merck, Sharp, and Dohme; Dr. S. G. Knight, University of Wisconsin; Dr. L. S. McClung, Indiana University; Dr. W. J. Walter, Montana State College; Dr. E. D. Weinberg, Indiana University

American Society of Parasitologists: Dr. Norman Levine (Chairman), University of Illinois; Dr. David R. Lincicome, Howard University; Dr. O. Wilford Olsen, Colorado A & M College; Dr. Marietta Voge, University of California

American Society of Plant Taxonomists: Dr. C. Ritchie Bell (Chairman), University of North Carolina; Dr. L. Constance, University of California at Berkeley; Dr. Mildred Mathias, University of California at Los Angeles; Dr. J. Proskauer, University of California at Los Angeles; Dr. A. E. Radford, University of North Carolina; Dr. Peter Raven, Rancho Santa Ana Botanic Garden

American Society of Zoologists: Dr. Carl Gans, University of Buffalo; Dr. Clarence Goodnight, Purdue University; Dr. Ronald R. Novales, Northwestern University; Dr. J. Paul Scott, Jackson Memorial Laboratory

Biophysical Society: Dr. Richard S. Bear (Chairman), Boston University; Dr. N. A. Coulter, Jr., Ohio State University

Botanical Society of America: Dr. Adolph Hecht, State College of Washington; Dr. S. N. Postlethwait, Purdue University; Dr. John Thomson, University of Wisconsin

Council for Exceptional Children: Dr. Harry Passow (Chairman), Teachers College, Columbia University; Dr. Louis A. Fleigler, University of Denver; Dr. Virgil S. Ward, University of Virginia

Department of Rural Education: Mr. Fred Guffin, Fulton County Board of Education, Hapeville, Georgia

Ecological Society of America: Dr. Frank Golley (Chairman), University of Georgia; Dr. Paul Johnsgard, University of Nebraska

Entomological Society of America: Dr. Robert V. Travis (Chairman), Garden Pest Control; Mr. George Senechal, Valentine City Schools, Valentine, Nebraska

Genetics Society of America: Dr. David Nanney (Chairman), University of Illinois; Dr. Robert Edgar, California Institute of Technology; Dr. E. S. Russell, Roscoe B. Jackson Memorial Laboratory

National Association of Biology Teachers: Dr. Edward Frankel, Bureau of Educational Research, New York City Board of Education; Mr. William M. Smith, Thomas Carr Howe High School, Indianapolis, Indiana; Mr. Donald Winslow, Indiana University

National Association for Research in Science Teaching: Dr. W. C. VanDeventer (Chairman), Western Michigan College of Education; Dr. Ralph P. Frazier, College of Emporia; Dr. Joseph Novak, Purdue University

National Catholic Education Association: Rev. Mark H. Bauer, S.J. (Chairman), Georgetown University; Brother Bernardine C.F.X., Archbishop Stephinac High School, White Plains, New York; Rev. Donald M. Chigar, Mount Carmel High School, Houston, Texas; Sister Mary Ivo, B.V.M., The Immaculata, Chicago; Sister Julia Marie, O.S.F., Holy Family College, Manitowoc, Wisconsin; Rev. George A. Walsh, O.S.F.S., Cathedral Prep, Erie, Pennsylvania

National Science Teachers Association: Dr. Darwin Levine (Chairman), New York City Board of Education; Mrs. Leona Adler, New York University; Mr. Thomas Lawrence, Erasmus Hall High School, Brooklyn; Mr. Kenneth Meyer, Harrison, New York; Mr. Jesse Miller, Manhasset Public Schools, Long Island; Mr. Robert Weinberger, Flushing High School, New York

Poultry Science Association: Dr. Walter C. Morgan (Chairman), South Dakota State College; Dr. D. W. MacLaury, University of Kentucky; Dr. George D. Quigley, University of Maryland; Dr. E. A. Shano, Cornell University; Dr. D. W. Talmage, University of Connecticut.

Society of General Physiology: Dr. R. R. Ronkin (Chairman), University of Delaware

Society for Industrial Microbiology: Dr. John N. Porter (Chairman), Lederle Laboratories; Dr. Marlin A. Espenshade, Wyeth Laboratories, Inc.; Dr. B. Malin, Eli Lilly and Company

Society for the Study of Evolution: Dr. John S. Mecham (Chairman), Auburn University; Dr. David J. Merrell, University of Minnesota; Dr. Robert Sokal, University of Kansas; Dr. Robert K. Vickery, University of Utah

Society for the Study of Growth and Development: Dr. Arthur Galston (Chairman), Yale University; Dr. Robert L. DeHaan, Carnegie Institute of Washington

INDIVIDUAL REVIEWERS OF THE GREEN VERSION

Dr. Daniel Arnon, University of California

Mr. John A. Behnke, Ronald Press, New York

Mr. Wilbur Pieter Bijhouwer, Chicago, Illinois

Dr. W. D. Billings, Duke University

Dr. Robert E. Bills, University of Alabama

Dr. Harold C. Bold, University of Texas

Mr. Ernest C. Borden, Phillips Exeter Academy

Dr. J. K. Brierley, British Ministry of Education

Dr. Ralph Buchsbaum, University of Pittsburgh

Dr. J. A. Campbell, Chemical Education Material Study

Mr. L. C. Comber, British Embassy

Dr. Henry S. Conard, Grinnell College

Dr. David E. Davis, Pennsylvania State University

Dr. R. F. Dawson, Columbia University

Dr. Fred D. Emerson, Elon College

Miss Janice B. Footlik, Peoria, Illinois

Mr. S. E. Frederick, Denver, Colorado

Dr. Shelby Gerking, Indiana University

Dr. Ira Gordon, University of Florida

Dr. Victor A. Greulach, University of North Carolina

Dr. Earl D. Hanson, Wesleyan University

Dr. Rollin D. Hotchkiss, The Rockefeller Institute

Dr. S. Charles Kendeigh, University of Illinois

Dr. Harlan Lewis, University of California

Professor James W. McFarland, Air Force Academy

Dr. Lindsay Olive, Columbia University

Dr. Leonard Ornstein, The Mount Sinai Hospital

Dr. Ray F. Smith, University of California

Dr. Carl P. Swanson, Johns Hopkins University

Dr. Kenneth V. Thimann, Harvard Biological Laboratories

Dr. Ruth B. Thomas, Eastern New Mexico University

Dr. R. A. R. Tricker, Staff Inspector for Science, Great Britain

Dr. Jacob Uhrich, Trinity University

Dr. Wayne W. Umbreit, Rutgers University

Dr. Kenneth Wells, University of California

Mr. F. Wing, Carl Sandburg High School, Orland Park, Illinois

Dr. Orville Wyss, University of Texas

FOREWORD

With each new generation our fund of scientific knowledge increases five-fold; this remarkable growth indicates, in part, why there has been wide-spread dissatisfaction with the content and methods of science courses in our schools. The American Institute of Biological Sciences, a professional society representing 85,000 biologists, has become very sensitive to this situation. In January, 1959, the AIBS established the Biological Sciences Curriculum Study as a means of contributing to the improvement of secondary school biological education. For the purposes of formulating basic policy there was organized a BSCS Steering Committee, composed of college biologists, high school biology teachers, and other educators—all interested in improving the quality of the teaching of biology. Head-quarters for their study was established on the campus of the University of Colorado. Primary financial support for the Biological Sciences Cur-riculum Study has been provided by the National Science Foundation.

During the summer of 1960, the BSCS assembled a group of 70 high school biology teachers and university research biologists to prepare trial materials for a general biology course. The books produced were used in approximately 100 high schools throughout the country. On the basis of this classroom experience, the materials were thoroughly revised during the summer of 1961. They were then used in 500 schools during the 1961–62 academic year and in 950 schools the following year. A final, thorough revision of the materials was completed early in 1963—again based on responses from testing teachers. The books now available reflect this extensive experience with trial editions over several years. The BSCS appreciates the singularly important contributions to the improvement of biological education made by over 1000 teachers and 150,000 students through their use of the trial materials.

Perhaps the most significant feature in the development of the BSCS texts has been the fruitful coöperation between research biologists, on the frontiers of science, and high school teachers, on the frontiers of teaching.

There does not seem to be a single "best way" of presenting biology to the diversity of American secondary school students. Therefore, the BSCS has designed a variety of approaches to the study of high school biology. In all approaches, however, the primary emphasis has been on investigation and inquiry as means of acquiring significant knowledge in science. Also, the task of weaving modern biology into the new instructional materials without neglecting the wisdom of earlier scholars dictated that only selected current developments should be covered in depth. The materials that have resulted from this work are designed for all students in American high schools—regardless of aptitudes or career goals—and they can be studied at a level of sophistication that was heretofore thought completely unrealistic. Taken together, the BSCS publications comprise a series of balanced and enriched programs—not merely a set of independent books and films.

The BSCS writing conferences have produced three versions of a modern basic course in biological science for secondary school students. Each version consists of a basic text, student's manual, teacher's guide, handbook, and tests. Each version has its own flavor and thematic approach. The rationale of the *Green Version* is fully presented in the "Introduction" and "Part One" of this guide.

The BSCS has initiated other projects intended to improve biological education in the high school. Some of the other BSCS publications are listed on page i. For information about these programs, interested persons may write to the Director, AIBS Biological Sciences Curriculum Study, University of Colorado, Boulder, Colorado.

Hundreds of the nation's biological scientists and teachers have worked diligently on BSCS materials; we hope that high school students and their teachers will continue to find their efforts of value.

BENTLEY GLASS, *Chairman*
Baltimore, Maryland

ARNOLD B. GROBMAN, *Director*
Boulder, Colorado

February 1, 1963

PREFACE

For four years the team charged by the Biological Sciences Curriculum Study with the development of the *Green Version* has had the advice and assistance of high school biology teachers, college biology teachers, research biologists, psychologists, and many others. The team hopes that this magnificent example of academic coöperation will be perpetuated. Curriculum evaluation, curriculum development, curriculum revision, can never safely cease. Every student, every teacher, every reviewer of the educational program, is invited to contribute to the obsolescence of these materials.

But the team would like to keep abreast of the tide of change. Criticisms, comments, and calumnies may be addressed either to the Biological Sciences Curriculum Study, University of Colorado, Boulder, or to the publisher.

HAVEN KOLB, *Supervisor*
HAROLD DURST
VICTOR LARSEN
WILLIAM MILLER
ELRA PALMER
JONATHAN WESTFALL

Baltimore, Maryland
February 1, 1963

CONTENTS

Introduction

The current revolution in secondary school science education has resulted not only in the publication of textbooks and
laboratory manuals; it has blazed a pathway for more effective
and efficient teaching. It has united the efforts of research
scientists, collegiate and high school science teachers, and
professional educators. It has brought into sharp focus the
objectives of science-teaching.

For most teachers the changes implicit in this revolution
demand a reorientation of teaching with respect both to major
viewpoints and to specific daily practices. Yet, as in all rev-
olutions, the roots of this reorientation have long existed. The
practices of good teachers—usually isolated and often hampered
by discouraging circumstances—have provided the meristems for
change in the science curriculum. Now these practices of ex-
cellence, gathered from a diversity of situations and directed
toward educational objectives appropriate to the modern world,
are presented for the use of all teachers and for the consideration of administrators, who must determine the educational
climate of the future.

The purpose of this guide is to provide each teacher with
materials for initiating his own reorientation—great or small—
in the teaching of biology. The materials in it, like those in the
textbook and student's manual, have been developed in the course
of the most extensive and intensive classroom-testing ever given
any curricular program in the history of American education.
Before work on the present edition began, this program had been
used by 500 teachers and 65,000 pupils in 1600 classes. Most of
the teachers submitted weekly, detailed reports, which have been
the basis for two thorough revisions of the textbook and the
student's manual. From these weekly reports also have come
the notes, cautions, and suggestions embodied in this guide. Thus,
this program has a unique validation.

But careful use of day-to-day advice does not guarantee a
successful reorientation of instruction. The ultimate factor in
teaching-learning endeavors is the truly professional teacher—
enthusiastic, skillful, and learned. Such a teacher will not begin
the daily task without first understanding the framework within
which it is to be performed.

Therefore, Part One of this guide begins with a general statement of the philosophy of the Biological Sciences Curriculum Study and of the points of view that are particularly stressed in the Green Version. Then, against this background, it presents overviews of the textbook's content and of the laboratory work. Part Two deals with specific teaching problems associated with each chapter and exercise.

PART **1**

THE COURSE:
GENERAL CONSIDERATIONS

The BSCS

The determination of educational objectives is a creative and continuing process. In all fields, objectives need to be reconsidered from time to time. In the field of science, such reconsideration has long been past due. Not only is science itself changing at an accelerating rate, but its relation to society has altered significantly in a period during which educational objectives have only slowly shifted. This disparity was already clear to a few scientists and to some educators when Sputnik I suddenly brought the general public to an intense but confused awareness of difficulty.

Biological science plays a crucial role in the determination of objectives in science education because biology touches more students at the high school level than does any other science. Realization of this fact has been paramount in the attempt of the Biological Sciences Curriculum Study to bring about changes in biology-teaching. For a large proportion of students, the objectives of science education will be the objectives of their high school biology course, since they will receive no further formal instruction in science after they leave the biology classroom.

OBJECTIVES

Early in the history of the BSCS, attention was directed to objectives. To provide a background, Dr. Paul Hurd studied

the history of biology-teaching in the United States.[1] On the
basis of this study, and after deep consideration of the present
state of science, society, and the American educational system,
in the summer of 1960 the Committee on the Content of the
Curriculum, under the chairmanship of Dr. John Moore of
Columbia University, formulated objectives that guided the
initial development of the BSCS curricular materials. Through
succeeding revisions these objectives have been refined and
restated. Any effective use of BSCS materials requires that
they be kept in mind. In abbreviated form (and rearranged
for present purposes) they are:

1. An understanding of the diversity of life and of the
    interrelations of all organisms.
2. An understanding of the nature of scientific inquiry:
    Science is an open-ended intellectual activity, and
    what is presently "known" or believed is subject to
    change at any time.
3. An understanding of the limitations of science and of
    the scientific method: Many problems, some of the
    greatest importance, cannot be dealt with scientifically.
4. An understanding of the biological basis of problems
    in medicine, public health, agriculture, and
    conservation.
5. An appreciation of the beauty, drama, and tragedy of
    the living world.
6. An understanding of the historical development of the
    concepts of biology and their dependence on the nature
    of the society and technology of each age.
7. An understanding of what biologists presently know
    regarding the basic biological problems of evolution,
    development, and inheritance.
8. An understanding of man's own place in the scheme of
    nature; namely, that he is a living organism, that he
    has much in common with other organisms, and that
    he interacts with all organisms in the biological system
    of the earth.

Anyone familiar with curricular statements will recognize
many of these objectives. In themselves they are not revolu-
tionary. As with teaching methods, the BSCS has not so much
invented new things as it has distilled the best from current
practice and synthesized a new blend. What has been discarded
is as significant as what has been retained. And the presence

---

[1]Hurd, Paul deHart. Biological Education in American
Secondary Schools, 1890-1960. Boulder, Colo.: Biological
Sciences Curriculum Study, 1961.

of Items 2 and 3—rare in statements of objectives a decade ago—
must be noted. But, of course, to state objectives is often only
a pleasant pastime; the task in the summer of 1960 was to im-
plement the objectives in courses.

CONTENT

The content of biology is vast. Much thought was given by
the Committee on the Content of the Curriculum and by the whole
BSCS Steering Committee to subject matter that would constitute
the best biology courses for the tenth grade. Naturally, there
have been differences of opinion on points of emphasis. The
three versions of the BSCS materials reflect some of these differences. But all the BSCS versions have been built around
nine themes:
1. Change of Living Things through Time: Evolution
2. Diversity of Type and Unity of Pattern in Living Things
3. The Genetic Continuity of Life
4. The Complementarity of Organism and Environment
5. The Biological Roots of Behavior
6. The Complementarity of Structure and Function
7. Regulation and Homeostasis: Preservation of Life
   in the Face of Change
8. Science as Enquiry
9. The History of Biological Conceptions
Obviously, these themes do not present a scheme of organization. Rather, they are threads of thought that ought to
run through any organization of biological subject matter. At
one point in the organization, one theme may predominate; at
some other point, another. But each should at least be in the
background at all times. And all should permeate the efforts
of the teacher. The prospective BSCS teacher should become
familiar with them. An elaboration of the themes appears in
Chapter 3 of the BSCS Biology Teacher's Handbook (New York:
John Wiley and Sons, Inc., 1963).
Except for development of the themes, the BSCS committees
left selection of content to the teams designing the three versions: Blue (biochemical), Green (ecological), and Yellow (de-
velopmental). Despite the differences in approach and the sharp
divergence in the backgrounds, attitudes, and temperaments of
the writers, the content that has been incorporated into the
three versions shows a high degree of overlap. But in all BSCS
versions the content differs considerably from the content in
other commercially published courses (see Handbook, pages
13-18).

This guide does not replace the <u>Handbook</u>. It is the task of the <u>Handbook</u> to elaborate upon the history and implications of the revolution in biology-teaching and to provide materials for the development of classroom skills appropriate to BSCS views. It is the task of this guide to deal specifically with the materials of the <u>Green</u> <u>Version</u>, and its authors assume that the teacher has derived orientation from the <u>Handbook</u>.

The *Green Version*

Within the framework of the BSCS, the <u>Green Version</u> has been developed on the basis of the following facts: (a) The great majority of ninth- or tenth-grade students take biology. (b) A large number of these students will take no more science in school. (c) Very few will become research biologists, and only a slightly larger proportion will enter the biological professions. (d) All are potential voting citizens.

AIMS

To the writers of the <u>Green Version</u>, these facts mean that the high school biology course should encourage a scientific viewpoint in the student and provide him with a background in biology that is as advanced as the fifteen-to-sixteen-year-old mind will permit. Subject matter should be selected to increase his effectiveness as a future citizen. A course that does these things will serve the interests of all. It will be of value to the filling-station attendant, the housewife, the physician, the biochemist.

Therefore, the aims of the <u>Green Version</u> are to interest the student in the living world, to direct him toward some appreciation of the points of view and working techniques of

scientists, and to provide information that may be useful to
him as a human being and as a citizen. The writers believe
that secondary school science should be presented as an aspect
of the humanities. If, in some cases, a secondary school
course arouses the student to pursue further biological studies,
fine—but this should be an incidental rather than a primary
aim. The high school is not the place to begin the training of
biological scientists.

The ecological aspects of biology have been neglected in high
school teaching, and this is unfortunate. An understanding
of the way in which the biological community functions is at
least as important as an understanding of the way one's own
body functions. The problems created by increasing human
populations, by depletion of resources, by pollution, and the
like, are (in part at least) ecological problems. All require
intelligent community or governmental action for solution;
therefore, in a democracy every citizen should have some
awareness of their significance.

These views have been maintained steadily in the Green
Version since its inception. In the first draft of the text (1960),
Dr. Marston Bates wrote:

"The word 'ecology' was proposed by Ernst Haeckel in 1870
to cover what he called 'outer physiology.' It is the point
of view in biology that takes the individual organism as the
primary unit of study, and is concerned with how these
individuals are organized into populations, species, and
communities; with what organisms do and how they do it.

"This contrasts with 'inner physiology,' the study of
how the individual is constructed and how the parts work.
Obviously the inside and outside of the organism are completely interdependent, and one cannot be understood without
constant reference to the other. The division is arbitrary,
but so are all of the ways in which biological subject matter
might be split. We stress the outside rather than the inside
on the assumption that this is more familiar and more
easily understood. We believe, too, that it is more important for the citizen, who must participate in decisions
about urban development, flood control, public health,
conservation—always as a voter and sometimes as a member of the town council or state legislature.

"For disorders of inner physiology the citizen should
consult his physician. But there is no specialist for outer
physiology, for disorders of the human biological community. Here each citizen shares responsibility, and
biological knowledge is greatly needed for some kinds of
decisions."

After three years of successful testing in the classroom, these considerations remain the foundation of the Green Version. They explain what is included and what is excluded. They explain the manner as well as the matter. Whoever undertakes to use the Green Version in his teaching must understand this position.

The BSCS Steering Committee instructed the writers to design courses suitable for the middle 60 percent in the range of interest and ability found among tenth-grade students. This charge has been conscientiously carried out. The Green Version may dismay the poorer students (the lowest 20 percent), though experience since 1960 has shown that they learn as much from it as from conventional courses—and seem happier in doing so. (This last may well be a result of the great emphasis placed upon direct observation and investigation in BSCS courses as opposed to "reading" courses.) No classroom course will completely satisfy the needs of the better students (the uppermost 20 percent). However, by wise use of the "Problems" and "Suggested Readings" appended to each text chapter and of the suggestions "For Further Investigation" following many of the exercises in the student's manual, the teacher of the Green Version may carry the better students beyond the classroom and into other BSCS materials. (See, for example, the more sophisticated "invitations to Enquiry" in the Biology Teacher's Handbook, and Research Problems in Biology: Investigations for Students [New York: Doubleday & Co., Inc., 1963].)

SOME POINTS OF VIEW

This guide concerns a complete course, not just a textbook or a lab manual. The text is written in a manner that requires the laboratory work for full interpretation—indeed, the text may seem enigmatic at times without the background of the laboratory. On the other hand, a year devoted entirely to laboratory work could give only a most episodic view of biology. Laboratory work is stressed at points in the course where firsthand experience is most pertinent, most feasible, and most efficient in the utilization of student time.

"Laboratory" has been interpreted broadly. The laboratory is where the work of the scientist is done; it need not be bounded by four walls. Moreover, some of the exercises in the student's manual involve much reasoning and little or no doing. These also may be legitimately regarded as laboratory activities. Conversely, there is very little of what the student

(and, perhaps, the teacher) may be used to thinking of as biological laboratory work—the sterile repetition of activities that
excited Agassiz's students a century ago but serve only to re-
strict the modern student's views of biological science.

This course rejects the unit organization so prevalent for
thirty years past—and paradoxically, it does so in order to
unify. In practice, the unit organization tends to compart-
mentalize—though such was certainly not the original aim. In
practice, the student takes the unit test, breathes a sigh of
relief, and murmurs, "Now I can forget all that; tomorrow we
start a new unit." And too often he has been quite correct.

The writers of the Green Version intend to give the student
no relief at any time from the healthy tension of learning. The
course is designed to build up ideas from beginning to end. Everywhere an effort is made to relate what is immediately in front
of the student with what has preceded—and with what the student
may be reasonably expected to know. At the end, the course
returns to the beginning—like the Chinese dragon with its tail
in its mouth—and relates all aspects of the course to a biologi—
cal world view.

In the tenth grade we are not teaching children, and we
are not teaching adults. Teachers who regard tenth graders
as children may be appalled by the degree of mental sophistication demanded in this course, by the lack of clear-cut definition, by the emphasis on chiaroscuro rather than on the
black-and-white thought patterns whose beautiful simplicity we
have absorbed from our Greco-Hebraic heritage. On the other
hand, teachers who ignore the difference between the adolescent
and the adult may be scornful of the control of running vocabulary, the attention to development of ideas, the paucity of
esoteric detail. But of all teachers, biology teachers ought
best to know that Homo sapiens of fifteen or sixteen years,
while in statu parentis in posse (and, indeed, occasionally in
esse), still has not cut all his third molars.

Long antedating the Iron Curtain, a "Mensural Screen"
has divided the nations of the world into two camps. Even
within nations this screen has divided brother from brother,
scientist from engineer. It has long been apparent that for
one camp the tide is running out, slowly but inexorably;
economics, not science, is the "moon" in this affair.

In high school science it has been customary to talk about
the metric system, to spend much time converting units from
system to system, to express quantities in metric units during
some laboratory procedures. But consistent use of the metric
system has usually been lacking, and students have gained the
impression that it is of ritualistic importance only—on a par
with academic gowns and Old Church Slavonic.

In the Green Version the metric system is used throughout.
For explicatory purposes, equivalents are sometimes given;
for designating a few pieces of equipment, sizes are expressed
in British units. However, no exercises on conversion of units
are offered. In this, a modern principle of language-teaching
has been followed: "The word to the object, not to another
word." We want the student to use centimeter measurements
so frequently that he will have a mental image of 10 centimeters, not a recollection of "about 4 inches."

THE TEXT: AN OVERVIEW

Before specific suggestions for teaching can be meaningful, the teacher must be acquainted with the organization of
the course, with the variations in organization that experience
has shown to be feasible, and with the teaching aids supplied
in text and student's manual. This section is intended to provide such general background with respect to the text.[2]

Organization

The organization of the text is the organization of the
course. The text is divided into twenty chapters (grouped in
six sections) and an appendix. Sections and chapters are of
unequal lengths, but the number of pages devoted to a topic is
not necessarily an indication of that topic's relative importance or of the amount of time to be spent upon it. In general,
the first three sections are discursive, with a rather low density of ideas. The last three are more compact, with an increasing load of ideas per page.

Section One
"THE WORLD OF LIFE: THE BIOSPHERE"

It is the whole individual organism with which the
student has had experience—he is one himself. Therefore,

---

[2] The material beginning on page 25 provides similar background for the manual.

the course begins with the individual and treats the ways in
which such biological units interact.

Chapter 1: "The Web of Life." The introductory chapter
is designed chiefly to lay some groundwork, to establish the
direction of the course. The interdependence of plants, animals, and protists in the transfer of energy and in the cy-
cling of matter; the interdependence of the living system and
the physical environment: These things will never be stated
again quite so baldly and simply, but they will persist in the
background throughout the course. "Scientific method" is not
preached extensively in the text; instead, the laboratory work
is relied upon to introduce such basic matters as observation,
measurement, experimentation, instrumentation.

Chapter 2: "Individuals and Populations." The units of
ecological study form a series—from the individual (the most
concrete) to the ecosystem (the most abstract). This chapter
deals with individuals and the various groupings of individuals
that can be called populations. The concept of a population
is very useful in biology, and it will keep turning up: species
populations form the basis of classification in Section Two;
contemporary genetic and evolutionary theory, dealt with
later in the book, turn largely on population studies.

Chapter 3: "Communities and Ecosystems." The actual
field study of a community—even the community in a crack in
a city sidewalk—is essential to this chapter. Since the
communities available for study will differ greatly among
schools, a brief description of a community is provided as a
basis for comparison. Much of the textbook material is concerned with the kinds of ecological relationships that exist in
communities. Finally, the concept of an ecosystem—the
biotic community and all the abiotic environmental conditions
that affect it—is introduced.

Section Two
"DIVERSITY AMONG LIVING THINGS"

The student should have some idea of the diversity of
organisms and of their classification before going further
into the patterns of ecological organization. But there is no
need for a "type study" of living things. Emphasis is on the
variety of forms in which life can occur and on those aspects
of form and function that are relevant to a useful and meaningful organization of such diversity.

Chapter 4: "Animals." On the principle of starting with
the familiar, the chapter begins with mammals. This, of
course, makes for difficulties. But the idea that a sponge or
a coelenterate is "simple" or "primitive" can be misleading,
and at this point there is no basis for a meaningful discussion
of phylogeny, anyway. Instead, diversity of form within the
animal kingdom is stressed. But this diversity is not endless;
patterns are discernible. And the theory of evolution is offered
as a possible explanation for the apparent order within the
general diversity.

Chapter 5: "Plants." Plants are treated in the same
general way that animals were in Chapter 4. The concept of
a classification scheme does not need repetition, but another
abstract idea is developed—that of nomenclature. Historically, nomenclature and classification have developed together, but this is not sufficient pedagogical reason for presenting
them to the student together. Objects can be classified without being named, and vice versa. Considerable experience
has suggested that these concepts are better understood when
they are presented to the student separately rather than as a
single large block of abstract material.

Chapter 6: "Protists." The teacher may not agree with
the system of kingdoms that has been used in the text or with
the way particular groups have been assigned to these kingdoms. The authors did not agree among themselves. But
some standard of classification was needed. The classification used by Simpson, Pittendrigh, and Tiffany in Life: An
Introduction to Biology was decided upon, just as you might
decide to use some particular dictionary as your standard for
spelling. If the teacher disagrees with this particular system,
pointing out the reasons for disagreement ought to give students
an idea of the nature of the problem. Obviously, there is no
classification on which all biologists agree.

Section Three
"PATTERNS IN THE BIOSPHERE"

In Section One the organization of communities was
developed. Now a world viewpoint is adopted. There are
three bases on which patterns of distribution may be constructed: ecological, historical, and biogeographical. Each
of these is used in turn.

Chapter 7: "Patterns of Life in the Microscopic World."
A number of laboratory exercises involving microorganisms
have been started during the work on Chapter 6; therefore, to

facilitate continuity of laboratory procedures it seems convenient to begin this section with ecological groupings of microorganisms. These groupings are essentially independent of
the pattern schemes developed in the following chapters.

Chapter 8: "Patterns of Life on Land. " The theme here
is the ecological distribution of macroscopic organisms. The
relation of physiological tolerances to the global distribution
of abiotic environmental factors adds up to an ordered world-
view—the kind of view that contributes to "liberal education"
in the old sense of the term. Of course it is necessary for each
teacher to expand on the characteristics of the biome in which
his school is located.

Chapter 9: "Patterns of Life in the Water. " From Chapter
8 the student has an idea of the principles of ecological
distribution, so the extension of these to the aquatic environment is easy. Ponds are everywhere, and they are probably
more easily visualized as ecological systems than any other
part of the biosphere. If the school is near the seacoast, the
latter part of this chapter holds special interest. But if the
school is inland, it seems equally desirable that the student
obtain some idea of marine life—which is certain to become
increasingly important as a resource for man.

Chapter 10: "Patterns of Life in the Past. " From this
chapter the student should get an idea of the sweep of biological events through time, of the continuity of life processes,
and of the time dimension of ecological relationships. This is
not the chapter on evolution. It is, however, important in
building up one phase of the evolutionary concept and in presenting the fossil evidence.

Chapter 11: "The Geography of Life. " Many curious
patterns of geographical distribution make sense only in terms
of evolution; the discussion of geographical distribution in
The Origin of Species was fundamental to Darwin's argument.
Most of the cases cited in this chapter involve mammals,
because mammalian examples are likely to be most familiar
to students. But the teacher with special interest or knowledge
can easily supplement the text.

Section Four
"WITHIN THE INDIVIDUAL ORGANISM"

Having devoted several months of the school year to the
supra-individual levels of biological organization, the student
now turns attention to the infra-individual levels. Tradition-

ally, in the general biology course the latter have been magnified far out of proportion to their lasting value for the
learner. But some acquaintance with "inner physiology" is
essential—not only for appreciation of the growing points of
modern biology but also for developing topics, such as "Genetics"
and "Evolution," that are important parts of the biological
understanding required for the functioning citizen.

Chapter 12: "The Cell." One of the principal characteristics of the BSCS Green Version is the late introduction
of the cell. But there is no need to make a fetish of this.
If, happily, students arrive from junior high school already
bearing some acquaintance with the cell, then the teacher may
freely use the term earlier in the course if it seems to improve
the flow of ideas—but let the teacher beware lest it impede
the flow of ideas. The objective of this necessarily long
chapter is to provide the student with the basic understanding
of cellular structure and function needed to interpret subsequent chapters. Energy flow in the living system has been
a fundamental idea from the beginning of the course, so
attention is focused on energy-release and energy-storage
in the cell.

Chapter 13: "The Functioning Plant." In a discussion of
the physiology of multicellular plants, photosynthesis is of
primary importance because of its key role in the energy
scheme of the biosphere. The biochemistry of photosynthesis
is used to illustrate the fundamental importance—and complexity—of biochemical research. The remainder of the chapter
concerns the structure and function of those plants with which
the student comes in contact most frequently--the vascular
plants.

Chapter 14: "The Functioning Animal." This chapter is
not an abbreviation of Gray's Anatomy. If the rest of the
Green Version is presented adequately, time limitations alone
demand considerable cutting of traditionalism here. It is
hoped that students will recall from previous years much of
the gross anatomy of mammalian systems. The chapter's
theme is the variety of ways in which fundamental problems
of animal function are "solved" in different animal groups.

Chapter 15: "Reproduction." Because reproduction is
not essential to the welfare of the individual organism, it is
treated separately from other life processes, and in a different
way. Thus, while attention to "inner physiology" still dominates,
there is a turning outward again, to the population.

Chapter 16: "Heredity." It is difficult to overestimate
the importance of genetics in biology, but balance in the biology
course demands that genetics not be allowed to get out of hand.
The topic is developed historically, and from this development some ideas concerning the logic of evidence are de-

rived. Mathematics is not shunned, but by suitable choice of laboratory exercises it can be either minimized or maximized.

Section Five
"ADAPTATION"

The swing "outward," which began in Chapter 15 and was prominent in Chapter 16, is now complete. Adaptation is, of course, not a new idea at this point. It is to be interpreted broadly—as the yoke for the two rather diverse but essential chapters of this section.

Chapter 17: "Genetic Adaptation: Evolution." The entire course—indeed, any biology course—can be regarded as a summary of the evidence for evolution. The main objective here, then, is not to give the evidence for evolution—that has already been done in several ways, both implicit and explicit; instead, the chief aim is to give the student some idea of how evolution works, the mechanism of evolution. Darwin is presented as one who provided an explanation of how evolution operates, not as the originator of evolution as a concept.

Chapter 18: "Individual Adaptation: Behavior." The text avoids defining "behavior," just as it has avoided defining "life." There is good precedent. In the course of preparing the volume Behavior and Evolution (Yale University Press; Ann Roe and G. G. Simpson, eds.), a committee decided that the best policy was to avoid any attempt at defining "behavior"; to the Green Version writers it seemed possible that this policy might be advisable at the tenth-grade level, too. The big problem has been selection of topics. Topics have been chosen that seem to be stimulating, important, and fairly readily understood at ninth- and tenth-grade levels. There is no use in giving the impression that the study of animal behavior is in a nice settled state—though equally, there is no point to involving high school students in the basic controversies about it.

Section Six
"MAN AND THE BIOSPHERE"

Textbook-writing biologists seem to be divided into two camps, the pro- and the anti-humans. The "pros" use man all through the book as the type animal. The "antis" avoid him completely. The Green Version tries to steer a middle course, using man as an example whenever convenient in ecological, physiological, or anatomical discussion. One of the purposes of high school biology is to put man in perspective with the rest of nature. But we are human, and biology is surely one of the humanities. So here, at the end of the course, it seems a good idea to focus explicitly on man.

Chapter 19: "The Human Animal." Here are discussed some ways in which man differs anatomically and physiologically from fellow organisms. Since much of man's distinctiveness is behavioral rather than physiological or anatomical, the chapter inevitably becomes involved in borderline areas: between anthropology and biology, between sociology and biology. But the high school is no place for the purism of disciplines.

Chapter 20: "Man in the Web of Life." The authors hope they have woven the whole course together in this chapter. The student is confronted with topics that will concern him in the future as a citizen—topics for which biological information has some relevance. These topics, of course, all go beyond biology; the primary aim is to provoke the student into continuing to think about them.

In summary, the Green Version is not intended to provide an encyclopedic account of biology. Many topics are omitted; many are treated cursorily. The course is a tool for the good teacher. It provides no comfort to the administrator seeking a cheap substitute for a prepared, adept teacher and an equipped and spacious laboratory.

Organizational Alternatives

The material in the text has been organized so that vocabulary and concepts are sequential and accumulative. If this organization is followed, the teacher is freed from problems of extemporaneous course design—problems that are expensive of time when encyclopedic texts are used. More time can then be put into the tasks of actual teaching, especially the time-consuming organization and supervision of laboratory work, which are sine qua non for BSCS courses. Nevertheless, it is recognized that every wise teacher will look for adaptations to enhance the instructional opportunities available in his own situation or inherent in his own resources.

One of the most pressing problems in biology-teaching is the seasonal availability of materials. Using greenhouses, aquariums, and refrigerators can do much to circumvent this problem, but such use cannot entirely eliminate it. Locale, weather, class schedules, and other factors may create the need for a change in chapter sequence. For example, in some localities the field and laboratory work provided for Chapter 9 may make it desirable to postpone study of that chapter until spring. The chapter can then reintroduce outdoor aspects of biology, perhaps at the end of Section Four or even at the end of Section Five.

For various reasons it may seem desirable to omit or to treat lightly certain portions of the course. If the teacher uses a BSCS laboratory block,[3] some omission will certainly be necessary. In this case the portion to be omitted will depend upon the nature of the block that is used. For example, if the Animal Growth and Development block is used, Chapter 15 would be omitted or used as collateral reading. If the block Microbes: Their Growth, Nutrition, and Interaction is used, Chapters 6 and 7 would be omitted or used as collateral reading.

If the school year is simply too short for study of the entire textbook, it is recommended that Chapter 11 be considered the most expendable. Chapter 9 might also be dropped, since it involves no major principles beyond those developed in Chapter 8. In some school systems tenth-grade students have already gained considerable knowledge of the history of life; under such circumstances Chapter 10 might be omitted. However, whenever possible, these three chapters should at least be assigned as reading, with brief class discussion to follow.

In any case it must be emphasized that Sections One and Six are indispensable to the philosophy of the Green Version. If the teacher is disposed to omit them, then he is unconvinced by the arguments presented on pages 8-10 and would do better to choose some other course.

It is very easy to allow a course to fray out and expire merely by reason of the arrival of the term's last day. This must never happen with the Green Version. In the last chapter an attempt is made to bring the whole course into focus. Here are posed those biological problems man must face if he is to continue his existence on this planet and to venture forth into space. So that the teacher may put his laboratory in order, take his inventories, and close out the laboratory accounts while classes continue to meet, no laboratory activities are proposed for Chapter 20. The teacher is strongly urged—no matter where he may be in the course, no matter what his route through the course may have been— to reserve a few days at the end of the school year for dis-cussion of the last chapter.

---

[3] BSCS Laboratory Blocks, published by D. C. Heath & Company, Boston, 1963.

Teaching Resources in the Textbook

Every teacher has his own ways of using a textbook.
Because the Green Version has aims that are rather different
from those of conventional courses, the organization and style
of its textbook are rather different, too. Therefore, some
modification in conventional methods may be in order. General
suggestions for reading BSCS texts are given in Chapter 15 of
the Biology Teacher's Handbook.

Tenth-grade students do not automatically recognize the
uses of textual apparatus; the wise teacher will therefore devote a little time to familiarizing students with the textbook.
But first, of course, he himself will have to investigate its
resources. The following paragraphs discuss the intentions of
the authors. No doubt teachers will find many other ways to
use the text materials.

Section introductions. The several paragraphs introducing
each of the six sections are not informational. Rather, they
set the stage, present a viewpoint, relate the section to the whole
of the course.

Headings. One of the principal differences between good
and poor students, both in high school and in college, lies in
their use of textbook headings. Poor students plod through
printed matter, oblivious to organization; good students make
full use of the authors' typographical attempts to display the
relationships between ideas. Teachers can point at least some
poor students toward a higher degree of reading comprehension
merely by stressing the utility of headings.

Within chapters the Green Version text employs headings
in four orders: Boldface capitals set flush to the left margin
distinguish major chapter divisions. For example:

RABBITS AND RASPBERRIES

In some chapters there may be no further subdivision. Second-
order headings are set as indented, thinner capitals, thus:

ENERGY IN THE CELL

Boldface type run into the beginning of a paragraph dis-
tinguishes third-order heads:

Osmosis. Water molecules, of course, behave in the
same way that our hypothetical substance X does, but . . . .

In a few chapters centered small capitals are employed as
headings, thus:

SOIL ORGANISMS

These are intermediate between second- and third-order
headings and are used only where the chapter organization is
more complex than usual.

Italics. Within paragraphs, italics are used for two purposes:
(1) they indicate the first occurrence of technical (biological) terms, or (2) they indicate an emphasis. They are used
for the second purpose sparingly.

Vocabulary. In any science textbook, vocabulary is of two
kinds: technical and running. Technical vocabulary is part of
the course content because ideas cannot be divorced from terms.
But the learning of terminology is not a proper aim of science-
teaching; it is a means only.

High school biology has been particularly subject to
criticism for its high density of technical terms. In the Green
Version considerable effort has been made to keep technical
vocabulary within reasonable limits. This effort has inevitably resulted in the loss of some terms that may be favorites
with teachers. There is, of course, no reason why a teacher
cannot increase the load if he wishes—but the authors trust
that he will approach each addition with a penetrating WHY?

Though each technical term has been carefully considered before being admitted to the text, the load remains
large. Several levels of importance can be distinguished.
Some terms are of pervasive importance throughout the course
(photosynthesis, environment, evolution, for example). They
must be applied again and again, examined in many contexts,
approached from many viewpoints. Others are of less
pervasive importance, but fundamental to some major section
of biology (meiosis, predation, natural selection). Still others
are not important in themselves but are essential as steps
to larger ideas (natality, crossing-over, tropism). There are
still lower levels of technical vocabulary—names of things,
such as kinetochore, host, ATP. Finally, there are terms
that need not be learned at all, terms that serve merely as
handles for dealing with examples—the names of organisms,
for example. Certainly it would be a pedagogical error to treat
all technical terms in the same way.

The running vocabulary carries the narrative. In the
first part of the text, it is simplified, though no attempt is
made to "write down" to the student. In the latter part of the
book, the authors have made less effort to find simple synonyms,
and the running vocabulary probably approaches that of the
average ninth- or tenth-grader--with occasional excursions
beyond.

Marginal notes. The single-column format permits the use of a wide outer margin for a variety of purposes. Principally, it allows for the inclusion of aids to pronunciation and meaning—and in a position that makes such material available but optional. Students who have no need for this kind of help are able to read on without interruption, while those who require it have assistance immediately and visibly at hand.

The marginal notes provide pronunciations for technical words as a matter of routine. Pronunciations are also given for some running vocabulary—at first rather freely, later somewhat sparingly.

The notes provide derivations of many technical terms. For the most part, derivations give Latin and Greek roots; from these, students can accumulate a stock of word elements that will facilitate the building of scientific vocabulary throughout the course and (hopefully) beyond.

Some definitions are given in the notes. These are never definitions of technical vocabulary. (Technical terms are italicized and explained where they first occur in the body of the text.) They are definitions of words in the running vocabulary that might be unfamiliar to a considerable proportion of tenth-grade students. They become fewer in the latter parts of the book.

In addition, marginal notes call attention to related laboratory exercises, refer the student to appropriate illustrations in other parts of the book, and give brief biographical notes on scientists mentioned in the text.

All marginal notes are printed in green. All are to be regarded as optional material. The meat is in the black print; the green is salad. The marginal notes should never be deliberately set up as an obstacle in the path of the bright and quick student; but students should be reminded—frequently, at first—that the notes are present to help when help is needed. They do not take the place of a good high school or college dictionary.

Illustrations. In a textbook that stresses the biology of whole individual organisms, constant reference to kinds of organisms is necessary to provide examples of the general principles discussed. But tenth-grade students vary greatly in their previous experience with living things. Therefore, pictures of many of the organisms mentioned in the text are provided, in many cases simply to strengthen general discussion with visual images. Like the marginal notes, these illustrations, usually placed in marginal position, are to be used as needed.

All other illustrations in the textbook are teaching materials. No illustration has been selected or designed for decorative purposes alone, though an effort has been made

to obtain pictures that are as attractive as possible. Captions
have been written to tie in with the text and, often, to extend
it. The questions that frequently occur in the captions are by
no means rhetorical; they should be thought of as additional
"guide questions" (see below), and they are worthy of class
discussion.

Wherever the practice might be helpful, illustrations are
accompanied by indications of the size of the pictured organism
or subject. In all such instances, the ratio of the picture size
to life size is given (X 1/4 = reduced to one-fourth life size;
X 1 = life size; X 2 = enlarged to twice life size).

Summaries. Each chapter ends with a summary (set on
a longer type measure and bounded by horizontal green lines).
A summary is not an outline, and the student will soon discover that it is no substitute for studying the chapter. However,
summaries do bring together major ideas in their chapters,
sometimes in new relationships with each other; they should
prove useful to students as a clinching device and to teachers
as a basis for launching discussions.

"Guide Questions." These are based directly upon the
chapter materials (text and illustrations). They require recall
rather than reasoning, though there is some departure from
this generalization in later chapters. The sequence of questions is exactly that of the ideas in the chapter. Thus, when
parts of chapters are assigned, the corresponding guide questions can readily be located.

It is intended that these questions be used for the student's guidance during his study. With some classes they may
be used for checking student understanding of text materials.
If confined to the guide questions, however, discussion will
proceed on a very low level and will result in the neglect of
much material. Therefore, even with very slow classes the
teacher needs to supplement the guide questions with some of
his own, based on his understanding of the interests and
attitudes of the students in each class. With average classes
such supplemental questions should call for reasoning with the
text materials. With above-average classes the guide questions should receive little attention in class discussion.

"Problems." Unlike the "Guide Questions," the
"Problems" require reasoning, computation, or research—
sometimes all three. Their sequence has no relationship to
the sequence of ideas in the text. They vary widely with respect to degree of difficulty. They are not intended as guides for
the student while he studies the chapter, but as extensions
beyond the chapter. Although the problems may in some cases
serve as material for class discussion, they should not be
assigned en masse.

No attempt has been made to control either the vocabulary or the sentence structure of the problems. New terms are sometimes used without explanation. It is assumed that students who are sufficiently advanced to use the problems will also know how to use dictionaries and other references. However, it is not possible to rank the problems according to difficulty. Assignment should be made only after consideration of the interests as well as the abilities of individual students.

For the teacher the principal value of the problems should be to provide suggestions for the invention of problems of his own. Problems with a local flavor or that bear upon biological topics currently receiving notice in news media or magazines are particularly valuable. Problems that lead the student into experimentation will, of course, be indistinguishable from the items entitled "For Further Investigation" in the student's manual. Better students may be encouraged to develop their own problems.

"Suggested Readings." The rationale of the "Suggested Readings" is given in Appendix A of this guide. Since it is desirable to encourage further reading on the part of all students—not only among the "gifted"—some easy references have been selected as well as some that will challenge the most advanced pupils. Additional material for the advanced student can also be obtained from the reference lists provided in Part Two of this guide.

Periodical references in the textbook have been confined to articles in Scientific American. This sparse selection from periodical literature does not imply that worthwhile material is lacking elsewhere, but desired single copies of most periodicals are often hard to find and many Scientific American articles are available in reprint form. Librarians often keep back files of National Geographic, Natural History, Audubon Magazine, and other periodicals with excellent material. The American Biology Teacher regularly carries a column noting appropriate biological articles appearing in current issues of "popular" magazines.

Appendix. The scheme of classification adopted in the Green Version (see page 14 of this guide) is outlined in Section Two of the text. In the Appendix this scheme is presented in conspectus, enabling the student to see the levels of organization in close relationship to each other. The language has been kept as nontechnical as possible, but not all terms will necessarily be comprehensible at the time the student is studying Section Two. Illustrations—all simple drawings—are juxtaposed to the descriptions. This material is, of course, strictly for reference purposes. It would be desirable for the teacher to present an outline of one or two other schemes of classification for comparison.

Index. By now the reader of this guide must realize that the memorization of definitions plays a very minor role in BSCS biology. The discussion of word meanings in context, the usage of words—these are important matters. But they are not served by a list of pat definitions. Therefore, BSCS biology texts do not contain glossaries. However, the index of the textbook is quite comprehensive, so that the student has ready access to all the material in the text, including definitions in context whenever they occur (see, for example, "abiotic environment," "biosphere," "ganglion," but note also "diseases" and "virus") And, of course, a good, full dictionary is indispensable.

THE LABORATORY: AN OVERVIEW

The importance of laboratory work in the BSCS programs has already been indicated (pages 10-11). Textbook and manual are but two faces to the same coin. Only matters of portability and usage have forced their physical separation. Only matters of convenience separate their consideration in this part of the guide.

The Basis of Laboratory Work

The first function of the laboratory is to present from nature the evidence for the basic biological concepts. This illustrative function was probably the principal one in Thomas Henry Huxley's mind when he introduced the teaching laboratory into science education. His insight was a simple one: Seeing is believing. In teaching science one must appeal not to the authority of a teacher or a book; one must look squarely at the facts, at the infinitely varied phenomena of nature. Unfortunately, the illus- trative function has been so heavily emphasized that students have come to spend most of their time watching demonstrations, looking through microscopes, dissecting animals or plants, learning names, labeling drawings—but rarely doing an experi- ment in the sense of really investigating a problem, the answer to which is unknown.

Today something more must be expected from school lab- oratory work. Active participation of the learner in some scien- tific investigation is needed if he is ever to glimpse the true nature and meaning of science, ever to appreciate the forces that motivate and activate the scientist (see manual pages ix-x).

This _investigative_ function of laboratory work requires a different approach, a revision of goals, and (often) a shift in the teacher's orientation. It requires different and (often) more expensive kinds of materials. It makes desirable more extensive laboratory facilities.

The investigative function of laboratory work does not displace the illustrative function; it complements it. For at least thirty years perspicacious biology teachers have striven to introduce this twentieth-century function to a place beside the honored nineteenth-century function. Their efforts were brought to focus in the _Laboratory_ _and_ _Field_ _Studies_ _in_ _Biology_, edited by Lawson and Paulson (New York: Holt, Rinehart & Winston, Inc., 1960). The writers of the BSCS _Green_ _Version_ are pleased to cite this book as a major source of inspiration and take pleasure in expressing indebtedness to the teachers and scientists who contributed to it.

The Student's Manual

The student's manual is divided into sections and chapters paralleling those of the text. For each chapter (except the last) several exercises are provided. Some of these are studies in seeing nature; some are problems to be solved; some are experiments. In one way or another, all involve techniques of investigating problems scientifically.

Classification of exercises. There are 85 exercises in the manual, far more than any class can accomplish in a year. In Part Two of this guide they are designated as "basic" or "highly recommended" or "optional." The 45 basic exercises are the most important for achieving the objectives of the course. The highly recommended exercises are closely related to the major ideas of the chapters; they frequently present concepts or terms not treated elsewhere. The optional exercises are less central to the mainstream of the course.

It is a good practice to have students read over all the exercises, and especially the passages marked "Introduction" or "Background Information." Under some of these headings can be found explanations that are assumed in later discussions in the textbook. Moreover, this practice may lead individuals or groups of students to undertake work that time does not permit the whole class to do.

A few exercises are recommended as demonstrations. For the most part these are exercises in which the replication of the procedure by many students would seem to serve no useful purpose or would involve an inordinate amount of equipment. From the discussion of laboratory aims (pages 25-26), it is clear that the number of demonstrated exercises ought to be kept to a minimum, even though many exercises not recommended for demonstration could be presented in this manner. It might be argued that any exercise deemed unsuited for class participation would gain as a demonstration by employing the superior skill (if any!) of the teacher. But from a pedagogical viewpoint, demonstrations performed by selected groups of students usually are superior to those done by the teacher—though neither procedure is ever a substitute for the direct involvement of all students.

Organization of exercises. Because individual exercises contribute in different ways to the advancement of the student's biological knowledge, no set pattern of internal organization is followed. There should be no strait-jacket formulation of scientific investigation in the high school laboratory; there is none in the laboratory of the scientist. However, two subheadings do occur in all exercises—"Purpose" and "Procedure." There is always something to do, and the doing is never aimless.

Every effort must be made to create in each student an awareness of the purpose of his activity. He may see the purpose and still flounder about. But if he sees the purpose, he is the less likely to flounder and the more likely to grasp and carry out the procedure.

Almost all exercises have a "Materials and Equipment" list, which is of more importance for the teacher and his laboratory aides than for the student. Most exercises have some kind of follow-up to the procedure. This often involves a section called "Studying the Data," in which directions are given for arranging data into tabular or graphic form and the meaning of data is elicited by suitable questions. Sometimes this is followed by a "Summary." If an experimental situation justifies the use of the term, "Conclusions" are called for.

Most exercises begin with an "Introduction," which points out relationships to other exercises or to ideas developed in the textbook. Frequently the introduction extends ideas beyond the level on which they are developed elsewhere. Sometimes exercises include "Background Information," material needed for understanding the procedure of the exercise. Still other subheadings are used occasionally.

Suggestions "For Further Investigation" are found at the end of some exercises. These are materials that can be explored by individual students who have more than average energy and drive— and, hopefully, above-average ability. Some call for fairly simple extensions of the procedure in the foregoing exercise; some entail original thought and attention to design. In most cases, specific directions are lacking; the student must work out his own procedures. Such further investigations represent a step between the exercises for classroom use (necessarily structured to meet logistical considerations) and the open-ended experimental projects found in BSCS Research Problems in Biology: Investigations for Students, two volumes (New York: Doubleday & Co., Inc., 1963).

Questions are inserted in the exercises wherever they seem appropriate—even in an introduction. Most, of course, occur in a section such as "Studying the Data," "Discussion," or "Conclusion." In some exercises questions are woven into the procedure (Exercises 1.4 and 1.5, for example), and in others the whole procedure advances by means of questions (see Exercises 17.4 and 19.1). These methods make it desirable to place an identifying number (in parentheses) after a question rather than before it, so that the number does not separate the question from the foregoing statements that lead to the question. This placement of numbers has been used consistently throughout the manual.

Use of the manual. In almost every exercise many variations are possible. Some of these variations are noted in Part Two of this guide. Others will be dictated by necessity. In the early part of the year, it is best to stick as closely to the printed directions as the local situation will permit. At this time the connection between variations in procedure and variations in results must be established. It is therefore desirable to train the student to follow directions; and the fewer changes he has to cope with, the better. If many changes must be made, it would be best for the teacher to rewrite the directions entirely.

Later, strict adherence to the printed procedures is not necessary—not even desirable. With more able classes, merely throwing out hints concerning possible changes may suffice to introduce valuable variations, variations that may increase the teaching possibilities in the results. But beware of breaks in the reasoning process. Variations in procedure can degenerate into mere tinkering if links between procedure, data, and conclusions are not strongly forged.

Finally, the exercises in the manual should in no way inhibit the teacher's efforts to devise exercises better suited to his own facilities and situation. Rather, they should encourage him to do so.

The data book. Because the manual is not an expendable book, the student must record his data elsewhere. Experience has shown that the most convenient way to handle this is by means of a bound (sewn) notebook in which all data derived from exercises are written. The use of the data book is fully explained in the manual (pages xii-xiii).

The student should be encouraged to regard the data book as his place of primary record. As such it will have to meet the hazards of constant usage at the laboratory table and will receive records hurriedly made. Under such circumstances the data book cannot be a thing of beauty. Slovenly work cannot be tolerated; but many students, particularly the "better" ones, tend to equate slovenliness with mere lack of neatness. They must be taught to associate slovenliness with inaccuracy.

Although the data book is a personal record, not a report to the teacher, it must be checked to ensure that the student is using the most efficient methods of recording and organizing data. Checking should be accomplished on the spot, not by removing the book from the hands of the student. At first, checking should be frequent, less so as the year progresses.

Some Matters of Procedure

Good BSCS laboratory work has been accomplished in spacious and fully equipped high school laboratories; it has also been accomplished in small classrooms with primitive and improvised equipment. Obviously, in widely different physical environments the procedures used by excellent teachers must also vary widely. Therefore, no prescriptions can be written for successful laboratory teaching. The following paragraphs are intended simply to alert the teacher to sensitive areas of planning.

Initiating the work. If the importance of laboratory work is to be established in the minds of students, there must be no delay in getting into it. Because very little procedure is involved, it is possible to set a class to work on Exercise 1.1 at its second meeting. But before Exercise 1.2 is attempted, some ground rules of laboratory work must be laid down. Among the matters to be considered are:

1. Need for thorough familiarity with the purpose and the procedures to be followed
2. Location of work stations and regulation of student mobility during laboratory work
3. A scheme for distributing and collecting materials
4. Principles of teamwork—leadership, acceptance of responsibility, and coördination of efforts
5. Relationship between the data book, the record, and the completed exercise
6. Methods of evaluating student laboratory work

Every student must assume responsibility for knowing the purpose of each exercise; he must understand the procedure as a whole and, especially, his own part in it. The teacher has some responsibility for introducing each exercise, for adapting (when necessary) the material in the manual to his own classroom situation. The materials under "Introduction" or "Background

Information" often present ideas not found in the textbook; these ideas may require direct teaching. The teacher is wholly responsible for the provision of the "Materials and Equipment," though he may be able to delegate such responsibility to student assistants. All required materials and equipment must be on hand when work begins. Nothing is more detrimental to good laboratory work than lack of an essential item at a critical moment.

Looking ahead. Careful planning is a hallmark of the good teacher. It is especially important in science-teaching. In biological science it is crucial.

BSCS biology, with its emphasis upon experimental procedures involving living materials, calls for the utmost skill and ingenuity in planning. Simultaneously the teacher must often consider the disposal of materials from a completed exercise, the care of materials in one or more current exercises, the provision of materials for work to be accomplished in the next few days, and the procurement of materials for exercises that are two, four, six, or more weeks in the future.

Among these layers of planning responsibility, long-range foresight is the one most likely to be neglected. Yet it is essential. For example, in most parts of the country an exercise requiring young tomato plants will be impossible to accomplish in December unless the seeds have been planted in October. And the seeds may be difficult to obtain in October unless they have been bought in the spring or early summer.

Finding time. Having understood the basic importance of laboratory work and having leafed through the thick student's manual, the teacher immediately asks, "How can I find time to prepare all this material?"

No complete answer can be given to this question. Teachers have found the time—in one way or another. But during the years of BSCS testing, every device suggested by teachers for providing more time seemed merely to open up new opportunities for expanding laboratory activities. Thus teachers in the "best" situations are often as busy as those in the worst.

Where school systems have become convinced that extensive, truly investigative laboratory work is educationally important, various kinds of administrative action have been helpful. In some schools science teachers are scheduled for one less class per day than are other teachers. The period freed from class instruction is available for preparation of laboratory and demonstration materials. In other schools full-time laboratory assistants are employed. Still other schools provide part-time help by paying interested and qualified high school seniors to assist the biology teacher in setting up laboratory and demonstration work for his ninth- or tenth-grade biology classes.

Even without overt administrative backing, the individual

teacher can improve his ability to provide worthwhile laboratory work for his students. Something may be achieved by increased care in planning. In schools having more than one biology teacher, the sharing of preparatory tasks is time-saving and labor-saving—particularly when special skills are utilized. And much time can be saved by attention to organization of materials; a stock room or preparation room where all items have a logical place will minimize waste motion.

Most important, however, is the enlisting of voluntary aid from the students. In almost every class some students will deem it a privilege and even an honor to be permitted to help in laboratory preparations. Not only will such students make a real contribution toward freeing the teacher from routine chores, but they will also gain a realization that a certain amount of "dish-washing" is an essential part of laboratory work.

There is, of course, nothing new in this practice, but some suggestions may be useful. The students should be selected on an informal basis and never to the exclusion of others who may later become interested in helping. They should not be expected to correct papers, score tests, monitor classes, or perform other tasks that place them in positions of real or supposed advantage. Although their assistance may be greatest in routine work, they should be given instruction in some laboratory skills—partly in return for their aid and in encouragement of their continued effort, partly in hopes of discovering a few who may be especially deserving of guidance into careers in science or laboratory technology.

Students who have already taken biology are often willing to become laboratory assistants during their free time. They can be assigned on a somewhat more formal basis than current students, since they are not members of the classes in which they assist. Among the criteria to be considered for the selection of such assistants might be (1) the students' interest in biology, (2) their scholarship in biology and related subjects, (3) their general scholarship, (4) their available free time, (5) their willingness to help other students, (6) their ability to get along with lowerclassmen, and (7) their general reliability and dependability. (CAUTION: No matter how much help he may have—paid or voluntary—the teacher retains sole responsibility for laboratory safety.)

Checking the work. It is possible to become so preoccupied with preparations for future laboratory activity, so enmeshed in the mechanics of present laboratory activity, and so fatigued by the chores of cleaning up past laboratory activity that the rounding out of the student's experience is neglected. Since there is little virtue in mere activity, this should never be allowed to happen. Every exercise should be followed by class discussion.

The kind of class discussion will vary with the kind of exercise. When an exercise is observational, the teacher will need to relate the observations to the purpose of the exercise. When the exercise is an experiment, the teacher will need to make sure that the course of the reasoning, from hypothesis through experimental design and data to conclusions, is understood. In any case, class discussion following a laboratory exercise is the milieu in which an understanding of the true nature of science is best developed. Not even the "Invitations to Enquiry" (which are always "dry runs") are as effective in placing before the student the rationale of science, the difficulties of research, the uncertainties of knowledge.

For many exercises a class discussion constitutes a satisfactory termination. Written reports for all exercises are neither necessary nor feasible. The teacher may easily be lured into a never ending race with paper work. The result is a poor use of student time—in excessive writing—and a poor use of teacher time—in excessive reading. Which exercises to select for written report is somewhat a matter of personal choice. But it seems more reasonable to require such a report for an experimental exercise (such as 1.2) than for an observational one (such as 1.4).

A ritualistic report that requires the student to copy much of the exercise is just plain busywork. It is a sure way to undermine the purpose of the laboratory. In general, a written report might consist of (a) a title, (b) relevant data worked up from the data book, and (c) answers to questions encountered in the exercise. If complete statements are required in answering questions, grading is easier, and—more important—vague thinking is discouraged. At the beginning of the year's work, questions may be discussed in class before a written report is required. Later, when a pattern of acceptable response has been developed, this sequence may be reversed.

Written reports should be submitted as soon as possible after completion of an exercise. Prompt evaluation and return of the report to the student make a follow-up discussion possible.

TESTS

No matter what the stated aims of a course may be, no matter how diligently the teacher may bend his efforts toward them, all is in vain unless the tests that are used to measure the student's progress reflect these aims. Whether much or little is made of marks in a school system, students remain realists; they will work toward tests. Therefore, it is of utmost importance that the tests used in BSCS teaching be based on BSCS aims.

If the memorization by the student of arbitrary, clear-cut definitions is the teacher's aim, then he should not be using BSCS materials, which are certain to engender frustration in both himself and his students. But if this is not his aim, then he must be sure that his tests do not require only rote memorization of terms. If the teacher really believes that the laboratory work is as important as the information in the textbook, then he must base his tests at least equally on laboratory and textbook work.

All of this is probably self-evident. But granting the principle, the constructing of tests that reflect BSCS aims remains difficult. For some of the aims, no good group-testing procedures are yet known. And for all of the aims, good testing procedures involve the investment of much time and effort. During the years in which BSCS materials were being tried out in classrooms, a committee of teachers, biologists, psychologists, and psychometricians worked to devise suitable tests to accompany the materials. Though it is realized that many problems remain to be solved, the committee has constructed, tested repeatedly with hundreds of classes, and (by 1965) will have normed quarterly tests for each of the three BSCS versions and a comprehensive final test. These tests represent the best current efforts to measure BSCS aims in the conventional paper-and-pencil way. The set of tests designed for the Green Version can be obtained through the publishers, Rand McNally & Company, Box 7600, Chicago, Illinois, 60680.

Of course, quarterly tests fall far short of meeting the teacher s testing needs. Much more frequent tests are needed to allow the teacher to determine his successes and failures, and to indicate the areas in which intensified review is required. There is no substitute for teacher-made tests. With the crowded schedules already existing for science teachers and the increased time requirements of BSCS laboratory methods, it is to be expected that, in his construction of test items, the teacher will not always be able to match his performance to his ideals. But something more than a casual nod to such ideals will be necessary if the student is not to be demoralized by his first encounter with the quarterly tests. The teacher must have previously provided him with some suitable test experience.

Chapter 16 of the Biology Teacher's Handbook discusses the problem of constructing the classroom test and gives examples of test items designed for a variety of testing purposes.

PART 2

SPECIFIC SUGGESTIONS
FOR TEXT AND LABORATORY

section One

THE WORLD OF LIFE: THE BIOSPHERE

Whole living organisms are the center of attention throughout Section One. The teacher should arrange to have the classroom plentifully supplied with them. This is the first and most important piece of advice that the authors of the Green Version can offer the teacher. Whether the room be large or small, whether provided with the latest biological equipment or not, it can be made a home for a variety of living things—ready, waiting, and conspicuous on the first day of school.

The first two pages of the "Introduction" in the Student's Manual should be read concurrently with the introduction to Section One in the text. Resist the impulse to test the student's understanding. Elaborate explanation at this stage can gain nothing, and it may destroy much. This material is bread cast upon the waters: some faith is necessary. If, however, the reading level of the class is very low, the manual and textbook pages cited above may be read to the students by the teacher before books are distributed.

In the latitude of Maryland, out-of-doors community studies are reasonably satisfactory until the end of October. If your school is in a region where inclement weather arrives earlier, Exercise 3.1 may be undertaken before the exercises that accompany Chapter 2, or even before the exercises on the microscope (1.4-1.6). With a little attention to some of the vocabulary developed in Chapter 2, you may take up Chapter 3 immediately after Chapter 1 in support of the fieldwork. Of course this violates the logic of the individual-population-community sequence, but such a violation is better than omission of Exercise 3.1.

CHAPTER 1

The Web of Life

MAJOR IDEAS

It is not intended that the ideas listed here be imposed on the student without some modification. They are merely an aid for the teacher as he plans class discussions of the chapter. Therefore, they are stated in adult language:

1. An understanding of the scientific enterprise—particularly the processes of scientific work—is basic to any worthwhile study of science.

2. Organisms tend to maintain a dynamic equilibrium, both internally and externally, in the face of change. This is the principle of homeostasis. (In some classes the teacher may wish to employ this word.)

3. Energy flows from the sun, through the living system, back into the abiotic environment, from which it is essentially irrecoverable.

4. In contrast to energy, matter moves cyclically between the living system and the nonliving world. The matter in living things is the same matter that is found in nonliving things.

5. Having once been introduced into the living system, energy is passed from organism to organism in chemical form. Food, therefore, represents the union of energy and materials.

6. The total living system may be conveniently conceptualized—on the model of atmosphere, lithosphere, and hydrosphere—as the "biosphere."

TEACHING SUGGESTIONS

Guidelines

If at all possible, begin the course with laboratory work instead of with the textbook. The procedure for Exercise 1.1 can be carried out as soon as routine organizational and administrative details have been disposed of. Then pages 2-6 of the text can be discussed.

As the succeeding laboratory exercises are pursued, Chapter 1 of the textbook can be considered in small portions: for example, pages 6-11, then 11-16, then 16-20. Short reading assignments are preferable to fairly long ones—at least, until the teacher can judge the capabilities of his classes.

In many modern school systems, students have gained quite enough physical and chemical knowledge in previous grades to provide a sufficient background for Chapter 1. In other systems a brief explanation of such basic terms as "element," "compound," "symbol," "formula," and "chemical change" is all that is needed.

The greatest danger the teacher faces in Chapter 1 is that of becoming enmeshed in the text. Remember that this is an introductory chapter. The dependence of producers on solar energy, the dependence of consumers on producers, the interdependence of the living system and the physical environment—throughout the course these things will always be in the background. Because they will be continually reappearing, the depth of understanding achieved at this point need not be great. Therefore, beware of bogging down in a morass of detail. Hit the laboratory hard; move through the text chapter quickly; and get on to Chapter 2 as soon as possible.

Some Notes

The biologist depicted in Figure 1.2 is Dr. Robert C. Stebbins of the University of California. He is shown in various phases of his work on the pineal eye of the fence lizard.

The terms "producer" and "consumer" are respectively equivalent to "autotroph" and "heterotroph." In some classes it may be desirable to use the latter pair (but see page 21).

It may not be necessary to define the terms used at the bottom of
Figure 1.4. All students will have heard of <u>some</u> of these,
at least.

The percentages in Figure 1.6 have been compiled from various
sources. It is to be expected that students may discover variations if they consult encyclopedias. This is a fine opportunity
for raising the problem of variability in data.

Student explanation of Figures 1.7, 1.8, and 1.9 takes the place
of several guide questions.

EXERCISES

1.1   Observing Living Things . . . . BASIC
1.2   An Experiment: The Germination of Seeds . . . BASIC
1.3   Interrelationships of Producers and Consumers. BASIC
1.4   Use of the Microscope: Introduction. . . . . . . BASIC
1.5   Use of the Microscope: Biological Material. . . BASIC
1.6   Use of the Stereoscopic Microscope . . . . . . Optional

Merely talking about scientific method is of little avail.
Something must be done to plunge the students into thinking and
doing, doing and thinking. The laboratory work for Chapter 1 can
accomplish this. Minimal discussional backing is provided by the
textbook (pages 4-6) and by the "Introduction" to the manual.

The sequence of exercises has been carefully planned. In
Exercise 1.1 the student employs the basic scientific activity,
observation, and (in part) he does this through an instrument—the
microscope—about which he presumably knows little. In Exercise
1.2 he is introduced to the method of experimentation. In Exercise 2.2, he is confronted with an experimental situation that
demands the use of this tool.

Five of the exercises for Chapter 1 are basic; this places a
heavy load upon the teacher at the beginning of the year. But the
load is necessary to establish the importance of laboratory work.

It is recommended that these exercises be done with as little
modification as possible. This will lessen confusion, point up
the importance of a careful reading of procedures, and build the
student's confidence. Later, of course, the teacher will often
want to modify procedures to take advantage of special local
circumstances.

Special attention must be given to the proper use of the data
book; for this, see pages xii-xiii in the student's manual.

Exercise 1.1
Observing Living Things

The process rather than the product is the teaching objective
of this exercise.

Setting up the laboratory. Living organisms are strongly
preferred here. In the early fall there is probably no school situation in which the procurement of a sufficient variety of living
specimens is impossible. Though it is desirable that this exercise
be started promptly, there are some advantages to enlisting the
aid of pupils in gathering the materials. Pupil contributions,
however, are likely to run to the more conspicuous animal forms;
therefore the teacher will have to supplement. Aim for a good
balance between plants, animals, and protists.

At this time, microscopes are passive instruments. The
teacher or assistant should set up the instruments so that illumination and focus are optimal. Cultures should be rich enough
so that no student manipulation of microscopes is needed. Students will simply observe. Of course, the microscopes will
arouse much student interest. It is good pedagogy to capitalize
on immediate interest; it is even better to avoid trying to do too
many things at once.

The following are lists of organisms that have been found
useful in this exercise:

For observation under the monocular microscope—Euglena,
Volvox, Spirogyra, yeasts, rotifers, nematodes

For observation under stereomicroscope (or hand lens)—
Rhizopus, liverworts, mosses, lichens, Planaria, small anne-
lids, small insects

For observation with naked eye—kelp, mushroom, fern,
Lemna, Anacharis (elodea), cactus, Pelargonium (flowering),
Begonia (flowering), sensitive plant, sponge, earthworm, clam,
snail, crayfish, centipede, spider, beetle, caterpillar, goldfish,
frog, toad, salamander, snake, turtle, lizard, canary, rabbit,
rat, hamster

Directing the work. Observation time should be at least a
minute and a half—for the first few specimens, somewhat longer.
The number of specimens to be observed must be gauged by the
time available in the period. Students may observe in pairs.

On the day before the observing, the teacher should go over
the directions with the students. The purpose must be made
clear. Each student (or pair of students) should be assigned the
number of the specimen with which he will begin, and the total
number of specimens should be announced. The signal for changing from one specimen to the next should be agreed upon.

During the observation period the teacher merely keeps time,
gives the signals for change of station, and makes sure that the

operation proceeds smoothly. Students will feel quite insecure and will ask innumerable questions about what to look for and how to record their observations. Answer no questions at this time. The difficulties of the students are part of learning to observe. They should be encouraged to write in their data books any questions that arise while they are observing.

Directing discussion. In the period following observation, some time should be taken for class discussion. By this time the students will have worked up their data in the manner described on page 4, student's manual ("Studying the Data"). The primary job of the teacher is to stress accuracy of observation. For example, does the student report roots on a geranium plant because he sees roots—or because he thinks that a plant in soil must have roots? Here the distinction is between observation and inference. Secondly, the teacher should try to arouse a critical attitude toward the points that students advance as characteristics of plants and animals, using the student's own knowledge of organisms to the greatest extent possible. Obviously no definite conclusion concerning the problem posed in the "Purpose" can be drawn from such limited data. This needs to be pointed out, and the student's natural uneasiness with the tentative and the unresolved must be quieted—perhaps after the teacher has conquered his own uneasiness. (See Chapter 14 of the Biology Teacher's Handbook.)

Remember: The process rather than the product is the teaching objective of this exercise.

Exercise 1. 2
An Experiment: The Germination of Seeds

This exercise introduces the student to experimental method. It is concerned primarily with the concepts encompassed by the terms "hypothesis," "variable," "control," "data," and "conclusions." The student should gain some insight into these concepts and should note the role of numbers and the use of graphic records in the recording of observations. He should also see the value of the team approach and the possibility of designing a single procedure for gathering data on two related hypotheses. The information concerning seed germination is incidental, though it is not without value for succeeding chapters where the influence of environmental factors on populations is discussed.

Materials. Many kinds of seeds are available in stores only during the spring and early summer. These may be purchased in advance and stored in insect-proof containers in a cool, dry

place. However, seeds used for pet food or for attracting wild
birds and also some cereal seeds may be purchased throughout
the year. The following are seeds that have proved satisfactory:
wheat, rye, corn, oats, barley, turnip, radish, vetch, bean
(subject to mold, even when treated with fungicide), carrot,
parsnip (slow), parsley (very slow), cucumber, squash, sunflower, marigold.

Baby-food jars are quite satisfactory as containers for
soaking seeds.

If there is a shortage of petri dishes, the soaked seeds can
be "planted" in sand in half-pint milk cartons. Before filling
the cartons, sterilize the sand in a hot oven for one hour. Punch
holes in the bottoms of the cartons for drainage.

If students cut their own circles of paper toweling, scissors
must be added to the list of materials.

Many seed fungicides are sold commercially. They may be
used according to the directions on the packages. However, several substances generally available in the high school laboratory
are quite satisfactory:

Ethyl or isopropyl alcohol (70%)—Soak seeds one minute.

Formaldehyde—Dilute commercial formalin 1:500 and soak
seeds twenty minutes.

Sodium hypochlorite—Dilute commercial bleaches (for
example, Clorox) 1:4 and soak seeds fifteen minutes.

Procedure. Team sizes must depend upon the availability
of materials, but 4 or 5 students per team is good. To test the
second hypothesis, each team should use a different kind of seed.
Kinds that show a wide range of response should be selected.
Radish represents one extreme; parsley, the other.

Treatment of seeds with fungicide reduces loss of germination
due to injury caused by fungi on the seed.

All seeds must be "planted" at the same time. Therefore,
a schedule must be set up to insure that all groups of seeds are
soaked the proper length of time. Soaking of the 72-hour seeds
should begin three days before planting; soaking of the 48-hour
seeds should begin two days before planting; soaking of the
24-hour seeds should be started one day before planting. If
necessary the soaking time for the last group of seeds may vary
from 2 to 4 hours, depending upon the schedule on planting day.
Obviously, weekends must be included; it is convenient to set up
the soaking schedule on a Friday and have some students take
jars home, where soaking can begin on Saturday and Sunday. In
this way a week of observation is available before another
weekend occurs.

To avoid confusion of materials, all soaking jars and petri
dishes should be labeled with the class (period) and team symbols
in addition to the labeling called for in the exercise.

Finishing the work. Though the actual work occupies little time except on the first day and planting day, the procedure for this exercise extends over many days. During this time it is easy to lose sight of the purpose. Therefore particular attention must be placed on rounding out the experiment after the procedure is completed.

Many ninth- or tenth-grade students require help in drawing bar graphs. Check the data forms to be sure that data are cumulated from day to day. Go over the sample bar graph given in the manual (page 8). Be sure a form for the recording of data from different kinds of seeds is provided on the chalkboard. Check to see that teams record on this form only the results from seeds soaked 0 hours.

These are small matters, but attention to such details is especially needed at the outset; the reward for such attention will be clearer discussion at the end of this exercise and better work in succeeding ones.

Class discussion of the questions at the end of the exercise is essential. During this discussion constant reference should be made to the "Introduction" and "Purpose." Note that the questions are concerned entirely with experimental method, not with seed germination.

Exercise 1.3
Interrelationships of Producers and Consumers

Unlike the other exercises for Chapter 1. this exercise is concerned primarily with the subject matter of the chapter, rather than the methodology of science. It is designed to show some producer-consumer relationships, particularly those involved in the carbon cycle. The exercise is best performed as a demonstration. It can easily be set up by a small team of students.

If the students have had little or no previous science. the teacher may demonstrate the properties of oxygen and of carbon dioxide. Directions for doing this can be obtained from any conventional manual for high school chemistry. But avoid becoming too deeply involved in the chemistry. Even if such demonstration is deemed unnecessary, a brief, silent demonstration of the effect of exhaled air on bromthymol blue would be advantageous.

Materials. If screw-cap culture tubes are not available. standard 20-X-120 mm test tubes. 4-oz prescription bottles. or 4-oz screw-cap specimen jars may be substituted. After the experimental materials are placed in them, containers should be tightly stoppered and sealed with paraffin.

Bromthymol blue is used because of its narrow pH range: pH 6.0 (yellow) to pH 7.6 (blue). A 0.1% stock solution may be prepared by dissolving 0.5 g of bromthymol-blue powder in 500 ml of distilled water. To the stock solution add, drop by drop, a very dilute solution of ammonium hydroxide until the solution turns blue. If the water in your community is alkaline, the addition of ammonium hydroxide may not be needed. (NOTE: Solutions of bromthymol blue purchased from supply houses are usually made up with alcohol; such solutions will kill the organisms.)

Discussion. In light a green plant appears to play a role in carbon-dioxide—oxygen exchange opposite to that of animals:

$$\text{Carbon dioxide} + \text{water} \underset{\text{respiration}}{\overset{\text{photosynthesis}}{\rightleftarrows}} \text{food} + \text{oxygen}$$

But respiration, of course, goes on continuously in both green plants and animals. During periods of light, the carbon dioxide released by green plants is usually reused almost immediately in photosynthesis, so it does not accumulate in the environment. During periods of darkness, however, photosynthesis does not occur, then the released carbon dioxide is not reused. Therefore, the bromthymol blue in a culture tube containing elodea turns green at night because carbon dioxide from respiration is accumulating. When photosynthesis begins in the morning, carbon dioxide is used more rapidly than it is released. After a short time, the plant must begin to extract carbon dioxide from the water; as the amount of carbon dioxide in the water decreases, the bromthymol blue reverts to its blue color. Hence the "A.M." observation should be made as early as possible in the morning.

If it happens that the snail in Tube 2 is near the top of the tube and the elodea plant at the bottom, the water in the tube may at times be green or yellow at the top and blue at the bottom.

Exercise 1.4
Use of the Microscope: Introduction

Students usually have an almost compelling interest in the microscope and the world it opens up for them. This motivating interest can be of great value in introducing some basic ideas about the role of instrumentation in biology. Among these are the following:

1. The microscope is a tool that enables the biologist to extend the range of his observations beyond what he can obtain via unaided vision.

2. The way the tool is used determines the kind and amount of information that the scientist can obtain.

3. Information made available through instruments has given rise to problems that would never have been recognized if these tools had not existed. If the biologist had never been able to see Euglena, Paramecium, or bacteria, the problem of deciding which organisms are plants and which are animals would be a far simpler one.

4. The development of many branches of science, including biology, has been closely tied to the development and improvement of instruments that made available crucial information. The microscope is an excellent example of such an instrument.

The foregoing ideas may be developed either when the exercise is introduced or at appropriate places during this and the following exercise.

Materials. Both slides and cover slips must be thoroughly dried before being stacked or put away in boxes. While not suitable for precise work at high magnification, No. 2 glass cover slips are entirely satisfactory for student use at both low and high power. They do not break as easily as the thinner No. 1 cover slips. Plastic cover slips soon become scratched and unusable; it is therefore debatable whether they represent any saving. Better use glass from the beginning, and stress proper handling.

Lens paper is usually supplied in the form of booklets or large sheets. The latter should be cut up into small pieces before being distributed for use. Both books and pieces should be stored in dustproof containers. Each piece of lens paper should be used only once and then discarded. Be sure students understand that lens paper is to be used only for cleaning lenses —not for cleaning slides.

Slides may be cleaned with ordinary paper towels, but a softer grade of paper or cloth is preferable. Facial tissues such as Kleenex are satisfactory.

The print used in financial reports and sports statistics in newspapers is small enough to fit into the low-power field of view. Try to find pieces of newspaper with printing on one side only. The strips should be only about 1 cm long. Halftone pictures printed on paper such as that used in Life magazine are more satisfactory than those from newspapers.

Ordinary 1-foot, transparent plastic rulers (bearing a metric scale on one margin) may be cut into several pieces with a saw. Short pieces are easy to handle on the stage of the microscope.

Almost any kind of water container can be used in place of finger bowls or beakers.

Procedure. Because many different kinds of microscopes are available, directions are necessarily presented in general

terms. For the same reason. details concerning the identification and description of the parts of the microscope have been
omitted from the laboratory directions. The microscope shown
in the manual (page 14) represents the type that was standard
for most of the last half-century. It is still found in thousands
of schools. But during the last decade several radical changes
have occurred in microscope design. The best course. then.
is for the teacher to exhibit an example of the type to be used
by the students, pointing out on it the nomenclature of the parts.

Adequate illumination is essential for effective work with
microscopes. The most elaborate microscope can be of only
limited usefulness if illumination is poor. In many cases a
dependable light of suitable color and intensity can be secured
only by providing a lamp for each microscope.

Previous student experience, the amount and kind of equipment available, the level of student ability—these and many more
factors will determine the rate of progress of any particular class.
However. most classes will require part of a period for introduction of the microscope by the teacher and two full periods for
student procedure. Undue haste at this time will result in faulty
techniques and the development of poor attitudes toward careful
laboratory work. Enough time must be provided so that the
student can proceed carefully and can have an opportunity to do
work of high quality.

Students should make notes in their data books as they work
through the exercise. The questions in the "Procedure" should
be discussed briefly after work is completed. Encourage the
use of notes as the basis for discussion. Check the students'
notes at random and informally, during the discussion; notes
are not to be rewritten and handed in.

Exercise 1.5
Use of the Microscope: Biological Material

Having learned something about his instrument, the student
now uses it to observe biological materials.

Materials. To prepare the iodine—potassium-iodide ($I_2 KI$)
solution. dissolve 15 g of KI in 1 liter of water. Dissolve about
3 g of iodine in this solution. This forms a stock solution. For
use in staining dilute the stock solution with water, 1:10. Small
bottles with dropper caps are useful for dispensing the stain.

White potato should be cut into pieces approximately
3 X 3 X 3 mm in size. If placed in a petri dish that is lined with
moist paper toweling, they can be kept through several periods
of the day.

To prepare the yeast cultures, add approximately 1 g of dried yeast to an equal volume of tap water, and mix to form a thick paste. Fill a glass jar (approximately 250-cc capacity) with molasses diluted to the color of strong tea. Pour the paste into the jar, and stir to disperse the yeast. Place the uncovered jar in a warm, dark place. Cultures should be set up the night before they are required for use.

In many parts of the country, excellent material for observing microorganisms can still be obtained from the nearest pond during September. Rich growths of algae, rotifers, and ciliates may simply be dipped up in glass jars. If opportunities to make natural collections are lacking, laboratory cultures may be prepared. These should be set up ten to fourteen days before use, as follows: Boil 10 g of chopped hay in 1 liter of water (spring or pond water, to avoid metallic ions) for about thirty minutes. Filter, and add one or two drops of 1 normal NaOH. Cool, and inoculate with a pinch of soil. Then add two crushed wheat grains that have been boiled for ten minutes. After a day inoculate with Ameba, Paramecium, Stentor, Blepharisma, Spirostomum, Colpoda, Colpidium, or Euplotes, all of which can be cultured with this medium. Each week add one or two boiled wheat grains. This culture can be continued by subculturing once every four to six weeks.

Procedure. If starch grains turn up in the yeast preparations, students have not used sufficient care in cleaning their slides. Point out the difference between starch grains and yeasts in reaction to the stain. Later in the year the characteristic reaction of starch will be used several times.

Be sure that cleanup at the end of the laboratory period is quick and complete. If attention to this is neglected now, bad laboratory habits will plague the teacher for the rest of the year.

Students may have difficulty recognizing that the presence of smaller organisms attached to larger ones indicates the occurrence of budding (Item 7). An explanatory drawing may be needed. This may be recalled when the question of defining "individual" is discussed, in Chapter 2.

The lack of perfect identity between image and object was brought up in Exercise 1.4 (page 17, items 1-4). This idea should now be extended. Three opportunities present themselves: First, Item 11 brings up the matter of depth of focus. A chalkboard drawing will help to clarify the way in which the shallow depth of focus obtained with the microscope influences the interpretation of three-dimensional shape. Second, movements of yeast, caused by water currents, must be distinguished from motion of the motile microorganisms observed in Procedure C. Third, the speed of motile microorganisms may be mentioned. (For this exercise there is no need to attempt to slow down the movements of microorganisms.) In magnifying dimensions the

SAINT MARY'S COLLEGE, CALIF.

microscope necessarily magnifies velocity. On an absolute basis, however, a turtle can run rings around the average Paramecium.

As in Exercise 1.4, students should jot down in their data books the answers to the questions in the "Procedure." This should be done in the laboratory, at the time the observations are made. A brief class discussion should follow the laboratory work, but there is no need to achieve consensus on all observations.

Exercise 1.6
Use of the Stereoscopic Microscope

The stereoscopic microscope is useful in many subsequent exercises; in a few it is indispensable. However, many schools still lack an adequate stock of these instruments, so this exercise must be considered optional. If a few stereomicroscopes are available, the exercise may be done by students with special interest. Later these students may serve as demonstrators in exercises that call for use of stereomicroscopes.

With stereomicroscopes good illumination is an even greater problem than with ordinary monocular microscopes. A gooseneck lamp with a 75-watt frosted daylight bulb provides fair illumination. Even better are small 75-watt spot lamps; these can be used with holders improvised from ring stands and clamps. If such lamps are used for extended periods, overheating of living specimens may cause trouble. This problem can be solved by placing a simple water cell (consisting of a flat-sided bottle or a Florence flask, filled with a dilute solution of copper sulfate) between lamp and specimen. More elaborate lamps, with field diaphragms, condensing lenses, and filter holders, are commercially available, of course. Although such lamps are expensive, one or more will be extremely valuable for setting up demonstrations with both monocular and stereoscopic microscopes.

SUPPLEMENTARY MATERIALS

Testing

The problem of constructing classroom tests was discussed on pages 32-33.

The provision of ready-made test items is not within the
scope of this guide. However, at the beginning of the year, the
teacher may welcome some means of comparing his own attempts
at test-making with those of others. Listed below are some
examples of test items for Chapter 1 (textbook and manual, including the introductory material in the latter). These items are
the result of feedback from teachers who worked with the preliminary editions. No effort has been made to select a set of ideal
items—obviously, some are better than others. In any case, the
basic criterion of a test is its balance. A test might consist of
an aggregation of excellent items and still be a poor test. In a
well-balanced test even a few items of bare, factual recall might
find a legitimate place.

1. A hamburger is food. This means it contains energy in
   what form?
   (A) light
   (B) chemical
   (C) kinetic
   (D) nuclear
   (E) heat

2. When a fox eats a rabbit, it is acting as a
   (A) producer.
   (B) first-order consumer.
   (C) decomposer.
   (D) second-order consumer.
   (E) parasite.

3. During photosynthesis light energy is converted into
   (A) chemical energy.
   (B) heat energy.
   (C) electric energy.
   (D) kinetic energy.
   (E) nuclear energy.

4. Of the following statements, which one is not true of
   science?
   (A) It builds on accumulated knowledge from the past.
   (B) It uses measurement to make observation precise.
   (C) It is subject to change as knowledge accumulates.
   (D) It is based on precise and verifiable observations.
   (E) It is made up of true and unchangeable theories.

5. Using the low power of a microscope, you observe an
   image having a diameter one-third the diameter of the
   field of view. You conclude that the object you are
   observing has a diameter of approximately
   (A) 1000 microns.
   (B) 1.5 microns.
   (C) 500 microns.
   (D) 349 microns.
   (E) 0.5 microns.

6. To test the hypothesis that the length of time required
   for germination of seeds varies with the kind of plant,
   it is necessary to design an experiment in which
   (A) several soaking times are provided.
   (B) seeds are planted in sand.
   (C) several kinds of seeds are used.
   (D) observations are made on several days.
   (E) seeds of different ages are used.

7. Because science is concerned with verifiable knowledge,
   it is important that scientists
   (A) observe things with a microscope.
   (B) stay in their laboratories.
   (C) observe things firsthand.
   (D) communicate their findings.
   (E) work for the government.

8. Scientific knowledge is best described as
   (A) reliable and confirmable.
   (B) secret and dangerous.
   (C) theoretical and useless.
   (D) certain and unchangeable.
   (E) measurable and magical.

9. Consumers receive their energy in the form of
   (A) light.
   (B) chemical energy.
   (C) heat.
   (D) kinetic energy.
   (E) matter.

Invitations to Enquiry

The "Invitations to Enquiry" in the Biology Teacher's
Handbook are valuable resources. In using them, the teacher
must keep in mind both the subject-matter background of the
students and their degree of sophistication in scientific methodology. For students of average ability and little background in
biology, the following "invitations" are recommended:

Invitation 3 (pp. 57-59 of the Handbook). Both the subject
(seed germination) and the topic (misinterpretation of data) are
so closely aligned with the work of Chapter 1 that this invitation
might almost be considered basic to the chapter. Because the
written materials to be given the student are brief, this invitation
lends itself to presentation by means of a series of transparencies
on an overhead projector.

Invitation 11 (pp. 83-84 of the Handbook). The subject
matter requires no special knowledge on the part of the student.
The topic (construction of hypotheses) provides greater depth
for Exercise 1.2.

Audiovisual Materials

In a broad sense, specimens and all the paraphernalia of the
laboratory can be thought of as audiovisual materials. In this
guide the term is obviously used in a restricted sense. Primarily, it means motion-picture films and filmstrips; occasionally
it refers to phonograph records and a few miscellaneous items.
At the outset it is desirable to establish firmly the biologist's
primary concern with living things and his need to work with them
firsthand. Because such establishment requires a large amount
of time in the laboratory, and because it is important to move
rather quickly through the textbook material of Chapter 1 (see
page 38), it is recommended that little or no time be devoted to
audiovisual materials. However, for those who wish to use
them, the following items are suitable:
Filmstrip: "Energy and Life." (Young America Films:
Principles of Biology, Part 1). Black & White. McGraw-Hill
Book Co., Inc. An excellent summary of textbook Chapter 1.
But the somewhat juvenile character of the first few frames
may make its use undesirable in classes sensitive to their
senior-high status.
Motion-picture film: "The World of Life." (AIBS Secondary
Film Series). 16 mm. Color. 20 min. McGraw-Hill Book Co., Inc.
Dr. Bentley Glass discusses the nature of biological science.
The film does not follow the content of Chapter 1, but it clearly
develops the attitudes discussed in the "Introduction" to the
manual and implicit in the exercises.
Phonograph record: "The Scientists Speak: Biology."
Harcourt Brace and Co., 1959. The first talk on this record
(by Dr. George Gaylord Simpson) has the same purpose as the
film "The World of Life." It is, of course, less vivid, but it
is shorter and has qualities that make it appeal to some students
who are overwhelmed by the film. Moreover, it does not become
involved in cellular and molecular biology.

Teacher's References

The "Suggested Readings" in the textbook also will be useful to the teacher; conversely, some materials in the following list may be of value as assignments to certain students:

BATES, M. The Nature of Natural History. (Rev. ed.). New York: Charles Scribner's Sons, 1962. (Chapter 18 provides good background on the nature of biological investigation.)

GATES, D. M. Energy Exchange in the Biosphere. New York: Harper and Row, 1962. (This goes far deeper than the understanding essential for teaching Chapter 1; but the teacher who reads it—even if he skips most of the mathematics—will gain an appreciation of a concept basic not only to the chapter but to the whole Green Version.)

MILNE, L. J., and M. MILNE. The Balance of Nature. New York: Alfred A. Knopf, Inc., 1960. (Good background material. but not profound.)

VAN NORMAN, R. W. Experimental Biology. Englewood Cliffs, N. J.: Prentice-Hall. Inc. 1963. (Useful far beyond this chapter.)

Individuals and Populations

MAJOR IDEAS

    1. The individual—regardless of difficulties in definition—
is a primary unit of biological study.

    2. For purposes of study, individuals may be grouped in
different ways. The indefinite but versatile term "population"
is useful for such groupings.

    3. Quantitative study of populations is based on the idea of
density—the number of individuals per unit of space.

    4. As do all units of the biosphere, populations constantly
change. Changes in density are determined by the interaction
of four rates: natality, mortality, immigration, and emigration.

    5. These rates are affected by biotic and abiotic environ-
mental factors that are themselves constantly interacting.

    6. Therefore, the study of natural populations is immensely
complicated, and the application of results from experimental
populations is fraught with uncertainties.

    7. Mathematics is an essential tool in the science of biology.

    8. The species population is an entity of great practical and
theoretical importance in biology.

TEACHING SUGGESTIONS

    Exercise 2.2 is an extensive undertaking. Careful, early
planning is necessary.

Guidelines

The light touch recommended for the teaching of Chapter 1 cannot be continued into Chapter 2. The concepts of "individual" and "population," first encountered here, form a foundation on which much of the remainder of the course rests. In Chapter 3 communities are regarded as interacting populations. In Section Two the species population is the unit of taxonomy. The "patterns" discussed in Section Three are composed of individuals grouped as species populations. Though these concepts sink into the background in the first part of Section Four, the individual emerges again as a unit in Chapters 15 and 16. From then on, individuals and populations remain the focus of attention. Consequently, thorough study of Chapter 2 is essential.

Again in contrast to the recommendations for Chapter 1, work on this chapter should begin with the textbook. After a brief overview to enable students to discover its scheme of organization, Chapter 2 can best be assigned in three bites: pages 22-30 (guide questions 1-6), pages 30-43 (guide questions 7-12), and pages 43-48 (guide questions 13-15). Soon after students have been exposed to the first of these assignments, attention may be shifted to Exercise 2.1. After Exercise 2.2 has been started, the mathematical ideas in the first assignment can be more extensively developed. The materials in the second and third assignments may also be taken up during the ten days required for growing the yeast populations of Exercise 2.2. Although the graphing in Exercise 2.3 can be done before Exercise 2.2 is finished, the questions cannot, for they furnish a conclusion to the whole series—Exercise 2.1 through 2.3.

The student will encounter many difficulties in this chapter, and the teacher must be prepared to assist him. The major difficulties are: abstract ideas (both in the textbook and in the manual); new vocabulary (often disguised as familiar words); a long, difficult laboratory procedure in Exercise 2.2; and, worst of all (from the viewpoint of many students), mathematics.

For teachers and students who regard textbooks merely as fodder for memory work, the Green Version has proved to be disconcerting: it brings up issues and then fails to resolve them. On the other hand, teachers and students who use textbooks as a jumping-off point—a basis for discussion—welcome this characteristic. Of course, the responsiveness of students and the amount of time available will determine which of the informal invitations to discussion are to be pursued and which must be passed over.

This characteristic—the recurrence of unresolved, "open-ended" exposition—is not applicable to Chapter 2 alone, but specific examples can be pointed out here: On page 24, para-

graph 2, opportunity exists for pursuing the matter of definition
in science. On page 25, paragraph 1 raises a point that reap-
pears as an important theme in Chapter 17. On page 32, paragraph 2 suggests a search of current literature to see whether
the inconsistency between the Wisconsin and England experiments
has been resolved by later experiments. On page 41, last paragraph, and on page 42, last paragraph, other unresolved problems
appear. Watch for the same kinds of opportunity in later chapters. The teacher who disregards <u>all</u> such opportunities will
largely fail to achieve the second BSCS objective (see this guide,
page 5).

Study of population density and of the interaction of rates
must be guided by the methods of the mathematics teacher; that
is, examples must be worked through with the class, and then
students must practice with numerous problems. Some practice
can be obtained from Problems 1 and 2, textbook page 49, and
from the problems on pages 68-69 of this guide. But the teacher
will have to devise many problems of his own. Problems with a
local flavor are, of course, best. Review of such problems
should occur occasionally during the several months following
"completion" of work on Chapter 2.

Both at the beginning and at the end of Chapter 2, the difficulty of definition is discussed—first in connection with individuals, finally with regard to species. From this the student might
get the impression that slipshod language is a characteristic of
science. Fortunately the interposition of the concepts of density
and rate, with their mathematical expression, helps to counteract
such an impression. The intention of the authors, of course, is
to show that the use of pseudo-precise language where ideas are
imprecise involves just as much falsity as does the use of imprecise language for ideas that are precise.

Some Notes

(In the following notes, references are to textbook pages and
figures unless otherwise stated.)

Make use of Figures 2.4 and 2.5 in class discussion. In Figure
2.5 densities of blazing star and goldenrod can also be calculated
and compared. This figure is based upon studies of old-field
succession in Michigan (S. A. Cain and F. C. Evans, <u>Contribu-
tions from the Laboratory of Vertebrate Biology</u>, 52 : 1-11, 1952
[University of Michigan]).

Discuss Figure 2.6, and relate the meaning of a change in slope to the interpretation of the line graph drawn in Exercise 2.1.

Be sure that students consider each of the rhetorical questions on page 29.

Figure 2.7 is a retouched photograph of one of the pens used by Dr. Charles Southwick (now of Johns Hopkins) in the "crowding" experiment at the University of Wisconsin. The "English" experiments were conducted at Oxford by Drs. Peter Croweroft and F. P. Rowe. The original reports of these experiments appeared in Ecology, 36 : 212-225, 1955, and in the Proceedings of the Zoological Society of London, 129 : 359-370, 1937.

Figure 2.8: The upper photograph was taken in Arizona, the lower one in Idaho.

Figure 2.12: The investigators estimated that their counting methods involved about 10-percent error. Of course, rats may have immigrated from surrounding blocks, but Davis and his students found that rats seldom crossed streets unless the population was quite dense.

On page 41 the word "cycle" should be given special attention because its sense here is, on the surface, rather different from its sense in Chapter 1—particularly when Figures 1.7, 1.8, and 1.9 are compared with Figure 2.13.

Page 42: In common language the words "hypothesis" and "theory" are frequently interchanged. In this course, hypothesis is used for specific "guesses" that are amenable to experiment; theory is used as indicated on this page (see also page 547).

Figure 2.18: Dimorphism related to sex and age is quite common in many organisms. Birds are used as examples because they are colorful and generally familiar. For other examples of dimorphism, see Figures 17.7 and 17.8. Specimens of monarch and viceroy butterflies can be used to demonstrate similarity in two populations that are completely isolated reproductively. (In this case the species are even placed in separate subfamilies.)

EXERCISES

The three basic exercises form a series: a hypothetical
population without limiting factors; a closed population with a
fixed food supply and no provision for elimination of wastes; a
natural, open population. The series involves comparisons
among the three component exercises and comparisons with
the populations described and graphed in the textbook.

In addition to Exercise 2. 4, Exercise 15. 6 is also concerned with the effect of an abiotic factor on a population. If
a team of students wishes to set up Exercise 15. 6 now, a second
generation of seeds might be obtained before the end of the school
year. In most parts of the country, however, a greenhouse would
be needed for this.

Exercise 2. 1
Population Growth: A Model

This exercise on a hypothetical population provides a basis
for comparing the real populations encountered in Exercises 2. 2
and 2. 3. But it also continues the task begun in Exercise 1. 1—
to introduce the student to scientific methodology. Therefore,
attention must first be directed to the introduction (manual page
26), where the use of conceptual models and the role of assumptions are briefly discussed.

Materials. Semi-log graph paper may be obtained in 1, 2,
3, 4, 5, or more cycles. Such paper is logarithmic on one axis
and regularly spaced on the other. The 1967 population of house
sparrows will be 156, 250 birds; six-cycle paper is needed to plot
this figure. But if the 1967 generation is deleted from the directions (page 28), five-cycle paper can be used. Printed semi-log
paper is expensive. Paper satisfactory for this exercise can be
produced on school duplicators from stencils prepared by the
teacher. The finer subdivisions shown on commercial paper
may be omitted.

Procedure. The computations and the construction of the
graph on the ordinary grid can be done at home. However, some
previous groundwork must be laid in class. This should include
at least some discussion of assumptions. In addition, many
teachers find a review of line-graph construction advantageous.

After the students have discovered the difficulties of choosing a suitable scale for the ordinary grid, the semi-log grid must
be explained. It is not necessary to become deeply involved in
mathematics. Briefly develop the series 10^1, 10^2, 10^3, 10^4,

etc. ; note the correspondence of the exponents to the number of zeros in the series 10, 100, 1000, 10,000, etc. Direct students to label the cycles on the semi-log graph paper "units," "tens," "hundreds," etc. Point out that each succeeding cycle represents numbers ten times greater than those represented by the preceding cycle. Link this idea with the fact that within each cycle the system of second-order subdivisions separates spaces of decreasing width. Then illustrate the plotting of points, using numbers different from those used in the exercise.

Discussion. In this exercise the principal advantage of semi-log paper is that it permits the plotting of very large numbers in later generations while showing clearly the small increments in earlier generations. The straight line obtained on the semi-log paper indicates a constantly accelerating growth rate. If it is known that a rate is of this kind, the plotting of only two points will establish the slope. Extrapolation is then easy. With most classes only the principal advantage need be stressed.

Unfortunately, many students with competency in making graphs have little knowledge of how to interpret them. Therefore, considerable attention should be given the concept of slope. The relation of slope to rate is basic in the interpretation of graphs. Here it is discussed simply, since all slopes in the graphs for this exercise are positive. But if there seems to be no danger of confusing the students, the significance of zero slopes and negative slopes can also be discussed, reducing the difficulties to be encountered in Exercise 2.2. The graphs in Chapter 2 of the textbook should be helpful—especially Figure 2.6.

Further investigations. Exercise 2.1 is the first to which materials titled "For Further Investigation" are appended. For their use, see pages 27-28 of this guide.

The last of these investigations invites the student to devise other problems by further changing the assumptions. The usual difficulty here is vagueness in stating the assumptions.

Exercise 2.2
Study of a Yeast Population

This is an essential exercise; students must obtain some firsthand experience with population dynamics. The exercise forms the hard core of such experience in the laboratory, and without it Exercises 2.1 and 2.3 are meaningless. Exercise 2.2 builds upon the student's experience with experimental methods (Exercise 1.2) and applies the results of his efforts to learn the use of the microscope (Exercises 1.4 and 1.5). Furthermore, it greatly extends his conception of teamwork in science and his appreciation of the value of replication. The teacher _must_ overcome any temptation to retreat before the manifold difficulties that are certainly present. Remember: This exercise has been done, over and over again and in a wide variety of classroom situations!

Considerations of time and space severely limit the choice of organisms. On both counts macroscopic organisms are ruled out. Algae reproduce somewhat too slowly; bacteria are too small. Common yeast seems to be the most suitable organism: it reproduces rapidly, its requirements are simple, it is easily visible with the "high dry" lens of the microscope, it responds readily to decrease in food concentration and increase in toxic substances, and it is an economically important organism already well known to students by name and appearance (Exercise 1.5).

Because of the time span it requires, this exercise should be set up early in the work on Chapter 2. Ideally, Exercise 2.1 should be completed before 2.2 is started, but this is not absolutely necessary; the purpose of Exercise 2.2 will be clear any time after 2.1 has been begun.

From start to finish, this exercise requires two weeks, but much of the class time during this span will be utilized in other work. Time needs can be broken down as follows:

1. Procedure A should be done outside of class time. It requires about two hours. If a sufficiently large sterilizer is available, medium for several classes can be prepared at one time. To prepare medium for five classes, two rounds of preparation probably will be necessary—a total of four hours.

2. Procedure B requires about two-thirds of a class period.

3. In each subsequent class period, inoculation requires not more than five minutes—and involves only three students.

4. Procedure C requires two full class periods.

5. Discussion of the results will require at least one full period, if it is properly done.

Materials. Few high schools have access to an autoclave. But a large pressure cooker of the kind used for home canning is an essential investment; many later exercises involving microorganisms require it. For Exercise 2.2, however, it is possible to get along without a pressure cooker. With luck, a sufficient degree of sterilization may be obtained by boiling the medium and the tubes for ten minutes.

Aluminum-foil caps are easy to make. Use a square of foil having a width a little more than three times the diameter of the test tube. Place the mouth of the test tube in the center of the square; fold the foil edges down by running the tube through a hole made by curving the forefinger around to the base of the thumb. It is desirable—though not essential—to use a heavier foil than the usual kitchen brands. A roll of commercial heavy-

duty aluminum foil 18 inches wide and 1000 feet long can be purchased from restaurant-supply dealers for about fifteen dollars.
It will be useful in many subsequent exercises. Bacteriological
cotton plugs can be used instead of foil, but they require an extra
skill—and they are messy.

For yeast extract, brewers' yeast tablets, obtainable at any
drugstore, may be substituted. Mix the tablets in about one-fifth
the amount of water to be used in making medium sufficient for
one class. Let stand overnight, decant, and then filter.

Sodium phosphate or dibasic potassium phosphate may be
substituted for monobasic potassium phosphate.

Sucrose may be substituted for glucose, but this is the least
desirable of the possible substitutions.

Beef-bouillon cubes may be substituted for peptone. Two
cubes are sufficient for 1000 ml of hot water. To remove the fat,
cool the mixture somewhat and filter.

If the mineral content of the local water is low, tap water
may be used in place of distilled water. Or the water may be
treated with a demineralizer.

If any of the materials for preparation of medium and their
substitutes are simply impossible to obtain, a solution of molasses (about 10-percent, not containing sulfur dioxide) may be used.

Procedure A.   The exercise is written with a class of 30
students in mind—three teams of 10. Each student is responsible
for inoculating a tube. Students are numbered according to tube
numbers; each tube number corresponds to the number of days
the tube has been incubated before counting day. On counting day
students work in pairs—No. 1 with No. 2, No. 3 with No. 4, etc.

Of course, few classes will consist of exactly 30 students.
If there are fewer than 30, the number of incubation days can be
reduced to 8 (requiring teams of 8 students), but then the chances
of obtaining a clear decline in population are reduced. A better
plan would be to have some of the better students take responsibility for more than one tube. Such "doubling-up" should be done
with tubes having lower numbers, because they are less likely to
require dilution on counting day.

For classes of more than 30 students, other kinds of adjustment are necessary. First, an additional student may be assigned
to work with the tube inoculated on counting day, making the number of students on each team 11. Second, extra students may be
assigned general duties connected with distribution of and account-
ing for materials—and they can also substitute for the inevitable
absentees. Finally, a small separate team may be assigned the
task of preparing the medium.

Though 10 ml represents a convenient and efficient amount
of medium per student, as little as 8 ml may be used—or as
much as 15. But the amount in all test tubes must be the same.
If all the tubes have the same diameter, time can be saved in dis-

pensing the medium by making a water "blank." Carefully measure out 10 ml of water and pour into the "blank" tube; then pour
medium into each tube to the level of the water in the "blank."

When a pressure cooker is used, care must be taken to bring
the contents back to room pressure slowly, to avoid having the
caps blown off the tubes.

Procedure B. For ease in handling the sets of tubes, it is
advisable to designate each team with an individual letter that is
not repeated in other classes: Teams A, B, and C might be in
one class; Teams D, E, and F might be in another; and so on.
With this system, containers holding each team's set of tubes
can be distinctively labeled. The containers may be bacteriological culture baskets, or students may be asked to bring No. 3
cans from home.

Each team should have a captain and a cocaptain. They are
responsible for seeing that the tubes are inoculated according to
schedule by team members. A chart should be made, showing
classes, teams, and tube numbers, with the names of assigned
students opposite each of the numbers. Placed on the bulletin
board, such a chart will help remind students of their tube numbers and may be used to check daily inoculations.

Students may experience some difficulty using the glass-
marking crayon on test tubes. Small pieces of masking adhesive
or Labelon tape may be used. Both team letter and tube number
may then be written with ordinary pencil. Ordinary adhesive tape
is difficult to remove from the tubes when cleaning; masking tape
is not. If desired, the eleventh tube may be placed with the team
sets at the beginning of the exercise and marked 0.

Experience has shown that fairly uniform initial populations
can be obtained by the apparently haphazard method of inoculation described in the manual. It is important to exercise some
care in picking out grains that are as close to the same size as
possible. It is not necessary that uniformity of grain size be
obtained among teams—only within teams.

No matter which day of the week is chosen for beginning the
inoculations, at least one weekend will be involved in the schedule.
How can inoculations be made on weekends? One solution: the
teacher may do the work himself. Or students may take the tubes
home and inoculate them at the proper time there. The main
objection to this solution is not so much the small error that is
likely to result from the change in environmental conditions, but
rather the danger involved in students' carrying glassware—
especially on a crowded school bus.

The cultures may be incubated at room temperature (normally
considered to be $22^{\circ}C$). At this temperature the populations
should be declining (the so-called "death phase" of the growth
curve) during the ninth and tenth days. It is important to keep

the cultures from drafts and sudden changes in temperature. The cultures may be most conveniently kept in a cupboard against an inside wall of the building. The development of the population may be accelerated by increasing the temperature of incubation or, conversely, slowed down by lowering the temperature. If facilities for maintaining higher or lower temperatures are available, some classes might be assigned to incubate their cultures at such temperatures. On the whole, however, this is not recommended, and for two reasons: (1) It introduces a variable that, while interesting, is irrelevant to the purpose of the experiment; and (2) it reduces the number of replications available for "smoothing out" the population curve.

Procedure C. In Exercise 1.5 students observed yeast organisms; but they have not attempted counts before, and they are still novices in the manipulation of the microscope. With no preparation (except closely supervised reading of the directions) students have made counts that yielded reasonably smooth curves —but at the cost of three class periods. With some practice better results can be obtained in less time.

A day or two before counting day (the day after Tube 1 has been inoculated), students may be given opportunity to practice the counting technique. Provide a fairly dense culture of yeasts. Just as they will on counting day, have the students work in pairs, checking each other's counts. Have all students practice diluting, even though not all will need to do this on counting day. With such practice behind them, students have sometimes been able to complete the actual counts in one period.

If counting cannot be completed in one day, the cultures must be stored in a refrigerator, so that the population of the first day is maintained with as little change as possible. There is no need for sterile techniques on counting day, because the cultures will not be used again.

One of the most common sources of error in making cell counts is an uneven distribution of cells in the medium when the sample is removed. The student should shake the tube vigorously and then make a quick transfer to the slide. Since maintenance of sterile conditions is not essential, adequate shaking should be no problem. The dropper should be thoroughly rinsed after each sampling. Before counting, organisms should be allowed to come to rest.

Adequate instructions for making counts are included in the student's manual. At this point the best advice for the teacher is to read the manual carefully and to anticipate (on the basis of his knowledge of students) as many difficulties as possible, taking steps to obviate them. And insist that students follow directions.

Discussion. Check to see that all students have included the dilution factor (X 1, if no dilution is made) in their calculations. The form shown in Figure T-2.2a is a convenient one for gathering the data of all teams.

DAYS

TEAM	0	1	2	3	4	5	6	7	8	9	10
A	18	218	219	162	355	95	175	132	167	485	136
B	24	63	69	283	281	161	147	365	199	227	314
C	39	61	363	56	20	114	322	41	66	87	38
D	36	53	75	710	56	240	230	190	200	630	340
E		30	210	45	59	46	82	453	93	60	88
F	47	71	73	170	20		242	660	73	110	55
G	16	25	35	980	540	50	350	165	14	160	212
H	48	42	36	650	760	500	305	356	313	65	69
K	23	344	60	45	90	330	54	250	37	138	74
Total	251	907	1140	3101	2181	1536	1907	2612	1162	1962	1326
Average	31	101	127	345	242	192	212	290	129	218	147

Figure T-2.2a

A wide range of numbers is likely to appear when counts of
different teams are gathered together. Furthermore, fluctuations
in the population —as measured by any one team—are likely to be
so great that to detect any pattern of growth may be difficult.
However, when the data from many teams are averaged, a fairly
good growth curve usually results. Figure T-2. 2a shows data
obtained by three classes of somewhat less than average ability,
and Figure T-2. 2b is a graph based on the average of all nine
teams.

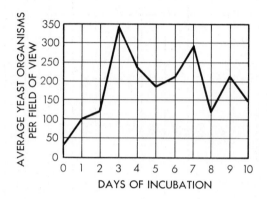

Figure T-2.2b

To obtain a curve that is explicable in terms of population
theory is, of course, desirable and very satisfying to students.
But failure to obtain such a curve must not be interpreted as
failure of the exercise. Item 1 on page 35 of the manual is the
pivot on which the exercise turns. No matter what the results,
they will provide material for a fruitful discussion of sources of
error in an experimental procedure and of the need for teamwork
in cooperative scientific work.

Responses to Items 2, 3, and 4 will, of course, depend upon
the nature of the graph obtained from experimental results. Comparison of Figure T-2. 2b with the graph obtained in Exercise 2. 1
shows that, initially, the growth rate of the yeast population
accelerated somewhat as did the hypothetical sparrow population.
But the yeast population soon reached a peak and began to fluc-
tuate; moreover, superposed upon the fluctuations is a decline in
the population. To explain the similarities and differences in simplest terms, you need only point out that both the sparrow and
the yeast populations were initially small populations in a presumably favorable environment. However, assumptions in
Exercise 2. 1 made no allowances for the "facts of life"—the
finite quantity of resources on the island. On the other hand,
the yeasts exploited a constantly declining food supply and en-

countered an increasing accumulation of waste products in the
environment. In other words, environmental resistance oper-
ated only in the yeast experiment.

It is rather difficult to conceive of any run of Exercise 2. 2
(as now written) that would confirm the hypothesis on manual
page 29.

Exercise 2. 3
Factors Limiting Populations

The graph for this exercise can be prepared at home—and at
any time after Exercise 2. 1 has been completed. Consideration
of the questions, however, should be delayed until Exercise 2. 2
has been discussed. The conclusion to Exercise 2. 3 is a conclusion to all three exercises.

Exercise 2. 4
Effect of an Abiotic Environmental Factor on a Population

Most high school students probably prefer working with animals to working with either plants or microorganisms. Yet work
with animals presents numerous difficulties. Flour beetles
(Tribolium), fruit flies, and Daphnia are possibilities—and enter-
prising students should be encouraged to attempt to culture these
organisms. Effects of temperature on population growth can be
tested with any of these organisms. (Mealworms [Tenebrio] are
easy to culture, but their life cycle is too long for population
studies in a school year.)

Hydra has been selected for use in this exercise partly because results can be obtained in a short time, partly because
students find this animal quite interesting, and partly because
favorable experience has accumulated from a similar exercise
in Animal Growth and Development, a BSCS Laboratory Block
by Florence Moog (Boston: D. C. Heath & Co. , 1963).

Brine shrimp (Artemia), used to feed the hydra, are interesting organisms, too, and they are likely to entice some students
into devising additional experiments. Brine-shrimp eggs can be
obtained at most aquarium dealers, since the young brine shrimp
are much used as food for tropical fish. At room temperature
the eggs hatch in about forty-eight hours.

The artificial medium for culturing hydra is made up as
follows:

Solution A: Dissolve 8.32 g $CaCl_2$, 1.9 g KCl, and 0.2 g KI
in 259 ml of distilled water.

Solution B: Dissolve 6.22 g $NaH_2 PO_4 \cdot H_2O$, 32 g $Na_2 HPO_4$,
and 0.5 g of Disodium Versonate[1] in 250 ml of
distilled water.

To 1 liter of distilled or deionized water add, separately, 1 ml
each of Solutions A and B.   Do not combine Solutions A and B
before placing them in the water; combining them will cause some
of the components to precipitate out.

A Temperature Gradient Box (shown in Figure T-2.4a) is
highly recommended.   It is useful here and in other exercises,
and in many projects that will occur to the resourceful teacher
or student.   In this exercise it allows a finer gradation of temperature control than can otherwise be conveniently obtained.
The Temperature Gradient Box is one of the pieces of apparatus
developed by the BSCS Laboratory Block Committee.   It is made
of masonite panels held together by tape.   The heat source—an
incandescent bulb—is regulated by a brooder thermostat.   The
box is placed in a refrigerator from which the shelves have been
removed.   The top joints of the box should be well sealed to
prevent escape of warm air.   The height of the wooden blocks
and the cooling capacity of the refrigerator determine the lowest
temperature.   Figure T-2.4b shows the temperature curve for
eight stacked plastic refrigerator dishes.   Petri dishes, small
finger bowls, or any other containers that can be stacked are
also acceptable.   One box will hold four stacks of dishes.

This exercise might be done by just one team in each class.
Data from the several classes can then be combined.   Dishes
should, of course, be labeled with a team symbol.

SUPPLEMENTARY MATERIALS

Additional Problems

As indicated previously (page 55), the ideas concerning population change must be developed chiefly through the consideration of
problems.   As much as possible, problems should be given local
flavor.   Those appearing below are far from adequate in number,
but they may serve as a stimulus to the teacher's own ingenuity.

---

[1] Disodium Versonate may be obtained from Fisher Scientific
Company: Order S-311 Sodium (di) ethylene-diamine-tetraacetate.

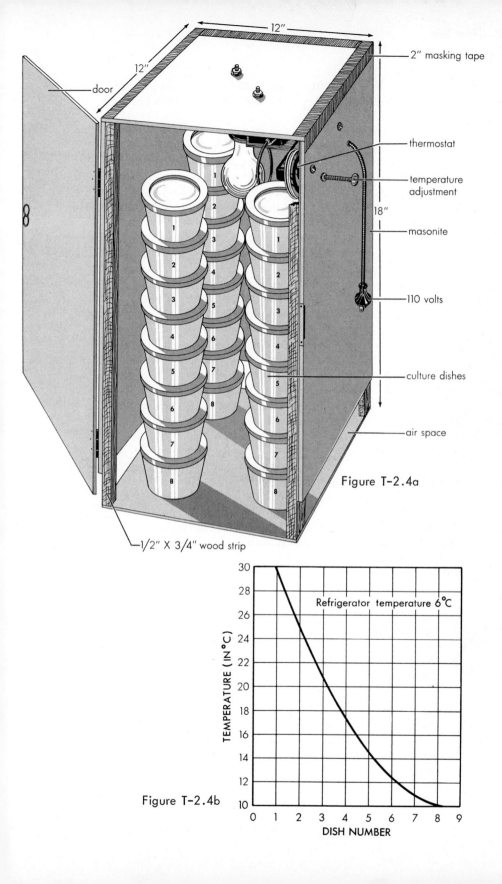

12"

2" masking tape

12"

door

thermostat

temperature adjustment

18"

masonite

110 volts

culture dishes

air space

Figure T-2.4a

1/2" X 3/4" wood strip

Refrigerator temperature 6°C

Figure T-2.4b

TEMPERATURE (IN°C)

DISH NUMBER

1. What is the density of the student population in your English classroom compared with the density in your biology classroom?

2. On October 15, 1960, the beginning of the squirrel-hunting season for that year, biologists counted 75 gray squirrels in a 30-hectare woods. On December 15, 1960, 42 gray squirrels were counted in the same woods. What was the density of the squirrel population on October 15? On December 15? What determiners could have interacted to affect the density? What determiners must have predominated? (NOTE: Many students might be expected to know that the breeding season of gray squirrels is virtually concluded by October 15 and that hunting mortality would probably be high.)

3. In a certain city an eight-block area contained 1056 human beings and an estimated population of 1400 rats. Then an Urban Renewal Commission razed the wooden buildings on the area and constructed eight large apartment houses. Following this action the area was occupied by 2480 human beings and an estimated population of 150 rats. Calculate the change in population density of both organisms. What determiners probably were predominant in effecting the change in density of each species?

4. On a range of 450 hectares is a total of 1275 jackrabbits. Studies indicate the following rates for this population:

Mortality..... 2225/year   Natality....... 3400/year
Emigration.... 775/year   Immigration.... 150/year

Is the population increasing? Decreasing? At what rate? Predict the population at the end of four years. What is likely to happen to the population of producers in this area during the four years?

5. In a cornfield the population of weeds (that is, all plants other than corn) is estimated at $35/m^2$. Half the field is treated with chemical A, and half is treated with chemical B. The density of living weeds in the "A" half:

end of first week..... $22/m^2$
end of second week... $13/m^2$
end of third week ..... $8/m^2$
end of fourth week .... $6/m^2$
end of fifth week...... $7/m^2$

The density of living weeds in the "B" half:

end of first week..... $32/m^2$
end of second week... $26/m^2$
end of third week .... $18/m^2$
end of fourth week .... $7/m^2$
end of fifth week...... $5/m^2$

During the five weeks what is the net rate of decline in the density of the weed population in each half of the field? Compare

the rates of decline in the two halves during the first week after
treatment. What population determiner is dominant in this
situation? What population determiner is probably operating
in the "A" half of the field between the fourth and fifth weeks?
(NOTE: Many more questions can be based on these data.)
6.   In a certain year observations were made of a mule-deer
population on a 105-hectare island off the coast of British Columbia. Data:

Number of does, January 1....... 90
Number of bucks, January 1...... 20
Births during year 75
Deaths during year 50
Number of deer, December 31... 155

What was the density of the population at the beginning of the year?
At the end of the year? What were the effects of immigration and
emigration on this population?

Invitations to Enquiry

The following "invitations" are recommended for use with
Chapter 2:
Invitation 5 (pp. 64-67 of the Handbook). A good background
for one of the major points encountered in the discussion of
Exercise 2.2.
Invitation 9 (pp. 76-78 of the Handbook). Has priority over
No. 5. Both subject matter and topic (the problem of sampling)
fit closely with the materials of Chapter 2.
Invitation 31 (pp. 167-171 of the Handbook). The last of a
series concerned with quantitative relations in biology. With
slight adaptation, however, it can be useful without the rest of
the series. The subject matter (population growth in bacteria)
directly parallels work in Exercises 2.1 and 2.2. Students who
have reached second-year algebra should be exposed to this
"invitation."

Audiovisual Materials

Films and filmstrips: The writers have been unable to discover first-rate audiovisual aids to accompany Chapter 2. It is

probable that more is to be gained by concentration on problems than by use of time for films and filmstrips. However, an imaginative teacher equipped with a good camera could make 2-X-2 slides of local scenes that would stimulate discussion and possibly serve as the basis for problems.

Teacher's References

ALLEE, W. C., A. E. EMERSON, O. PARK, T. PARK, and F. P. SCHMIDT. Principles of Animal Ecology. Philadelphia: W. B. Saunders Co., 1950. (Though "the Great AEPPS" is showing its age, and though major advances have been made on many ecological fronts since its publication, it remains a basic reference. Section III deals with populations.)

ANDREWARTHA, H. G., and L. BIRCH. The Distribution and Abundance of Animals. Chicago: University of Chicago Press, 1954. (A rather technical book that sets forth views still stirring population research.)

BROWNING, T. O. Animal Populations. New York: Harper and Row, Publishers, Inc., 1963. ("For a quick elementary understanding. . . . Deals with experimentally tested concepts . . . . How environment influences populations and maintains the balance of nature"—AIBS Journal.)

CRAGG, J. B. (ed.). Advances in Ecological Research, Vol. I. New York: Academic Press, Inc., 1962. (Several population papers appear in this first volume of a new series presenting reviews of research. Watch for later volumes.)

GALTSOFF, P. S., F. E. LUTZ, P. L. WELCH, and J. G. NEEDHAM. Culture Methods for Invertebrate Animals. Reprint edition. New York: Dover Publications, Inc. (Laboratory studies of population dynamics depend upon the ability of the investigator to culture organisms. This is an old stand-by in its field.)

GREIG-SMITH, P. Quantitative Plant Ecology. New York: Academic Press, Inc., 1957. (This book is primarily concerned with techniques, but it is useful for illustrating the role of mathematics in the study of plant populations.)

LACK, D. The Natural Regulation of Animal Numbers. New York: Oxford University Press, 1954. (Much of this book is concerned with populations of birds, a group of animals for which many data on natural populations exist. For balance it should read in conjunction with works concerning laboratory populations.)

MALTHUS, T., J. HUXLEY, and F. OSBORN. On Population:
Three Essays. New York: New American Library of World
Literature, Inc., 1960. (This paperback provides the most
ready access to Malthus. Since human population is not
stressed in Chapter 2 of the Green Version, the Huxley and
Osborn essays may be postponed until study of Chapter 20.)

MAYR, E. Systematics and the Origin of Species. New York:
Columbia University Press, 1942. (This old work contains
one of the best discussions of the "biological definition" of
species. Most recent works on taxonomy—see pages 92 and
101-102 of this guide—include brief treatments of the topic.)

SLOBODKIN, L. B. Growth and Regulation of Animal Populations.
New York: Holt, Rinehart & Winston, Inc., 1961. (A short,
critical book dealing with theory, but reflecting much experimental work.)

CHAPTER 3

Communities and Ecosystems

MAJOR IDEAS

The break between Chapters 2 and 3 is one of convenience; the sequence from individual to ecosystem is a concept that over-arches both chapters. However, the following are distinguishing ideas for Chapter 3.

1. A biotic community consists of the sum of all interactions among the species populations in the community.

2. In attempting to describe the ecological relationships among species in biotic communities, ecologists have developed a multiplicity of terms. These terms often have overlapping meanings.

3. The significance of a community relationship is best de-termined by measuring the relationship's effect upon population densities of the species involved.

4. The delimiting of communities is a subjective process; in nature there is always continuity in both space and time.

5. The more or less orderly transition of communities through time is termed "succession."

6. Since every biotic community exists in an abiotic setting, the study of communities only partially realizes the goals of ecol-ogy. Every biotic community is part of an ecosystem which is a complex of all biotic and abiotic relationships within a definable unit of space and time.

TEACHING SUGGESTIONS

Guidelines

The concept of a biotic community cannot be adequately developed merely through verbalization. Pictures, especially
motion pictures, will help. But it is essential that the student
gain direct experience with communities. Within the classroom
walls simple laboratory communities can, of course, be maintained. Aquariums and terrariums are old standbys. Exercises
6.1, 7.1, and 9.2 concern laboratory communities. In many
schoolrooms, students, their lunches, and their viruses, houseflies, house mice (and, sometimes, crickets, dermestid beetles,
and cockroaches) form a community that the alert teacher will
use—especially in illustrating parasitism and commensalism.
    In the view of the Green Version writers, however, all this is
still inadequate. In city schools especially, it is important to
get beyond the walls of the classroom, to show students that life
is not entirely an in vitro phenomenon—that community interactions normally are not confined within glass test tubes, glass
tanks, and glass buildings.
    The previous sentence stresses the urban situation because
teachers in city schools have the most difficulty finding natural
biotic communities. But the need may be as great in other
locales. Even students who live on family farms often do not
see that their fathers' business is based on attempts to control
biotic communities by encouraging some species and discouraging others. In a word, Exercise 3.1 is essential.
    In addition to providing firsthand experience with a commu-
nity (Exercise 3.1), it is desirable to furnish students with descriptions—and if possible, pictures—of several communities in
the local region. Teachers who have studied local communities
and who have the ability to write well can contribute valuable
materials to their colleagues.
    In the textbook, Chapter 3 fills only twenty-three pages,
three of which are purely descriptive. It does not lend itself
well to short assignments. However, a fairly logical division
can be made at page 63. The first part of the chapter should be
read before the fieldwork of Exercise 3.1 is done; the second
part, afterward. And if the season is growing late, work on
the chapter may begin with the exercise.
    With classes that can be trusted to glean the more obvious
ideas from the textbook with a minimum of discussion, the teacher
can take time to stress some of the more abstract features of the

chapter. First, the terminology of community relationships offers him an opportunity to extend the discussion (begun in Chapter 2) of definitions in science. Second, the paradox of change vs. constancy—of dynamic equilibrium—is an idea that recurs frequently; it came up early in Chapter 1 and again in Chapter 2. Its relationship to the theme of homeostasis is obvious. Third, the continuity of communities and ecosystems in time and space without real boundaries is merely a special example of the unity of biology.

Chapter 3 completes the series of ecological units begun in Chapter 2 and also marks the end of Section One. Therefore, it should be brought to a close with a careful review of the series—individual, population, species population, community, ecosystem. This is the time for a "unit test" (if the teacher wishes to preserve that term), but the student must understand that the test is only an "interim summary" (see the Handbook) and ends nothing.

Some Notes

(References are to textbook pages and figures unless otherwise stated.)

One of the Florida rivers plotted in Figure 3.1 is shown at the head of the chapter (page 51). The description of the Florida river community is based on the work of Dr. John Crenshaw, now at the University of Maryland.

Do not confuse a community with a society. In the usage adopted in this course, a community involves interspecific relationships; a society involves intraspecific relationships only. In a beehive there is a society, not a community (unless species in addition to the bees are considered).

The most likely victim of the lions shown in Figure 3.4 would be a zebra.

Figure 3.6: How does the position of the flea on the food chain differ from the position of the louse or the mite?

Figure 3.11: The graph is based on work of D. A. MacLulick, University of Toronto Studies 43 : 1-136, 1937.

Figure 3.12: The graph is based on studies by J. Davidson, Transactions of the Royal Society of South Australia 62 : 342-346, 1938.

Figure 3.13: The succession shown here is in the Colorado Rockies. The trees are aspens.

EXERCISES

3.1 The Study of a Biotic Community. . . . . . BASIC
3.2 Competition Between Two Species of Plants . . . . Optional
3.3 A Comparative Study of Habitats . . . . . . Highly Recommended

Exercise 3.1 requires such a great amount of time that few teachers are likely to be able to do many other exercises while working on Chapter 3. But it should be noted that in addition to the exercises listed above, Exercise 7.3 concerns a parasite-host relationship, Exercise 7.4 involves an example of mutualism, Exercises 8.3 and 9.5 deal with the effects of abiotic factors on communities, and Exercise 9.2 deals with succession. The last of these might well be set up at this time, while materials are easily available out of doors, and then examined at intervals during the earlier part of the winter.

Exercise 3.1
The Study of a Biotic Community

NOTE: If a pond is readily available, the purposes of this exercise can be accomplished by substituting Exercise 9.1.

Every exercise should be planned carefully, but any exercise that takes students out of the school building demands doubled care. Unless both teacher and students know exactly what is to be done, this exercise can easily become a lark, without educational value. Given the time and attention it demands, however, it can be one of the most rewarding experiences of the year.

For reasons given in the manual (page 47), it is impossible to prescribe a single procedure for this exercise. Nevertheless, enough information has been given the student to enable him to take an active part in the planning. The teacher, of course, should know considerably more about the methods of community study than is provided in the manual. He will find Ecology of Land Plants and Animals, a BSCS laboratory block by E. A. Phillips (Boulder, Colorado: Biological Science Curriculum Study, 1961), valuable.

First, the area to be studied must be selected. The teacher, if not the students, should be thoroughly acquainted with the potentialities of his region. It is desirable that the area be as close to the school as possible so that repeated visits may be made. However, the desirability of repetitive visits may be outweighed by other considerations. If the resources in the immediate vicinity of the school are poor, and if administrative conditions permit, an excursion to a desirable site at greater distance may be preferred. However, in no school is this exercise impossible. Biotic communities exist even in the most urban situation. Look for vacant lots, the area around a billboard, even cracks in cement and asphalt—all these contain plants, insects, nematodes. Though the chief producers may be miles away, the city environment also contains larger organisms—mice, rats, cats, pigeons. The urban biology teacher should be acquainted with the following books:

BEEBE, W. Unseen Life of New York as a Naturalist Sees It. Boston: Little, Brown & Co., 1953.

FITTER, R. S. London's Natural History. London: William Collins Sons & Co., Ltd., 1945.

KIERAN, J. Natural History of New York City. Boston: Houghton Mifflin Co., 1959.

Remember that this exercise has been done under a wide variety of conditions. For example: At the beginning of the 1960 school year, Dundalk High School, Baltimore County, Maryland, had just been completed. No landscaping had been started at the time this exercise was to be done. After a dry summer the "campus" resembled the less agreeable parts of the Sahara— an excellent setting for comparisons of gravels, clays, and sands (there were even miniature dunes), but devoid of macroscopic life except for physical-education classes braving the dust. Adjacent, however, was the old wartime motor pool of Fort Holabird, once rather generously strewn with crushed stone and parked trucks, but now semicovered by heath asters and hardy goldenrods, with here and there some tufts of weedy grasses. This sparse producer life did have an associated fauna—even some quite obvious consumers, such as butterflies and occasional small birds. Soil-sampling was impracticable because of the layers of crushed stone, but an abundance of other material for Exercise 3.1 was present.

Having chosen the area for study, the teacher should visit it—together with a committee of students, if possible. With the area under direct observation, the possibilities can be sketched out.

Next, on the basis of the directly observed possibilities and the procedures suggested in the manual, the class can proceed to make detailed plans. The plans must be fitted to the personnel. Each student must have a definite place in the plans. He must have something to do, he must know what his responsibility is, and he must know how to carry it out.   Each team leader must know the overall plan for his team.   Figure T-3.1 is an example of a form (used in a woodland study) that provides the teacher and team leaders with a way of checking on individual responsibilities.

EXERCISE 3.1   JOB SHEET

TEAM _____   TEAM LEADER _____

PREPARATIONS

Staking out the area: General description:

_____   _____   _____

_____   _____   _____

_____   _____   _____

_____   _____   _____

_____   _____   _____

DATA COLLECTION

Trees:

_____   _____

Shrubs and saplings:

_____   _____

Herbs and seedlings:

_____   _____

Searching:

_____   _____

Litter and soil samples:

_____   _____

TEAM EQUIPMENT

Stakes, 8	Hammer, 1	Rubber bands, 4
String, 50 m	Old magazines, 6	Plastic bags, 2
Meter sticks, 2	Collecting bottles, 4	Wire circles, 2
Rulers (metric), 4	Forceps, 2	Trowels, 2

Figure T-3.1

Written instructions are essential. Forms for recording data in the field may be devised; these, of course, will vary with the nature of the area to be explored. Some teachers have found it desirable to go through a "dry run" with their team leaders to check out directions and data forms.

If at all possible, Exercise 3.1 should be a comparative study. For example: the border of a woods may be compared with the interior; a grazed pasture may be compared with a mowed meadow; a well-trodden section of the school campus, with a less-disturbed section. Population densities of several selected species may be obtained by counting individuals on measured quadrats. The mean densities in one habitat can then be compared with the mean densities in the other. If a large number of quadrats is used, the difference between the means can be treated statistically against a null hypothesis; but at the level of sophistication appropriate for the tenth grade, it is probably sufficient in most cases to let the students decide subjectively whether or not the degree of numerical difference is "significant." Choice of species depends upon the habitats being compared. For instance, in comparing a much-trodden lawn with an out-of-the-way one, not grass but dandelions and plantains should be counted.

Get the fieldwork done while the weather permits. It is not necessary to process the data immediately; if a delay is necessary or seems desirable, take some 35-mm color photographs of the study area. These may be useful later, when the student's memory needs refreshing.

Some teachers find it desirable to use organisms collected during this exercise as a basis for considering diversity among living things—a concept to be stressed in the next three chapters. Thus Exercise 3.1 can serve as a connecting link between Sections One and Two. In particular, the exercise provides an opportunity to acquire numbers of insects for Exercise 4.3. But collecting is not an aim of Exercise 3.1, and care must be taken that the enthusiasm students often display for collecting does not interfere with the community study.

Exercise 3.2
Competition Between Two Species of Plants

This is a simple experiment that can easily be turned over to a small team. Though only a small part of the United States has a climate that permits Exercise 3.2 to be done out of doors in late autumn, the work can be done at home if sufficient window-space is available. However, growth of the plants in the laboratory will arouse interest and discussion that should make the team's report of the results more meaningful to the class.

The seeds may be treated with fungicide, as described in Exercise 1.2. If a greenhouse is available during the germination stage, glass sheets may not be needed.

In this experiment it is assumed that the roots of the tomato plants represent a negligible weight factor. If students object to this assumption, it is possible to harvest the whole plants by gently washing the soil away from the root systems.

"Intraspecific competition" is more closely related to the idea of crowding (discussed in Chapter 2) than to community study, but the introduction of the term may induce some students to consider the possibility of demonstrating this kind of competition. Such a demonstration could parallel Exercise 3.2. One kind of seed should be used. The intervals between seeds should be different in each of several flats. The effects of spacing can be measured by the dry weight. Peas, which are self-pollinating, may be used; then the effects of spacing can be correlated with the quantity of seed produced.

In summary, there is value in allowing students to see that pertinent data may be obtained from an experiment in a variety of ways.

Exercise 3.3
A Comparative Study of Habitats

This exercise should have precedence over Exercise 3.2. It not only concerns the concept of ecosystem, but it is related to matters of tolerance and ecological distribution that arise in Chapter 8. One team per class may be delegated to do the fieldwork. Even if this exercise is skipped, the "Introduction" (manual page 59) should be read for its explanation of the useful term "habitats."

Differences in temperature among the three habitats will be more pronounced earlier in the autumn. For best results vegetation should still be in an active condition, and the sun should be fairly high in the sky. Of course the work should be done on a sunny day. The three habitats should be as near to each other as possible, so that topographic differences will be minimal.

For meeting student questions concerning relative humidity, refer to H. J. Oosting, The Study of Plant Communities.

In this exercise, sling psychrometers are difficult to use—at the 0-cm height, impossible. But if available, they hold the two thermometers conveniently. If the sleeves around the thermometer bulbs are to be used repeatedly, distilled water should be used to soak them.

SUPPLEMENTARY MATERIALS

Additional Problems

The frontier farm is often said to have been self-sufficient. What does this mean in terms of biotic communities?

Why may it be reasonable to include the wheat fields of Kansas, the cotton fields of Texas, and the fishing banks of Newfoundland in the biotic community of New York City? [A modern city may be thought of as a biotic community, but its energy system cannot be understood unless study is extended far beyond the city limits.]

In Figure 3.12 the "smoothing" of a graph line between plotted points is shown. To explain this further the teacher may present other examples of population data plotted on a grid and have the class draw smoothed curves for each set of data. (See W. C. Allee et al., Principles of Animal Ecology, pp. 309, 329, 385, and E. P. Odum, Fundamentals of Ecology, pp. 199, 232.)

Invitations to Enquiry

Invitation 8 (pp. 72-76 of the Handbook). An excellent "invitation." It ties together Chapters 2 and 3 and introduces an important methodological matter—the handling of "second-best" data.

Audiovisual Materials

The concepts introduced in Chapter 3 lend themselves rather well to visual instruction. Many relevant filmstrips and motion pictures are available, but most are pitched on a level too superficial for tenth graders. An opportunity exists here for an imaginative film producer who has a respect for the intellectual capabilities of the high school student.

Filmstrips: "Symbiosis—Strange Partners in Nature." ("Darwin's World of Nature," Part VIII). Color. New York: LIFE Filmstrips, 1960. The pictures are good, but the captions are full of teleology and anthropomorphism. The term "symbiosis" is used in the restricted sense—i.e., equivalent to "mutualism."

"The Ecological Succession. " (McGraw-Hill Text Films, Ecology Series). Color. New York: McGraw-Hill Book Co. , Inc. , 1960. Contains accurate terminology, though rather more than necessary. The picturing of bare-rock succession parallels the description in the Green Version textbook.

Motion-picture films: "Life in a Woodlot. " National Film Board of Canada. 16 mm. Color. 17 minutes. Shows the factors that affect the dynamic balance of populations in a woodlot community through the cycle of the seasons.

"The Community. " Encyclopaedia Britannica Films. 16 mm. Color. 11 minutes. Depicts the interrelationships that comprise a biotic community. Food webs of several communities are illustrated.

"Succession—From Sand Dune to Forest. " Encyclopaedia Britannica Films. 16 mm. Color. 16 minutes. Deals with one of the most thoroughly studied examples of succession—that on the southeast shore of Lake Michigan. In developing this story many good examples of community relationships are illustrated. The alert teacher can exploit these more effectively than the narrator does.

Teacher's References

References for Chapter 3 overlap those for Chapter 2 because the division between these two chapters is rather arbitrary. Of the "Suggested Readings" listed in the textbook, the books by Odum and by Oosting are of particular importance to the teacher.

ALLEE, W. C. , A. E. EMERSON, O. PARK, T. PARK, and F. P. SCHMIDT. Principles of Animal Ecology. Philadelphia: W. B. Saunders Co. , 1949. (Pertinent materials are mostly in Section IV.)

DICE, L. R. Natural Communities. Ann Arbor, Michigan: University of Michigan Press, 1952. (Dice attempts to interweave materials from both plant and animal ecology.)

HANSON, H. C. , and E. D. CHURCHILL. The Plant Community. New York: Reinhold Publishing Corp. , 1961. (A more recent book than Oosting's. Contains a considerable amount of material on the methodology of community analysis.)

RUTTNER, F. Fundamentals of Limnology, 3rd ed. Toronto: University of Toronto Press, 1963. (This book is a good place to begin an acquaintance with the limnologist's view of communities.)

TEAL, J. M. "Energy Flow in the Salt Marsh Ecosystem of Georgia, " in Ecology 43 : 614-624, 1962. (This article is an excellent example of the unifying effect the concept of energy-flow has had on community studies by ecologists.)

section Two

DIVERSITY AMONG LIVING THINGS

During the twentieth century all the major developments in biology have tended to strengthen the concept of a fundamental unity in life processes. Yet diversity remains an obvious characteristic of living things. Whether this diversity is of any importance to the man who is devoting his life to the study of mitochondria in rat liver cells is perhaps debatable. But the diversity of living forms is an inescapable fact. Biologists—at least some biologists— must deal with it. Certainly any biology course having primarily cultural aims (see guide page 5) ought to deal with it. And diversity should be considered early in the course; the student needs a mental map on which to arrange the numerous organisms that are used later in illustrating the workings of biological principles and processes.

The number of concepts in this section is fewer than the number of pages might indicate. Pictures are many, and the text is somewhat discursive, so it behooves the teacher to adopt a schedule that is in proportion to the density of ideas rather than to the number of pages. Even allowing time for continued review of the important ideas from Chapters 2 and 3, study of Section Two should probably not extend over more than four weeks.

The chief intellectual burden of the section is not the characteristics of the numerous groupings into which taxonomists have sorted organisms. All such groupings involve a large element of subjectivity; they are mutable, if not ephemeral. Much depends upon still-accumulating paleontological evidence—and much depends upon the way in which the groups are defined. "The alligator belongs to the class Reptilia" is a kind of statement frequently heard—as if the class Reptilia were an a priori entity to which alligators must conform. Today such a statement is merely a matter of convenience; to the modern biologist it does not have Aristotelian implications. But it certainly will have such implications for the student unless he is cautioned to interpret the statement thus: "Alligators have characteristics that allow us most conveniently to place them in the Reptilia—as that class is defined by most zoologists." With such an interpretation, drill on the proper disposition of organisms into one of the many possible schemes of classification becomes absurd.

The chief intellectual burden of the section does lie in three abstract ideas: first, the purposes and the nature of biological classification (Chapter 4); second, the scheme of biological nomenclature (Chapter 5); third, the difficulties inherent in attempts to fit the facts of nature into a conceptual mold (Chapter 6). Whatever time the teacher allows for class discussion should be devoted primarily to these three ideas.

Throughout the work on Section Two, every effort should be made to bring into the laboratory or classroom as many examples of living organisms as possible. Both teacher and students may collect organisms for temporary display. Local hobbyists, pet shops, and florists, and state game and wildlife agencies are possible sources.

Then, too, students can be taken to organisms; zoos, aquariums, botanical gardens, and natural-history museums should all figure in the teacher's plans for Section Two.

CHAPTER 4

Animals

MAJOR IDEAS

1. Despite the bewildering diversity of animal forms, some major patterns of structural characteristics can be discerned in the animal kingdom. These patterns form the basis for the hier- archical ordering of taxonomic groups.

2. Because the taxonomist often finds it convenient to work with dead specimens—and, in the case of extinct species, must do so—the structural characteristics of organisms have been em- phasized in classification. But other kinds of characteristics are increasingly employed by modern taxonomists.

3. In different species structures having obviously similar basic components vary in detail; these variations appear to fit the structures to efficient functioning in different environments. This is the concept of structural adaptation—an important element in all evolutionary theories, but equally applicable to a theory of special creation.

4. Since the time of Darwin, the similarities among organ- isms have been ascribed to common evolutionary development. By means of levels of classification, the modern taxonomist seeks to express the varying degrees of evolutionary divergence; but simultaneously he seeks to provide biologists with con- venient means of grouping organisms.

TEACHING SUGGESTIONS

Guidelines

Work on this chapter may begin with Exercise 4.1.   The
first part of the exercise requires no acquaintance with classification beyond the vertebrate-invertebrate dichotomy, which
is known to most students. (If not known, it is easily explained.)
The necessary terminology is given (manual pages 66-67).

Or study of Chapter 4 may begin with textbook pages 78-83.
This is preferable if the teacher anticipates difficulty with the
basic concept of a hierarchical classification.   In this case the
teacher may wish to have students go through the procedure of
devising a classification for a group of objects that they can
manipulate—an assortment of bolts, screws, and nails of various sizes and types; or an assortment of geometrical forms
cut from cardboard.

If the first approach is adopted, the textbook material can
be conveniently divided into two assignments, thus: Pages 78 to
95—begin with the abstract notion of classification and proceed
with the organization of the chordate phylum; pages 95 to 117—
continue the description of "important" phyla of the animal kingdom and conclude with the meaning of biological classification,
a return to abstraction.   Between the two textbook assignments,
Exercise 4.1 can be concluded and Exercise 4.2 can be started.

If the second approach (starting with the textbook) is adopted,
all of Exercise 4.1 can be undertaken after the first textbook
assignment.   The remainder of the chapter can then be conveniently divided as follows: pages 83-103 and pages 103-117, with
Exercise 4.2 interjected at any convenient point.

Exercises 4.1, 4.3, and 4.4 provide opportunities to ac-
quaint students directly with many different animals.   But even
if all exercises are used, pictorial means will still have to be
used to give students a broader view of the diversity of animal
forms.   The pictures in the textbook should be fully exploited.
In addition, bulletin boards, filmstrips, and slides should be
employed.   For bulletin-board materials National Geographic
Magazine, Natural History, and LIFE magazine are particularly
good sources.   Students vary greatly in their acquaintance with
animals; the teacher must gauge the experiential background of
his classes and select materials accordingly.

Though incidental to the main purposes, some vocabulary
gain should result from study of Chapter 4.   Such terms as
"appendage," "adaptation," "internal," "external," "dorsal,"
"ventral," "marine," "alimentary canal," "anterior," "poste-

rior, " and "symmetry" will be useful in later work. Of course,
many students may already understand most of these terms.

Finally, the teacher should make frequent reference to the
appendix of the textbook, "A Catalogue of Living Things. " Though
several such references occur in the text, the teacher ought to
call attention to the introductory paragraphs on page 698 and to
point out the reversal of sequence.

Some Notes

Figure 4.1:   The technical form of each group name has
been used in the chart, but in class discussions teachers are
urged to employ the English forms whenever possible.   Thus,
say "chordates, " "arthropods, " "mammals, " even "canids";
leave "Chordata, " "Arthropoda, " and "Mammalia" for formal
use, in books.   Students should know that the technical forms
exist, but they do not need to burden themselves with exotic
spelling and pronunciation (unless they individually wish to do so).
The use of italics at the genus and species levels will be explained
in Chapter 5.   If a student asks about this practice now, let him
seek the answer himself.

Some teachers will undoubtedly consider the illustrations on pages
82 and 83 superfluous.   But with many tenth graders the mental
images of fox, wolf, shark, et al. , are quite vague.

Page 86: Blue pigments do not occur in birds, and green is rare,
not occurring in hummingbirds or quetzals.   Some student might
like to investigate "structural color. "

Figures 4.15 and 4.16: For background information consult N. J.
Berrill, The Origin of Vertebrates (New York: Oxford University
Press, 1955).

Page 95: The complete reference is F. Lutz, A Lot of Insects
(New York: G. P. Putnam's Sons, 1941).

Figures 4.21, 4.22, and 4.23: Though structural adaptation is
not mentioned in the captions, these figures (in addition to Figures
4.9 and 4.10) contain good material for discussion of that concept.

Figure 4.40: The question in the caption should not be overlooked.

EXERCISES

Exercise 4.1
Structural Characteristics in the Classification of Animals

Much of the advice given for Exercise 1.1 applies equally well
to this exercise.

The charts for Exercise 4.1 are rather cumbersome to draw.
Some teachers find it convenient to duplicate the charts and have
students paste the copies in their data books. The footnotes need
not be included, but students should read them over carefully
before the laboratory period and carry their manuals with them
for reference as they observe the organisms. The number of
columns in the charts depends upon the number of animals to be
observed.

At the beginning of observation, two minutes should be allowed
at each station. This time can be reduced as students become
familiar with the charts, but it is unlikely that more than 25
specimens can be examined in a single period. If diversity is
to be evident despite this limitation, a judicious choice of
specimens is important.

Since the keys in the second part of the exercise are very
simple, they do not take into consideration exceptional repre-
sentatives of the groups. Therefore, in choosing specimens,
take care to select those that will "key out." The following are
suggested:

> For Chart 1: rat or mouse, dogfish, frog
> or salamander, bat, canary or parakeet,
> snake, turtle, goldfish, lizard, lamprey.

> For Chart 2: earthworm, crayfish, jelly-
> fish, hydra, butterfly or moth, starfish,
> clam or oyster, beetle, spider, planarian,
> grasshopper, snail (but avoid slugs), clam-
> worm, millepede, centipede, tick.

Living animals should, of course, be used whenever possible.

When students have studied through page 95 in the textbook, the second part of the "Procedure" ("B. Using a Key," manual pages 68-70) can be assigned as homework. However, in classes where many students have reading difficulties, the teacher should assist in working several examples through the keys before leaving students to independent work. It is important to call especial attention to the cautions in the last two paragraphs of the "Procedure."

Exercise 4.2

The Levels of Classification

This exercise can be assigned any time after students encounter the vocabulary used in the textbook discussion of chordates and arthropods. For all students who have attained a ninth-grade reading level, Exercise 4.2 is quite feasible as an independent home assignment. For others, various degrees of assistance must be given—to the extreme of working out the whole exercise in class, with direct guidance by the teacher.

A few points where students may go wrong: (1) The peglike second incisors of the orangutan may be mistaken for extra canines. (2) On manual page 72 note that braincases—not whole skulls—are being compared. (3) The third upper incisors of the dog and cat may be mistaken for canines, but comparison with the teeth in the lower jaw will help to straighten this matter out.[1] (4) On manual page 76 both man and crayfish are in anomalous position for the interpretation of "dorsal" and "ventral."

The questions on manual page 77 follow directly from the preceding work. Students sometimes try to make them more complicated than they are, attempting to give reasons for the classification by repeating the structural features noted in the charts instead of merely citing the classification levels. The teacher should be sure to review answers to questions in class. If time is pressing, the rest of the work need not be considered in class except where related to specific questions from students.

---

[1] In all but the first printing of the manual, this difficulty has been eliminated; subsequent printings call for counts of dog and cat teeth in the lower jaw only.

Exercise 4. 3
A Dichotomous Key for Identification of Insects

If it is conceded that a primary aim of education is to provide the student with means for instructing himself, then teaching the use of a taxonomic key is surely justified. The basic principle in the use of such keys is introduced in Exercise 4. 1, but more extensive practice is required if the student is to gain some degree of independent skill.

Practice is conveniently obtained with a key to insect orders. Insects are usually available in sufficient variety to provide a number of pathways through the key and also in sufficient quantity to allow many students to work with the same species simultaneously—with replacements available after hard usage. The orders of insects are numerous enough for a key of some complexity, but not so numerous as to cause bewilderment. Finally, students are usually interested in insects, but not so familiar with them that a key is unnecessary for identification.

Time may not permit the use of the exercise by whole classes, but it can easily be assigned to groups of interested students, for it requires a minimum of teacher preparation and teacher direction.

If stereomicroscopes are available, they may be set up at convenient places in the laboratory. Students may use them whenever the magnification obtained with hand lenses is insufficient. Under this plan even a few microscopes may serve a whole class. Of course, by using nothing but larger insects, the teacher may avoid all need for microscopes.

The following insects are suggested for first attempts to use the key: grasshoppers, crickets, dragonflies, houseflies, ants, butterflies, chinch bugs, bumblebees, leafhoppers, termites. For this exercise, dead specimens are preferable to living ones. They need not be pinned specimens, however. After they are killed, the specimens may be thoroughly dried and stored in envelopes with a few crystals of paradichlorbenzene. Or specimens may be preserved in alcohol; these have the advantage of retaining some flexibility of parts.

Students who become especially interested in the use of keys for the identification of insects may be referred to H. E. Jaques, How to Know the Insects, 2nd ed. (Dubuque, Iowa: William C. Brown Co. , 1947). This carries identification to the family level, includes most of the common families in the United States, and uses the principle of the dichotomous key.

Exercise 4. 3 should be kept in mind for possible use in the spring, when the presence of living insects may again arouse student interest in them.

Exercise 4.4
Diversity in the Animal Kingdom: A Comparative Study

This exercise is not intended to be an abbreviated type study of animal phyla. Its primary purpose is to sharpen the student's observation of living animals. Secondarily, through it the student becomes acquainted with five major patterns of animal structure and obtains firsthand evidence for the structure-function relationship stressed in the textbook.

The principal teaching problem is one of logistics. It is sometimes difficult to assemble all the animals—in a healthy, active condition—simultaneously. Except for crayfish, all the species are used more than once in Green Version exercises, and all (including crayfish) are worth maintaining as permanent denizens of the laboratory. Therefore, some attention to culturing these animals on a permanent basis is justified. If cultures are routinely maintained, the problem of timing orders from suppliers is eliminated (see Galtsoff, et al., in "Teacher's References" for Chapter 2, this guide, page 70).

It is unlikely that Exercise 4.4 can be followed exactly as written. The teacher may direct students to omit some of the general questions (manual page 85) or to add others. (But be sure that any added questions can be answered from the material available; this is not the time to send students scurrying to the encyclopedia.) Some of the directions for specific animals may have to be bypassed—feeding the frog probably causes the most difficulty. Teachers may wish to add or substitute other animals. Suggestions: Daphnia, Tubifex, crickets, grasshoppers. Of course, if substitutions are made, the teacher must revise the specific directions.

The five stations should be as far from each other as the plan of the room permits. Movable tables and peripheral facilities allow the best arrangement, but adaptations can be made in other situations. Six students per station is perhaps ideal, but eight can be accommodated. Each group should be permitted about eight minutes at each station. Directions for observation must be thoroughly studied before the laboratory period begins.

SUPPLEMENTARY MATERIALS

Audiovisual Materials

Slides: Of materials for projection, the best for this chapter
are 2-X-2 slides. Large stocks of such slides, offering illustrations of almost all animal phyla, are available from the principal
biological suppliers: General Biological Supply House, Inc.,
8200 S. Hoyne Ave., Chicago, Ill. 60620; Carolina Biological
Supply Co., Burlington, N. C. 27216 (or Powell Laboratories,
Gladstone, Ore. 97027); Ward's Natural Science Establishment,
P. O. Box 1712, Rochester 3, N. Y. (or Ward's of California,
P. O. Box 1749, Monterey, Calif.). From these stocks the
teacher can select slides showing animals that are unavailable
as living specimens.

Filmstrips: Except for human physiology, no topic in biology
has been more abundantly treated in filmstrips than has classification. For the most part, however, the results have been medi-
ocre; the Green Version writers have seen none that they can
recommend ahead of others. As indicated above, the teaching
of animal diversity is better accomplished with slides; the teacher
is then free to discuss alternative systems of classification.

Motion-picture films: The comments on filmstrips apply in
some degree to films.

"Introducing Insects." 16 mm. Color. 17 minutes. National Film Board of Canada. Illustrates well the diversity among
insects and discusses classification. Includes some good slow-
motion and time-lapse sequences.

The following films are useful if other means of presenting the material are lacking; they are modern and well photo-
graphed in 16-mm color (all by Encyclopaedia Britannica Films):
"Stinging-celled Animals—Coelenterates"; "Flatworms";
"Segmentation—The Annelid Worms"; "The Jointed-legged
Animals—Arthropods"; "Echinoderms—Sea Stars and Their Relatives"; "What Is a Fish?" "What Is an Amphibian?"

See also "Life in the Ocean" (cited on page 153 of the guide),
which beautifully presents a number of marine animals.

Teacher's References

The literature in the field of animal systematics is vast and
rather easily accessible. Much of this literature is of little value

to the busy teacher of general biology. Each of the titles listed
below has been selected for some special relevancy. Beyond
this, the bibliographies in any good general zoology text will
lead to specialized works.

BORRADAILE, L. A. , and F. A. POTTS. The Invertebrata,
3rd ed. New York: Cambridge University Press, 1958.
(An excellent systematic reference on the invertebrates.
Contains numerous line drawings.)

HANSON, EARL D. Animal Diversity. Englewood Cliffs, N. J. :
Prentice-Hall, Inc. , 1961. (This short book goes rather
far beyond the materials in Green Version Chapter 4, but
its organization and viewpoints may prove stimulating to
the teacher.)

ROTHSCHILD, N. M. V. A Classification of Living Animals.
New York: John Wiley & Sons, Inc. , 1961. (Perhaps the
most recent systematic overview of the animal kingdom.)

SIMPSON, G. G. Principles of Animal Taxonomy. New York:
Columbia University Press, 1961. (An important summa-
rization by a paleontologist who has devoted many years of
careful thought to both the philosophy and the practice of
taxonomy.)

STORER, T. I. , and R. L. USINGER. Elements of Zoology,
2nd ed. New York: McGraw-Hill Book Co. , Inc. , 1961.
(A general textbook that approaches zoology from the viewpoint of systematics—but the system employed is rather
conventional.)

In addition to these references, the teacher will need books
for identification of various species. Instead of separate titles,
four "popular" series of guides are recommended: (1) The
"Pictured-Key to Nature" series, edited by H. E. Jaques and
published at Dubuque, Iowa, by the William C. Brown Co.
(2) The "Peterson Field Guides," edited by R. T. Peterson
and published at Boston by the Houghton Mifflin Co. (3) The
series of "Guides" published at Garden City, N. Y. , by Doubleday & Co. , Inc. (4) The series of "Fieldbooks" published in
New York by G. P. Putnam's Sons. Of these, the first covers
the widest variety of taxonomic groups; the second is most
generally useful in the field; the third has particularly excellent
illustrations; the fourth is distinguished as the pioneer series,
most of the titles being now well entrenched in librarians'
bibliographies.

CHAPTER 5

Plants

MAJOR IDEAS

Classification and structural adaptation continue to receive emphasis in Chapter 5. Additional ideas are:

1. In classifying plants, taxonomists have emphasized reproductive structures and life histories.

2. Binomial nomenclature grew out of the need for an orderly system that would provide distinctive names for each of the multitude of newly discovered organisms in the age of world exploration.

3. With the biologists' application of a few simple rules, the binomial system has resulted in relative stability and clarity in biological nomenclature for nearly two hundred years. Remarkably, this has occurred in the face of extraordinary scientific developments: the revolution in taxonomic thinking (evolution), the multiplication of languages in which scientific material is published, and the nearly hundredfold increase in known species.

TEACHING SUGGESTIONS

Guidelines

It has been customary to wrap the whole of taxonomy in a neat package of abstractions that are quickly and superficially covered and quickly and completely forgotten. The authors believe that taxonomy is not a thing apart, but that it explicitly or implicitly permeates all areas of biology. Moreover, they believe it to be an intellectual achievement, an important facet in the comprehension of human cultural development, and, therefore, a matter of importance in the high school biology course. The result of these beliefs is an attempt to avoid locking taxonomy into a compartment by itself. The writers' experience indicates that taxonomy is more clearly understood—and (we think) better appreciated as an intellectual achievement—when it is divided into parts and taught at several appropriate points than is the case when it is presented in one massive lump. So the species concept came first (Chapter 2); classification followed (Chapter 4); now comes nomenclature.

Work can begin with Exercise 5.1 if some special attention is given to a few terms: "rhizoids," "midribs," "spores," "parallel-veined," "net-veined," "lianas." Yet, with the exception of "midrib," these terms are in the textbook chapter, so work may just as well begin there. If this choice is made, Exercise 5.2 may be taken up before Exercise 5.1; the latter then becomes a means of reviewing the textbook chapter.

For assignment the most obvious divisions of the textbook chapter are pages 119-125, pages 126-139, and pages 139-149. The first of these is rather short, but, as has been mentioned previously, number of pages is not necessarily a good guide to the number of ideas. In this chapter nomenclature will require a major share of discussion time.

Refer to the "Teaching Suggestions" of Chapter 4 (guide pages 85-86) for guidance in handling diversity of plants. Avoid becoming entangled in alternation of generations—traditionally a "Slough of Despond" in the pilgrimage through the plant kingdom. What Marston Bates calls "the botanist's obsession with sex" should not at this time deter the student from gaining a panoramic view of plant diversity. In due time reproductive cycles will be dealt with, in Chapter 15.

Some Notes

The photograph at the head of the chapter shows saguaro cacti in Arizona.

A student report on the life of Linnaeus might be useful. Encyclopedia accounts are dull—as Linnaeus himself certainly was not. But even an average tenth grader ought to be able to contrive an interesting report from Green Laurels, by D. C. Peattie (New York: Simon & Schuster, Inc., 1936. Chapters 4, 5, and 6).

Some expansion of the discussion on text pages 124-125 may be interesting to students. Further examples of short generic epithets are Pica (magpies), Sus (pigs), Acer (maples), Bos (cattle), Rhus (sumacs), Erica (heathers), Ficus (figs), Ilex (hollies), Chen (snow geese), Anas ("puddle" ducks), Iva (marsh elders), Aix (wood chucks). On the other hand, the layman's view has some justification; consider Stongylocentrotus (sea urchins), Dolichocephalocyrtus (beetles), and Electroheliocopsyche (trichopteran)!

Some further examples of generic epithets far from classical Latin and Greek are Fothergilla, Forsythia, Cunninghamia, Koelreuteria, Torreya, Kickxia, Muhlenbergia, and, of course, Welwitschia—all these are plants named for botanists; Lama, Nasua, and Fayra—mammals with names derived from American Indian languages; Peggichisme—it looks like Greek, but try pronouncing it; Arizona, Sonora—snakes with names derived from geographical terms of American Indian origin; Ginkgo— a gymnosperm tree with a Chinese name.

Figure 5.14: The spines of cacti are modified leaves.

Figure 5.39: Answers to the question in the caption: Oscillatoria—Myxophyta; Ulva and Enteromorpha—Chlorophyta; Laminaria, Fucus, and Ascophyllum—Phaeophyta; Chondrus and Polysiphonia—Rhodophyta.

EXERCISES

    5.1 Diversity in the Plant Kingdom . . . . BASIC
    5.2 Diversity Among Angiosperms . . . . BASIC
    Taken together, these exercises should not require more than three class periods.

Exercise 5.1
Diversity in the Plant Kingdom

If time is pressing, the secondary purpose of this exercise
(manual page 89) may be treated lightly. Not so the primary
purpose. Students generally have far less acquaintance with
plants than with animals; therefore, more effort is required to
broaden the concept "plant." The easiest plants to obtain, of
course, are those that tend to confirm the popular stereotype.
Considerable effort (and, if necessary, money) should be ex-
pended to provide a true diversity of plants; perhaps not more
than three of the ten specimens should be angiosperms, and not
more than one of these should be herbaceous.

Materials. The student is being asked to observe. Inference
is to be kept at a minimum. Therefore the plant materials should
show as many as possible of the characteristics needed for correct scoring. For example, gymnosperm specimens should
include seeds; angiosperm specimens should have fruits or
flowers; mosses, ferns, and lycopods should bear spore cases.
Of course, some distinctions—as between shrub and tree—will
be difficult to exhibit with specimens.

Suggestions for plant materials follow: For microscope—
green algae (Spirogyra, Oedogonium, Ulothrix); blue-green algae
(Oscillatoria, Anabaena, Nostoc); yeasts. For hand lens or
stereomicroscope—molds (Rhizopus, Aspergillus); liverworts
(Marchantia, Conocephalum); mosses (Polytrichum, Mnium,
Pogonatum, Dicranum). For naked eye—Lycopodium; ferns
(Polystichum, Polypodium); pine; spruce; begonia; Zebrina;
household geranium; fire thorn (Pyracantha).

As always, fresh material is preferable to that which is
preserved. Most of the plants listed above are fairly easy to
obtain in the autumn. To obtain bread molds, start about ten
days before the exercise is scheduled. If possible, use home-
baked bread or rolls, since commercial bread usually contains
mold inhibitors. Break the bread into ten pieces to avoid later
handling. Spores of the mold are usually abundant in the air;
after the bread has been exposed to air in the laboratory for a
day, sprinkle it with a little water, place it in a covered dish,
and keep it in a warm, dark place.

Procedure. The chart on manual pages 90-91 bears a superficial resemblance to a dichotomous key. The resemblance
enables the student, who has had experience with keys in Exercises 4.1 and 4.3, to grasp the plan of work quickly. But of
course the chart is not a key, because it does not lead to
identification.

Begin the work by dividing the class into groups of 2 to 4
students and assigning each group to a station. Each station

should be supplied with a specimen of each kind of plant.   If sufficient specimens of each kind of plant are not available, some plan of rotation among stations is required.   By this time students should be able to move from station to station readily.   Work will be expedited if the teacher runs through the scoring of a specimen (one not included in the exercise) before setting students to work.

Discussion.   The secondary purpose of this exercise derives from the last portion of Chapter 4 (pages 111-116).   From the idea that classification reflects genetic (kinship) relationships, it logically follows that characteristics of organisms have diverged through successive generations in the past.   That some present-day organisms may have retained more, and others fewer, of their ancestors' characteristics is but a corollary of this proposition.

The numbers in the chart are quite arbitrary.   They have been worked out so that, when summed along possible courses through the chart, they will provide low scores for plants generally considered primitive by botanists and high scores for plants generally considered advanced.   For the purposes of this exercise, "primitive" and "advanced" are adequately explained in the "Introduction" (manual pages 88-89).   During the discussion at the conclusion of the work, the teacher must bear in mind and communicate to the students the subjective nature of the scores.   For example, it is probable that many mycologists would justifiably object to the rather low score that is assigned to fungi.

Exercise 5.2
Diversity Among Angiosperms

As the most abundant and conspicuous plants known to students, angiosperms deserve special attention.   The emphasis on flowers in this exercise corroborates the importance of reproductive structures in plant classification.   Though the memorization of names of plant structures is not encouraged, the student is certain to pick up some botanical terminology.   The terminology has, however, been reduced to a minimum, and the terms are "defined" in pictures rather than in words.

The key on manual pages 94-95 employs the same principle as that used in the keys of Chapter 4.   Only the format is new, and this is so obvious that the student does not require any explanation.   Indeed, all the teacher need do is provide the facilities and materials, then circulate among the working groups to offer suggestions on reading the key and observing the specimens. Motivation is usually good because the key presents a challenge; the student obtains satisfaction by demonstrating to himself his ability to identify organisms.

A convenient plan for carrying out this exercise follows:
Divide the class into groups of 3 or 4 students. Arrange as many
stations as there are groups. At each station provide hand lenses
and dissecting needles for each student and one good specimen of
each plant to be keyed out. Number, but do not name, each specimen. Depending upon the difficulty inherent in the plants and
the ability of the students, keying 4 or 5 species should require
about twenty-five minutes of work time.

The specimens used for this exercise must, of course,
belong to one of the seventeen families included in the key. If
any do not, then either they will not fit the alternatives in the
key at all or they will lead the student to the wrong family.

In most parts of the country, it is impossible to collect a
sufficient variety of specimens outdoors in the autumn. From
florists, however, it is often possible to obtain gladioli and
snapdragons—and, sometimes, sweet peas—that are not fresh
enough to sell but perfectly satisfactory for this exercise. Tradescantia and Zebrina may be maintained in the school greenhouse,
and paper-white narcissus may easily be grown from bulbs placed
in a little gravel and regularly watered. But, by and large, the
material for this exercise should have been collected during the
previous spring and summer. Such material can be kept in plastic
bags in a refrigerator. Or it can be dried under pressure, in
standard herbarium fashion. Flowers of dried material can be
dissected readily after being placed in gently boiling water for
a few minutes. With some families (orchid, iris, amaryllis,
water-plantain, buttercup, parsley), only the flowers are needed
for running the key. These flowers can be preserved in FAA
(formalin-acetic acid-alcohol). FAA can be purchased, or it
can be made up as follows: ethyl alcohol (95%), 50 ml; glacial
acetic acid, 2 ml; formalin (40% formaldehyde solution), 10 ml;
and water, 40 ml.

The following is a list of suggested plants for each family:

Orchid Family	Wild plants: rattlesnake plantain, Spiranthes, Habenaria, or any small-flowered wild orchid that is abundant. (But most wild orchids should not be picked.) Cultivated plants: any multiflowered greenhouse orchid
Amaryllis Family	Wild plants: yellow star grass, atamasco lily, zephyr lily (Zephyranthes) Cultivated plants: amaryllis, Narcissus, daffodil, spider lily (Lycorus), snowflake (Leucojum)

Iris Family	Wild plants: wild Iris species, blue-eyed grass, blackberry lily, celestial lily (Nemastylis), Alophia Cultivated plants: gladiolus, crocus, cultivated Iris
Grass Family	Wild plants: any of numerous wild species Cultivated plants: wheat, rye, oats, bluegrass, Johnson grass
Lily Family	Wild plants: wild onion, Yucca, Solomon's seal, false asphodel (Tofieldia), death camass (Zygadenus), trout lily (Erythronium), Calochortus Cultivated plants: day lily, hyacinth, cultivated lilies, lily of the valley
Sedge Family	Wild plants: nut grass, bulrush, spike rush, sedge Cultivated plants: Egyptian paper plant (Cyperus)
Spiderwort Family	Wild plants: spiderwort, roseling, dayflower (Commelina) Cultivated plants: Zebrina, Rhoeo, Tradescantia
Water-Plantain Family	Wild plants: water plantain (Alisma), arrowhead (Sagittaria), Damasonium, Echinodorus
Rose Family	Wild plants: five-finger, avens, wild rose, blackberry, hawthorn, mountain mahogany (Cercocarpus), antelope brush (Purshia) Cultivated plants: Spiraea, flowering quince, peach, apple, plum, strawberry
Buttercup Family	Wild plants: buttercup, pasqueflower, wild anemone, globeflower, monkshood Cultivated plants: Clematis, columbine, Christmas rose (Helleborus), anemone

Phlox Family

Wild plants: wild sweet William, blue phlox, Gilia, Jacob's ladder, Navarretia
Cultivated plants: perennial phlox, Drummond's phlox, trailing phlox

Figwort Family

Wild plants: butter-and-eggs, beard-tongue, turtlehead, speedwell, louse-wort, paintbrush
Cultivated plants: snapdragon, fox-glove, Torenia

Mustard Family

Wild plants: shepherd's purse, penny-cress, peppergrass, crinkleroot
Cultivated plants: radish, watercress, mustard, turnip, stock

Legume Family

Wild plants: partridge pea, locust, wild indigo, locoweed, rattlebox, mesquite, palo verde
Cultivated plants: sweet pea, Wisteria, lupine, vetch, bean, clover, alfalfa

Parsley Family

Wild plants: wild carrot, water parsnip, dog fennel (Lomatium), sweet fennel (Foeniculum)
Cultivated plants: dill, parsley, parsnip, caraway

Honeysuckle Family

Wild plants: elderberry, Viburnum, twinflower, snowberry, Japanese honeysuckle
Cultivated plants: Abelia, bush honey-suckle, Weigela

Sunflower Family

Wild plants: black-eyed Susan, dandelion, oxeye daisy, fleabane, aster, gaillardia
Cultivated plants: zinnia, sunflower, chrysanthemum, Shasta daisy, lettuce

SUPPLEMENTARY MATERIALS

Audiovisual Materials

The remarks concerning audiovisual materials for Chapter 4 (guide page 91) apply equally well to Chapter 5.

Filmstrips: "Classification of Plants." United World Films, Inc. Color. Although this filmstrip uses the ancient Cryptogam-Phanerogam classification, it is clearly organized in a way that can easily be related to more modern classification. The drawings are excellent. Only a few of the names in this British film will be unfamiliar. One error—roots of ferns and horsetails are called rhizoids.

"Kinds of Plants." Society for Visual Education. Color. A general review of the plant kingdom.

"Great Names in Biology: Carolus Linnaeus." Encyclopaedia Britannica Films. Color. Good for biographical background.

Films: "Fungi." Encyclopaedia Britannica Films. 16 mm. Color.

"Simple Plants: The Algae." Encyclopaedia Britannica Films. 16 mm. Color.

"Gymnosperms." Encyclopaedia Britannica Films. 16 mm. Color.

These three films are part of a series covering the plant kingdom. As a whole the series places too much emphasis on phylogeny for Section Two of the Green Version course; but taken individually, the films may be useful for emphasizing plant diversity with students who have poor experiential backgrounds.

Teacher's References

BENSON, L. Plant Classification. Boston: D. C. Heath & Co., 1957. (A general text on plant taxonomy, but it emphasizes vascular plants.)

FULLER, H. J., and O. TIPPO. College Botany. New York: Holt, Rinehart & Winston, 1954. (Uses Tippo's classification, which is close to that used in the Green Version.)

POPP, H. W., and A. R. GROVE. Botany: A Textbook for Colleges, 3rd ed. New York: McGraw-Hill Book Co., Inc., 1960. (Uses a good, up-to-date classification of the plant kingdom.)

SAVORY, T. Naming the Living World. New York: John Wiley
& Sons, Inc. , 1963. (An excellent introduction to the principles of biological nomenclature.)

SOKAL, R. R. , and P. H. A. SNEATH. Principles of Numerical
Taxonomy. San Francisco: W. H. Freeman & Co. , Publishers, 1963. (The Linnean system of binomial nomenclature is not likely to disappear overnight, but the teacher
ought to be aware of new developments in the field of biological nomenclature.)

The series of identification manuals cited at the end of
Chapter 4 (guide page 92) includes several that deal with plant
groups.

CHAPTER 6

Protists

MAJOR IDEAS

Structural adaptations, classification, and nomenclature should continue to receive emphasis during work on Chapter 6. Additional ideas are:

1. All that we know of microorganisms has come to light within the era of modern science. This knowledge—representing a whole new dimension in biology—has been integrated into the older biological knowledge slowly, with difficulty, and (still) incompletely.

2. Science is an international enterprise, sustained by the efforts of many men in many countries. (This, of course, is an idea that should carry through the entire year, but it is especially appropriate for emphasis in Chapter 6.)

3. The more one learns about nature, the less easy it is to fit the knowledge into compartments. The boundaries between taxonomic groups seem sharp when a scheme of classification is studied in a book—but indistinct when organisms themselves are observed.

TEACHING SUGGESTIONS

Guidelines

Animals are very familiar to students, plants (except in a general way) less familiar, and protists quite unfamiliar. Consequently, though shorter than Chapters 4 and 5, Chapter 6 presents more difficulties for the student. It seems best not to dwell unduly on the idea of diversity in the text, but to concentrate on building a concept of each phylum, leaving diversity to the illustrations.

Exercise 6.1 can be set up well before the textbook chapter is assigned. This is not just for the convenience of having organisms to observe early in the work. Also, many of them are plants rather than protists, so the exercise forms a good bridge between Chapters 5 and 6.

The chapter in the textbook cannot logically be divided for assignment purposes; it seems best to assign it as a whole.

In Chapters 4 and 5 ecological relationships were allowed to sink into the background. In Chapter 6 ideas and terms from Chapters 2 and 3 are picked up again—in fact, a new term, "symbiosis," is introduced. The teacher should be aware of this swing back toward ecology; he should actively exploit it, because it prepares the way for a full-fledged return to ecological concepts in Section Three.

The introductory part of the chapter, which provides historical background, and the central part, which catalogues the phyla of protists, do not lend themselves well to class discussion. Time available for discussion is best devoted to the problems involved in human attempts to impose order upon the facts of nature —as illustrated by difficulties of classification at the kingdom level, for example, or by doubts concerning the status of viruses. From the first chapter students have been exposed to the idea that learning science is not the memorizing of a prescribed system, into which facts are to be fitted with Procrustean determination, but rather a seeking after new and better ways to order an ever-widening array of facts. Said Abbé Galliani, "La science est plutôt destiné à étudier qu'à connaître, à chercher qu'à trouver la vérité." Chapter 6 offers a fine opportunity to bring this attitude to the forefront.

If students have studied cells in a previous course, the question of the cellularity of protists may be raised. Are ciliates, for example, single cells, or are they organisms that have lost cellularity—or did they ever have cells? How do we interpret cellularity in the slime molds?

Some Notes

The photograph at the head of the chapter shows a mixture of "protozoa," mostly ciliates.

Figures 6.2 and 6.3: Though the principle of the compound microscope was well known in his time, Leeuwenhoek's microscopes were simple lenses. But Leeuwenhoek ground his lenses so expertly that some produced magnifications of 270 diameters.

Figure 6.6: After the discussion of nomenclature in Chapter 5, take advantage of every opportunity to use technical names—but without ostentation. The names of microorganisms are suitable for this purpose, since most microorganisms lack other names.

Pages 160-161: Point out that in referring to an organism biologists often use only the generic epithet when a specific distinction does not seem necessary. This practice is not a violation of the binomial system; it is merely a convenient and legitimate way to avoid specific identification.

EXERCISES

6.1 A Garden of "Microorganisms" . . . . BASIC
6.2 Experiments on Spontaneous Generation. . . . . BASIC
6.3 Microscopic Study of Bacteria . . Highly Recommended
    The exercises for Chapter 7 are also concerned with microorganisms—in part, with protists. If convenient, any of these exercises may be started during the work on Chapter 6.

Exercise 6.1
A Garden of "Microorganisms"

    Terminological distinctions made in the introduction to this exercise are quite important.
    Exercise 6.1 allows the biology teacher to lay claim (temporarily) to some of the olfactory ill fame usually monopolized by the chemistry department. This is not necessarily bad public relations; in many schools it has called attention to the fact that there is life in the biology laboratory!

Materials. The media recommended in the manual have been chosen with an eye to culturing a wide variety of microorganisms; there are, of course, many other possible choices.

If finger bowls are in short supply, any glass or plastic container more than 10 cm in diameter and having more or less vertical sides 4 cm or more high may be substituted. Small plastic refrigerator dishes are good; but they cannot be stacked, so they require more space after being filled. It is desirable that all the containers used in any one class be alike.

If necessary the number of containers per team may be reduced, but the media recommended for Bowls 1, 3, 4, 5, and 8 should be retained. If the teacher plans to use Exercise 7.5, Bowl 9 should be omitted. Peppercorns (Bowl 10) are recommended because of their historical association with Leeuwenhoek's work. The kind of fruit for Bowl 1 can be varied from team to team; so can the kind of water for Bowl 3. Most of these materials can be supplied from students' homes.

Hand lenses may be used in place of stereomicroscopes, but they are not really an adequate substitute in this exercise.

Tap water may be used in setting up the cultures, but if the water contains much chlorine it should be allowed to stand twenty-four to forty-eight hours in a container that will provide a large exposed surface from which the chlorine can diffuse.

Procedure. It is convenient to set up three teams of 10 students each. Each student is responsible for 1 of the 10 bowls, and each bowl has three replicates. (Few classes have exactly 30 students; see guide page 60 for suggested alternatives.)

It is important to note that all bowls must be clean at the outset (and of course should be cleaned thoroughly afterwards). Here "clean" means not sterile, but chemically clean—that is, free of all soap or detergent. After washing the bowls, rinse them thoroughly at least four times.

If the bowls are set up on Friday, they may be observed macroscopically (and olfactorily) during the following week. Each day at the beginning of the class period, the bowls should be placed in an accessible place so that each student can observe all bowls—at least in a cursory way. But it is too time-consuming to have all students make detailed notes on all bowls; each should concentrate on the bowl he set up.

One week after the experiment has been set up, the materials in the bowls should be ripe for microscopic observation. Students having like bowl numbers should work together as a group. Provide each of these (ten) groups with whatever optical equipment the growths in its bowls seem to require. For example, students working with Bowl 3 will require monocular microscopes, but they will have little use for hand lenses or stereomicroscopes. In a classroom situation it is not feasible to attempt identification of microbes all the way to the genus and species levels; in most instances one must be content with identification at the phylum level. Some students may, however, wish to pursue the matter further with the aid of the references on page 103 of the manual.

The peppercorn infusion can be saved for use in Exercise 6.3. In fact, that exercise might be considered an extension of Exercise 6.1. It has been written up separately because many teachers do not want to become involved in staining techniques in Exercise 6.1; and this is probably wise, for "micro-observation day" can become complex enough without it.

Discussion. The first step is to have the reports of observations exchanged among the students either orally or by means of duplicated sheets.

The questions on page 103 of the manual present opportunities for discussion to proceed in many directions. It is particularly desirable to stress the fact that in this "garden," foods—not merely inorganic nutrients—are provided for the microorganisms since all are consumers (Item 6). Though there is no clear-cut way to distinguish the consumers that should be called decomposers, this exercise displays an array of them in situations where the decomposition process is obvious (Item 7).

From this point on, the discussion might be turned to such questions as: Why the odors, and why different kinds? Where did the microorganisms come from (a good prelude to Exercise 6.2)? How can you account for the changes in a given bowl over a period of time?

Exercise 6.2
Experiments on Spontaneous Generation

This is a demonstration exercise. There is no need for more than one setup per class. But if the teacher has more than one class, replication by classes may reveal that there can be some variation in the results.

A few students working outside of class time may prepare the materials. Those who prepared the medium for Exercise 2.2 can now prepare the medium for this exercise with a minimum of teacher supervision. The work with glass tubing is new, however. If preparation of the flasks is done after school, the sealing with paraffin can be delayed until next day and then performed in front of the class, after the demonstrators have briefly described their preparatory activities. Filtering can be avoided if peptone is available; use about 8 g of peptone in place of the bouillon cube.

At 15-lb pressure the temperature in the autoclave or pressure cooker is 120°C.

Typical results are as follows:

Flask 1 becomes turbid within a day or two. In this and the other
flasks that become turbid, patches of mold often develop on
the surface of the medium.

Flask 2 usually becomes turbid a day or two later than Flask 1.

Flask 3 may take a very long time to become turbid; indeed, it
may never become turbid. Nevertheless, though many
microbes are killed by boiling, the resistant spores of some
bacteria may survive and eventually produce turbidity.

Flask 4 usually becomes turbid at about the same time as Flask 2.

Flask 5, with its small opening, may not become turbid for many
days or (if there are few air currents) even weeks. But if it
is kept long enough, turbidity will appear.

Flask 6 often remains clear long after the experiment has been
concluded.

Flask 7 should remain perfectly clear for as long as it is undisturbed. Some flasks of this kind have been dated and kept
for years as exhibits. The design of the S-shaped tube is
comparable to that of Pasteur's "swan-neck" flask.

Students may doubt that the turbidity of the broth is caused by
bacteria. (If the course is doing what it should, they will demand
evidence.) The material from Flasks 2 and 4 can be used in doing the work of Exercise 6.3. Usually some good slides of bacilli
and cocci will be obtained, and these can be compared with prepared slides of known bacteria.

The chief point in the exercise involves Flasks 3 and 7:
Believers in abiogenesis argued that Spallanzani's sealed flask
did not develop microbes because heating had destroyed the
"power" of the air in the flask and there was no way for new air
to enter; Pasteur's "swan-neck" flask disposes of this argument.

Exercise 6.3
Microscopic Study of Bacteria

This is a fine exercise for arousing interest if time and facilities permit its use. All the work can be done in twenty minutes.
(This does not include time for studying directions beforehand
and cleaning up afterward.)

If the biology laboratory is not equipped with sufficient gas
outlets, and if alcohol burners are unavailable, the teacher may
be able to arrange an exchange of laboratories with the chemistry
teacher for one period.

To prepare crystal-violet stain, dissolve 2 g of crystal violet
(gentian violet) in 20 ml of ethyl alcohol (95%) and add 180 ml of
distilled water.

The teacher should demonstrate the use of the inoculating loop. Though sterile technique is not critical in this exercise, flaming the loop before and after use should be practiced for the sake of bacteriological principle and in preparation for Exercise 7.2.

The oil-immersion lens is not essential; after all, Leeuwenhoek observed bacteria in a peppercorn infusion with a lens magnifying 270X. But an oil-immersion microscope always adds some interest to the observation of stained bacteria. To point up the extent of magnification possible with the oil-immersion microscope, a simple comparison can be made: To the center of the chalkboard fasten a 1-mm square of white paper; around this mark off a 1-m square. The bacteria, when viewed under the oil-immersion microscope, are magnified to a similar degree. From this the students can get an indication of the minute size of bacteria.

Some teachers provide blank slide labels. The student may mark such a label with the name of the organism, the date, and his initials, affix the label, and keep the finished slide as a souvenir. Because students are often proud of these tokens of their achievement, knowledge of the activities of the biology classes may be disseminated through the school.

SUPPLEMENTARY MATERIALS

Audiovisual Materials

The remarks concerning audiovisual materials for Chapter 4 (guide page 91) apply equally well to Chapter 6.

Phonograph records: "The Scientists Speak: Biology." (Harcourt, Brace & World, Inc.). Includes a stimulating talk by René Dubos that weaves his personal experiences into the story of microbiology.

Filmstrip: "Great Names in Biology: Antony van Leeuwenhoek." (Encyclopaedia Britannica Filmstrips). Color. Good for biographical background.

Motion-picture films: "Bacteria: Laboratory Study." (Indiana University Films). 16 mm. Color. 15 minutes. Gives a more extended treatment of bacteriological techniques than does the BSCS film cited below.

"Bacteria." (Encyclopaedia Britannica Films). 16 mm. Color. Emphasizes the kinds of bacteria and their life processes.

"The Single-celled Animals: Protozoa. " (Encyclopaedia
Britannica Films). 16 mm. Color. The title may raise some
good questions.

"Bacteriological Techniques. " (Thorne Films—Boulder,
Colorado). 16 mm. Color. 5 minutes. Produced by the BSCS;
intended for the teacher who has not had a course in bacteriology.
Techniques demonstrated include making of cotton plugs, transfer
of cultures, preparing agar plates, spotting and streaking, form-
ing a microculture chamber.

Teacher's References

BROCK, T. D. (ed.). Milestones in Microbiology. Englewood
    Cliffs, N. J.: Prentice-Hall, Inc. (Includes papers by
    Spallanzani, Pasteur, Koch, Stanley. Beijerinck.)
DOBELL, C. (ed.). Antony van Leeuwenhoek and His Little
    Animals. New York: Dover Publications, Inc., 1960.
    (The letters Leeuwenhoek sent to the Royal Society, in
    which he described his discoveries.)
DUBOS, R. J. Louis Pasteur, Free Lance of Science. Boston:
    Little, Brown & Co., 1950. (An illuminating biography by
    a man who has himself contributed to microbiology in many
    ways.)
KUDO, R. Protozoology, 4th ed. Springfield, Ill.: Charles C.
    Thomas, Publisher, 1954. (A standard handbook for informa-
    tion on the protozoa.)
STANLEY, W. M., and E. G. VALENS. Viruses and the Nature
    of Life. New York: E. P. Dutton & Co., Inc., 1961.
    (Stanley is the scientist who crystallized the tobacco virus.
    The contents apply directly to the question raised at the end
    of Chapter 6, textbook page 168.)

section $Three$

PATTERNS IN THE BIOSPHERE

Although Chapter 6 concludes Section Two, it leads directly
into Section Three. Emphasis on the diversity of organisms comes to
an end with Chapter 6, but the protists—now viewed in their ecological settings—retain the center of attention in Chapter 7. In the
classroom the transition from section to section need not be conspicuous; the basic ideas of Section Two require no elaborate summa-
tion. In addition, work on some of the exercises for Chapter 6 may
have to extend beyond the time of transition (Exercise 6.2, for
example), and some exercises in Chapter 7 may already have been
started before Section Two is finished. In a word, the break between
Sections Two and Three is not a major one.

The textbook introduction to Section Three should be sufficient
to establish the change in viewpoint that characterizes the return
from taxonomic to ecological thinking. But it may be worthwhile
to dwell a bit upon the quotation from Hinshelwood (page 173). To
it may be added one from Henri Poincaré: "Science is built up of
facts as a house is built of bricks; but a collection of facts is no more
a science than a heap of bricks is a house."

Patterns of Life
in the Microscopic World

MAJOR IDEAS

1. Soil is an ecosystem consisting of living organisms as well as of organic remains and inorganic substances. The organisms vary in size, but the most significant ones are microscopic.

2. Microorganisms are sensitive to the chemical nature of the ecosystems in which they occur. Ionization is one of the significant chemical processes in the soil environment.

3. All the community relationships discussed in Chapter 3 can be found in soil microcommunities. Mycorrhizae are a special kind of symbiosis—probably mutualistic—that is characteristic of soil communities.

4. The biogeochemical cycle of the element nitrogen in large part turns upon the activities of soil microorganisms. In addition much of the return of other elements to the inorganic world is accomplished by soil microbes.

5. The human body is a microcosm of microbial populations that exist in various forms of symbiosis with the human organism. In general all macroscopic organisms are, in differing degrees, centers of symbiosis.

6. Disease is not a special curse of the human species, but a universal attribute of living things. An infectious disease is an ecological relationship between two organisms. (Note that viruses must here be considered organisms.)

7. Virulence is a characteristic of pathogens; resistance and immunity are characteristics of organisms that pathogens affect. The milieu in which pathogen and host meet is a third factor in the causation of disease.

8.   Different diseases prevail in different parts of the world as a result of different ecological conditions.   Among the ecological conditions necessary to the existence of some diseases is the presence of suitable vectors.

TEACHING SUGGESTIONS

Guidelines

Chapter 7 is long; it contains few pictures and a rather large number of ideas.   Moreover, these ideas are in some cases entirely unfamiliar to most students, or (and this is much harder to cope with) they are ideas involving unfamiliar ways of looking at superficially familiar things.   All of this calls for a slowing of the pace.

The textbook chapter is most logically broken into two assignments: pages 174-188 and pages 188-204.   "The Ecology of Micro-organisms" is clearly introductory and might be discussed along with the introduction to Section Three.   The first reading assignment would then begin on page 175.

Both Exercise 7.1 and Exercise 7.3 require a long time to bring to completion.   They will run far beyond the time needed for study of the textbook chapter.   Obviously Exercise 7.1 should be set up while soils are being discussed, and Exercise 7.3 while infectious diseases are under consideration.   Exercise 7.2 can be fitted in at any convenient time.   Meanwhile, observations on Exercise 6.2 should be continuing.

Exercise 9.5 concerns the measurement of pH.   If Chapter 9 is to be skipped, students might read the "Introduction" and "Background Information" for this exercise (manual pages 181-182) in connection with work on soil.   The teacher might also demonstrate the colorimetric measurement of pH—or, at least, the distinguishing of acid from base by litmus.

Curriculum-makers universally regard soil conservation and disease prevention as important topics.   So do the writers of the Green Version.   But at the tenth-grade level the time has passed for the building of terraces on the sand table and the morbid recital of disease symptoms.   If the student is ever to progress beyond the rote repetition of "right" prescriptions for conservation of soil and prevention of disease, he must be induced to wrestle

with the concepts embodied in the terms "soil" and "disease."
Chapter 7 aims to bring the student to grips with the biological
realities of these concepts.

There is, of course, need to apply the concepts in a local situation. Do you teach suburban students whose parents are struggling to make a lawn on subsoil hastily bulldozed into place by the
departing "developer"? Do your students know soil only as a
commodity that is sold in plastic bags at the variety store? Are
the agriculturists of your region coping with drained muck soils,
irrigated desert soils, acid soils, alkaline soils, sandy coastal
soils lacking humus, upland clay soils, lateritic soils?

In many situations tuberculosis is still an important infectious
disease; use it to point up the concepts of transmission, symptoms,
virulence, resistance, epidemiology. In New Orleans what has happened to yellow fever? In Charleston what has happened to malaria? In Norfolk and Baltimore what has happened to cholera? Even
the most voluminous textbook cannot adequately treat such local or
regional matters. A textbook may replace a teaching machine;
it cannot replace the alert teacher.

The appendix of the textbook was frequently referred to during
work on Section Two. The teacher should continue to call attention
to it. As various groups of organisms are mentioned in Chapter 7,
they should be placed in the framework of the classification
scheme.

Some Notes

Figure 7.8: Note that organisms are indicated by boldface type,
substances by thin type.

Pages 199-200: The terminology for kinds of immunity seems to
be quite unsettled. That used here follows Frobisher (Fundamentals of Microbiology) for the most part.

Pages 191-192: Recent work indicates that aspirin apparently
works by moderating the body's defensive response to disease.
See H. O. J. Collier, "Aspirin," in Scientific American. 209
(November. 1963), 96-108.

Figure 7.16: DDT is dichloro-diphenyl-trichloroethane, or more
precisely 1, 1, 1, trichloro-2, 2, -di-(p-chlorophenyl)-ethane.
Biology is not the only science that makes use of long terms!

EXERCISES

From the wide range of possible microbiological laboratory
exercises, these have been selected for their practicability and
their relevance to the discussion in the textbook. For the teacher
who wishes to proceed further with microbiological laboratory
work, the following reference is recommended: Committee on
Education, Society of American Bacteriologists, "Special Issue
on Microbiology in Introductory Biology," The American Biology
Teacher, 22 (June, 1960).

Exercise 7.1
Decomposing Action of Soil Microbes

This experiment shows the decomposing power of molds and
bacteria (including the actinomycetes) and also ties in with what
the student has learned about the chemical composition of plant
and animal structures. The exercise is not expected to generate
any great enthusiasm. It is neither colorful nor spectacular—and
it may seem interminable to a tenth grader. Yet its purposes are
important. And its length can help make the point that biological
processes are often slow and the biological investigator must be
patient.

Though Exercise 7.1 is basic, not all members of the class
need be involved in setting it up. Two or three setups per class
are quite sufficient for purposes of comparison; two to four students are ample for each setup. However, the whole class should
understand the procedure and participate in observing and recording the progress of decomposition.

Materials. Petri-dish lids fit snugly inside 4-inch flowerpots. Figure 7.1-1 shows a 5-inch (short form) flowerpot; petri-
dish lids leave considerable surface exposed in pots of this size.
The aluminum dishes in which frozen potpies are packed make
excellent substitutes for deep dishes if 4-inch flowerpots are
used. Cans may be substituted for flowerpots—but be sure to
punch several holes in the bottoms.

Obtain sharp builder's sand and wash it well; the less it has the qualities of a true soil, the better. On the other hand, the soil should be a humus-rich loam.

Considering the season in which this exercise is likely to be set up, it may be necessary to collect leaves, insects, and twigs in advance. These should be dried and stored without preservatives. Maple leaves are among the more rapidly decomposing leaves; oak leaves are among the slowest. Beetles, crickets, grasshoppers, and cockroaches are suitable insects.

Old stockings are good sources of nylon.

Procedure, observations, and conclusions. The surfaces of the pots should not be watered; they must be kept moist by capillarity from the dishes in which the pots sit. Therefore the dishes must be kept filled with water. Since observations occur at infrequent intervals, one student from each team should be delegated to check the water each day.

The observation times listed on the chart (manual page 114) may be varied. The general rate of decomposition depends on temperature. Four weeks is scarcely enough time even in well-heated buildings; eight weeks is closer to the average. Probably the first evidence of decomposition will be mold hyphae on the oats. Somewhat later, molds may appear on other items. Still later, the typical earthy odor of actinomycetes and the putrid odor of bacterial decay may be detected. Rates of decomposition on sand may or may not differ from rates on soil. Usually there are differences, decay of most items proceeding more slowly on the sand because of its smaller initial population of decomposers—but the facts should not be forced to fit the theory. In discussing results, stress the production of humus and the return of minerals to the soil, where they are used again as plant nutrients. In the economy of nature the decay of food, fiber, and wood is no different from the decomposition of other plant and animal remains. "Desirable" decomposition and "undesirable" decomposition are only expressions of man's point of view.

Exercise 7.2
Some Microbial Techniques

This is a complex exercise, but it is well worth the effort involved. It pays dividends in appreciation rather than in specific knowledge. Moreover it provides a good test of the extent to which students have learned to understand and follow directions, to work together in teams, and to relate procedures to outcomes. It is also a good test of the extent to which the teacher has mastered laboratory logistics.

Materials. Before any action is taken on the "Procedure," a careful check of materials must be made. Keeping in mind the quantities of glassware available, team sizes must be decided upon. Teams of 2—as suggested in the manual—may be entirely impracticable. Such teams require, for example, 600 test tubes, 150 beakers, and 375 petri dishes if a teacher has five classes of thirty students each. Using teams of 4 will cut these quantities in half and still provide opportunity for each student to participate actively. By staggering the scheduling of the exercise for different classes, the teacher may cut down the quantities still further.

A standard nutrient agar may be used in place of the separate ingredients. If the tap-water supply bears no unusual amount of minerals, it may be used in place of distilled water.

Serratia marcescens is a bacterium having a red pigmentation; Sarcina lutea is yellow. These organisms are relatively harmless. They are safe for use by high school students and are large enough to be easily studied. Cultures can be obtained from most biological supply houses.

Grids ruled on sheets of plastic are useful as guides in counting colonies; they, too, are available from supply houses.

Procedure. The teacher who has no bacteriological background should make use of the BSCS film "Bacteriological Techniques" (cited on page 110). In addition, the BSCS Laboratory Block "Microbes—Their Growth, Nutrition, and Interaction," by A. S. Sussman (Boston: D. C. Heath & Co., 1963) should be consulted. The BSCS technique film may be shown to classes. Since it is quite short, the showing can be repeated a number of times. But even with its use, the teacher should demonstrate all steps in the procedure.

In preparing the nutrient agar, have the required ingredients weighed out beforehand. Heat water (just below boiling), and dissolve the agar first; then add peptone and beef extract. Heat until the mixture comes to a boil, stirring continuously. While the liquid is still warm (above $55^{\circ}C$), pour it into the funnel, to which a short piece of rubber tubing, closed with a pinch clamp, has been attached. Use a 4- or 5-inch funnel held in a ring mounted on a ring stand. A little practice in using the pinch clamp will facilitate filling the marked tubes.

The manual does not give instructions for calculating the area of a petri dish. This is no great problem for many students, but signs of difficulty at this point should be watched for. Teacher assistance in carrying out the dilution calculation may also be needed.

Although the bacteria being cultured are ordinarily harmless, sterile procedure should be observed throughout the work, not only because the demonstration of safe handling of microorganisms is one of the purposes of the exercise but also because it is possible for pathogenic organisms accidentally to get into the medium and multiply. Therefore, at the conclusion of the exercise all tubes and petri dishes must be sterilized in an autoclave or pressure cooker before the medium is cleaned out of the glassware.

Discussion. Upon the completion of Exercise 7.2 the questions within the "Procedure" as well as those in the "Summary" should be discussed in class. Some additional questions that might be considered are:

1. What factors may affect the accuracy of population determination?

2. How might the kind of medium and the temperature of incubation influence the number of colonies?

3. How could you use the pour-plate method to compare rates of growth for two different kinds of bacteria in a mixed culture?

4. What are some possible sources of error in estimating the number of bacteria in a culture by the methods used in this exercise?

Exercise 7.3
Investigating an Infectious Disease

Even if this exercise cannot be performed, the "Introduction" is recommended reading because it lists Koch's postulates. However, the writers regard this as an extremely important exercise; it clearly demonstrates disease transmission, a topic that traditionally has been "talked to death." Moreover it applies the skills practiced by students in Exercises 6.3 and 7.2.

The interval between the beginning and end of this exercise is long, but the students' interest in the progress of the plants is easier to maintain than their interest in the progress of decomposition in Exercise 7.1. With three long-term exercises being observed concurrently (Exercise 6.2 will still be running), some effort must be made to keep students from forgetting which procedures belong with which setups.

Plants must be started at least a month before this exercise is set up. When ready for use, they should have three or four true leaves. Three-inch pots are large enough, or half-pint milk cartons may be used. Tomato is probably the species of choice. Pot labels are not essential; the pots themselves may be marked with a soft pencil.

Agrobacterium tumefaciens is not an animal pathogen. It is quite safe from the point of view of students. However, it should be handled carefully and with full attention to sterile technique, for it is dangerous to plants, and plants are important. The bacilli

are large enough to be studied under the 4-mm "high-dry" objective of the microscope. Though cultures of Agrobacterium are
available from biological supply houses, permits for shipment are
required from state and federal agricultural departments, so
ordering should be done early.

For crystal-violet solution, see Exercise 6.3.

The scalpel must be quite sharp; a razor blade is preferable.
To prepare culture tubes of dextrose agar, you need:

Peptone . . . . 5 g
Beef extract. . . . . 3 g
Agar. .15 g
Glucose (dextrose) . . . . .10 g
Distilled water . . . . 1000 ml

Heat water (just below boiling) and dissolve the agar in it; then
add peptone, beef extract, and dextrose, stirring the mixture
well. Pour 30 to 40 ml into cotton-plugged tubes. Sterilize tubes
in autoclave or pressure cooker, and cool them on a slant of about
30 degrees. (CAUTION: At the conclusion of the exercise, be
sure to sterilize in an autoclave or pressure cooker all plants,
pots, and soil that have been used.)

Exercise 7.4

Nodule-forming Bacteria

Though this exercise is not basic, it is interesting to many
students. A few teams in each class might set it up and show the
results to the rest of the students.

The quantities of dry ingredients given on manual page 126 are
large, to make weighing easier; several batches of medium can be
made from these amounts. One batch (made with 1 liter of water)
provides medium sufficient for about 40 tubes. If only one batch
is required, the amount of each ingredient may be calculated by
applying a factor of .15 to the quantities given in the manual, and
an analytical balance will be needed.

For sodium hypochlorite solution, a bleach such as Clorox
will do. Sterile water may be dispensed in small test tubes, but
it is easier to pick up the seeds from small, wide-mouth bottles.
If these have screw caps, loosen the caps before placing the
bottles in the pressure cooker.

Be sure to obtain Rhizobium inoculum that is designated for
clover, since each species of Rhizobium produces nodulation and
nitrogen fixation only with particular species of legumes. Commercial inoculum can be bought at most seed stores. The material comes in moist humus or as a dry powder.

Exercise 7.5
Growing Soil Microbes by the "Mud-Pie" Technique

One or two teams might set up this exercise. The quantities given will provide enough material for microscopic examination by several students. Bowl 9 of Exercise 6.1 possessed—on a small scale—the conditions of Exercise 7.5.

The richer and finer the soil, the better. If the soils used are heavy clays, there will be heaving of the soil due to accumulation of gases—principally carbon dioxide (CO_2) and hydrogen (H_2)—from the fermentation of starch and glucose by anaerobic bacteria. These bacteria will not appear as colonies on the surface, but will be imbedded in the soil.

If the atmosphere of the laboratory is extremely dry, it may be necessary to provide some kind of moist chamber to prevent the drying out of the mud pies. A plastic dishpan lined with wet paper towels and covered with a glass plate makes a good moist chamber for a large number of soil cultures.

To prepare methylene-blue stain, dissolve 0.3 g of methylene blue in 30 ml of 95% ethyl alcohol (C_2H_5OH) and add 100 ml of distilled water.

Colonies of small threadlike organisms are those of actino-mycetes, the "moldlike" bacteria. They give the soil its characteristic earthy odor. Most of them probably produce antibiotic substances. A student could use a culture rich in actinomycete colonies as a source for isolating producers of antibiotics.

Because soil contains many varieties of microorganisms, an interested student might do an extended study of the different types of microbes found in soil samples from different locations. One technique: With a stout knife make a slit in the soil. Place a clean glass slide in the slit, and press the soil firmly against it. The slide is left in the moistened soil for two or three weeks; then it is carefully withdrawn, and the largest soil particles are removed. The slide is fixed by heat, and the adhering film is stained. Preferably, microscopic observations are made with an oil-immersion objective. Bacteria, molds, and algae are likely to be the most numerous organisms present. This method permits rough comparisons of microbe populations in soils from different sources: garden; field; marsh; deciduous forest; coniferous forest; beach; or deposits from the bottoms of ponds, lakes, and rivers. Tests may also be run on soils obtained from a single site, but at differing depths.

Exercise 7.6
Soil Nematodes

This is a good exercise for use as a special project. It can be carried out by one interested student or by a small group.

Soil samples from a cabbage patch are ideal if nematocides have not been used on it. Otherwise use soil from a spot on which there is a heavy growth of vegetation. The apparatus shown in Figure 7.6-1 is known as a Baermann funnel. The funnel should be smooth-sided, not ribbed. A screw clamp may be used in place of the spring-compressor clamp. Tap water may contain enough chlorine to kill the nematodes; it is therefore desirable to use water that has been "aged" (see guide page 106). Scotties tissues are tough when wet and have been found satisfactory. Some teachers have had success with paper toweling.

The nematodes have been variously classified: They have been placed in a phylum (Nemathelminthes) along with the spiny-headed worms and horsehair worms. Because their body cavities are not lined by a definite mesodermal layer, they have been grouped with rotifers in the phylum Aschelminthes. Many zoologists regard them as a separate phylum, Nematoda, and they are classified this way in the appendix of the Green Version textbook.

The "nemas" are bilaterally symmetrical animals, cylindroid, unsegmented, bisexual, triploblastic. There are both free-living and parasitic species, with adaptations to a great variety of habitats. All, however, are basically aquatic—to remain active, even the soil forms require a film of moisture. In water they whip themselves about by rapidly contorting the body.

Nematodes are possibly second only to insects in number of species. In some species, dried-out specimens that have been dormant for many years have been known to revive upon being returned to water. It has been estimated that there are at least 80,000 species of "nemas" specifically parasitic on vertebrates, mollusks, crustaceans, and worms. Free-living "nemas" in soil and water run to (estimated) hundreds of thousands of species.

The first (1918) edition of Ward and Whipple's Fresh-water Biology (New York: John Wiley & Sons) has a good general discussion of soil nematodes, but the book is difficult to obtain now. Pennak's Fresh-water Invertebrates of the United States (New York: Ronald Press, 1953) is helpful for a general discussion of nematodes. The United States Department of Agriculture has a number of booklets on nematodes that injure specific crops. State land-grant colleges and county agents' offices also can provide information about nematodes.

Exercise 7.7
The Abundance of Airborne Microorganisms
in Various School Environments

If the class did a thorough job on Exercise 7.2, this exercise can be done easily—especially if the corps of student assistants who have learned the techniques of medium formulation and sterilization can be utilized again.   The exercise often generates a considerable amount of interest outside biology classes and is desirable for intramural public relations.

If teams from several classes undertake this exercise, the results for each location can be averaged; this will reduce chance variation.

The list of materials and equipment for preparing the nutrient agar calls for 200 ml of water.   As written, the exercise requires only 150 ml of medium; but it is possible to simplify the weighing by making up 200 ml.   And, of course, more plates may be poured.   An additional area to sample might be a stairwell immediately after a change of classes.

In this experiment incubation temperature of 35°C is desirable.   The Temperature Gradient Box (Figure T-2.4a) may be adapted as an incubator by taping cardboard over the open spaces at the bottom and setting it up in a place where an even room temperature is maintained.

(CAUTION: In this experiment pathogenic organisms are very likely to be picked up and cultivated.   Therefore, after exposure the plates must be taped closed.   Counting the colonies must be done without opening the dishes.   Only after dishes have been sterilized should they be opened for washing.)

SUPPLEMENTARY MATERIALS

Invitations to Enquiry

Invitation 10 (pp. 78-83 of the Handbook).   The relationship between environment and disease is used to show the role of hypothesis in scientific investigation.

Invitation 16 (pp. 103-105 of the Handbook).   The discovery of penicillin is used to illustrate serendipity in scientific investigation.

Audiovisual Materials

Phonograph record: "The Scientists Speak: Biology." (Harcourt, Brace & World, Inc.). René Dubos speaks on microorganisms, referring to the work of Pasteur, to his own work with antibiotic-producing microbes, and to the interrelationships among the scientific disciplines.

Filmstrip: "Jenner and the Story of Smallpox"—"Pasteur"—"Koch"—3 separate filmstrips. (The Metropolitan Life Insurance Co.). Black and white.

Motion-picture film: "Microorganisms—Harmful Activities." (University of Indiana Audiovisual Center). 16 mm. Color. 18 minutes. A good film to back up this chapter. Discusses specificity of infection, types of immunity, antibodies, and Koch's postulates. Shows part of the technique of Exercise 7.3.

Teacher's References

ALEXANDER, M. Introduction to Soil Microbiology. New York: John Wiley & Sons, Inc., 1961. (A current standard textbook of the subject.)

BURNET, SIR F. M. Natural History of Infectious Disease, 2nd ed. London: The Cambridge University Press, 1953. (Excellent background reading for the viewpoints expressed in the Green Version.)

NOTTINGHAM, ENG., UNIVERSITY, SCHOOL OF AGRICULTURE. Soil Zoology, ed. D. K. M. KEVAN. London: Butterworth & Co., Ltd., 1955. (Except for the economically important nematodes, the small animals that inhabit soils and often play an important role in the microcommunity have been much neglected—by the Green Version as well as by others. This book contributes to overcoming such neglect.)

RUSSELL, SIR JOHN. The World of the Soil. London: Longmans, Green & Co., Inc., 1950. (By the man who for thirty years headed Rothamstead, the British center for agricultural research; a cornerstone for any reading program on soils.)

CHAPTER 8

Patterns of Life on Land

MAJOR IDEAS

1. The organisms occurring naturally in any given area are those that can survive and successfully reproduce under the environmental conditions (abiotic and biotic) prevailing there.

2. Over large areas of the earth, organisms and environment produce characteristic landscape patterns—biomes.

3. Rainfall and temperature (both ultimately determined by the global pattern of solar radiation) are the major abiotic environmental factors that determine the distribution of biomes.

4. In general, as one approaches the equator from the poles, one passes through biomes of increasing richness (diversity of species) and increasing complexity (diversity of community interrelationships). This sequence is also characterized by an increasing depth of vegetation.

5. In the low and middle latitudes an additional sequence of biomes may be distinguished along a gradient characterized by a diminishing availability of water.

6. Man has been becoming an increasingly important element in determining the characteristics of landscapes. He has now succeeded in completely transforming large portions of some biomes; for example, he has transformed much of the middle-latitude deciduous forest into something closely resembling a grassland biome.

7. Most completely man-dominated are urban and suburban areas, where even the effects of climate are so highly modified that the eye of a trained geographer is needed to detect them, and where the major portion of biotic energy is derived from distant regions.

TEACHING SUGGESTIONS

Guidelines

Even though students should be developing greater facility in handling assignments, the length of textbook Chapter 8 makes division desirable. The most logical plan calls for four short assignments: pages 208-216, with the addition of whatever climate materials the teacher wants to use (see guide pages 135-142); pages 216-230 and pages 230-241, with one or the other of these to include additional materials on the natural biome in which the school is located; finally, pages 242-247. An alternative plan consists of two assignments—pages 216-230 and pages 230-247; this division is less complex but also less logical.

Obviously, emphasis in this chapter should be placed upon the biome in which the student lives. However, one of the aims of the course is to broaden the student's view of the world, so other biomes should not be neglected. In most cases direct experience with the local biome can be either assumed or secured, but concepts of other biomes must usually be developed through audio-visual means. The clearer and more immediate the student's view of his local biome, the clearer will be his understanding of other biomes.

Even becoming familiar with the local biome may be some-what difficult—especially in "inner city" schools. A field trip may be the best means of obtaining such familiarity. If the teacher himself is well acquainted with his region, he will undoubtedly be able to arrange an itinerary for a half- or full-day trip that will display the salient characteristics of the biome. Both municipal and state governments are becoming aware of the need for "wild" lands (not merely recreational areas studded with ball diamonds, tennis courts, and archery ranges) within easy reach of high-density human populations. Farseeing school systems cooperate in the development of these resources; administrators in such systems will welcome and facilitate the efforts of teachers to utilize the facilities.

Of course the pristine "climatic climax" of the local biome may long since have disappeared from any place within feasible traveling distance, but excellent examples of the influence of man on the biotic landscape, of successional stages, and of the "suburban forest" should be available. With a properly planned sequence of observations and a series of sharp, attention-fixing questions, the teacher can organize the immediate experiences of a field trip into an adequate acquaintance with the local biome.

Unlike the field work of Exercise 3.1, a field trip for Chapter 8 does not require growing-season conditions. The aspect of the landscape in early December is quite suitable for the study of biome characteristics unless deep snow prevails.

In the broad view, biomes are biotic expressions of climate. To understand biomes, then, the student must have some knowledge of (1) the atmospheric factors that—when statistically summarized —constitute climate, and (2) the astronomical and geophysical phenomena that determine the distribution of climates. As in the case of distant biota, an understanding of distant climates is best developed against a background of familiarity with the local climate.

The old "physical geography" taught in the upper elementary grades contained much of the material needed for understanding the world distribution of climates. Today in some school systems this material is well developed in junior-high general science courses; in other systems it seems to have dropped from view. The experimental editions of the Green Version textbook contained background material on climate distribution. Some teachers questioned its inclusion in a biology course—just as some questioned the inclusion of chemistry material. Others were glad to include it. They stated that even where students had previously studied the subject, the material on climate provided valuable review and directly linked biology to what the students had considered a separate field of science. Space considerations and the assurance that most students already possess at least some background on climate have forced it out of the present edition of the textbook. However, for those teachers who wish to use it, the material on climate appears on pages 135-142 of this guide.

An excellent source of information about distant biomes and climates is often overlooked—students who have lived in other biomes, who often have photographs as well as an eagerness to talk about their former surroundings. Teachers in schools located near installations of the armed forces or near large industrial plants that frequently shift their personnel are usually aware of this resource, but other teachers might discover unsuspected possibilities by looking into their student records or by direct questioning.

During discussion of the textbook descriptions of biomes, attention should be focused on the relation of the climatic factors (as graphed in the climatograms) to the biota. For example, in the climatogram for the tundra (text page 217) the graph indicates that the average monthly temperatures are above freezing—and not far above—only three months of the year; during most of the year the average monthly temperatures are far below freezing. Furthermore, the precipitation is quite low in all months of the

year. From these facts we can conclude that the producers of
the tundra biome are actively producing food during only a fraction
of the year and that the density of consumers must be low. But
the implications of the data presented by the climatogram need to
be explored. The amplitude of the yearly cycle of monthly average
temperatures implies a high latitude; this, in turn, assures a long
daily period of sunlight during the season when temperatures are
high. In addition, the low temperatures imply a low rate of evaporation. Thus conditions for plant growth during the brief summer
season are not as unfavorable as they seem at first glance. The
food production may be greater than resident consumers can exploit. These conditions suggest that a large migratory summer
population of consumers may be possible. Such reasoning should
be applied to all the climatograms.

Some Notes

The photograph at the head of the chapter shows typical North
American short-grass plains.

Figure 8.1: Alligators have more rounded snouts than caimans,
which come from Cuba and points south. Exportation of alligators
from Florida is illegal.

Figure 8.4: The map is quite generalized and is based on one in
Odum (see "Suggested Readings," textbook page 250). Its lack of
precision greatly pained the cartographers at Rand McNally. However, much of the world simply has not been studied sufficiently
from the biome point of view to make a better map possible at
present. Maps of vegetation only are many, and some are quite
detailed. A good one is that by a A. W. Kuchler, in E. B. Espenshade, Jr. (ed.), Goode's World Atlas, 11th ed. (Chicago: Rand
McNally & Co., 1960). For North America, Pitelka (American
Midland Naturalist 25 : 113-137—1941) compiled a fairly detailed biome map that has been widely reproduced (see Odum,
page 387).

Figure 8.8: Students will not automatically carry out the directions in the caption. But it is worth an effort by the teacher to see
that the student writes a brief account—and to resurrect it when
Chapter 17 is reached.

Figure 8.18: In part, the general greenish tinge to the light at
the floor of the tropical rain forest derives from the filtering out
of other colors by successive layers of foliage above.

Figure 8.19: In this figure the height of the dominant trees in the middle-latitude deciduous forest is typical of primeval sites on deep soils of Ohio, Indiana, and Kentucky. Almost everywhere these forests have been culled, and the average height is now rather less.

Figure 8.31: Even in the southern parts of the western United States, some mountains have sufficient altitude to exhibit the full range of zones. In the eastern states, however, an alpine zone occurs only in some of the higher mountains of New York and New England; the "balds" of the southern Appalachians are not comparable to tundra.

EXERCISES

8.1 Limiting Factors in Distribution . . . . . . BASIC
8.2 Temperature, Rainfall, and Biome Distribution . . . . BASIC
8.3 Effects of Fire On Biomes . . . . Highly Recommended

Some exercises from Chapter 7 will still be in progress during work on Chapter 8. Therefore, only one exercise requiring laboratory work is given for this chapter; neither Exercise 8.2 nor Exercise 8.3 involves the teacher in laboratory preparations and equipment problems.

Some botanists are of the opinion that plants are slighted in the high school laboratory; some teachers may feel that the Green Version has gone too far in the opposite direction. Any teacher who takes the latter view may substitute Exercise 14.7 for Exercise 8.1.

The concept of tolerance, developed in the first part of the textbook chapter, is illustrated by Exercise 9.3. The teacher may wish to use that exercise now, especially if he expects to omit Chapter 9.

Exercise 8.1
Limiting Factors in Distribution

This exercise makes use of some technical skills developed in Exercise 1.2. If students are made aware of this, most will strive to show that they did indeed learn something.

Teams of 5 or 6 students each are suitable. These are not too large to provide each student with a task, including assignment of one student as a team leader. Extra students can be used for distributing materials and coördinating the allocation of dishes to their proper environments.

Materials. The plant species selected for this exercise will provide a variety of responses to the conditions of the experiment. Other seeds may be substituted as follows:

For tomato.....beet, pepper, carrot, sunflower, cotton

For radish..... tobacco, corn, bindweed, flax

For lettuce..... African violet, evening primrose, mullein, onion, fireweed, phacelia

For vetch...... celery, larkspur, columbine, henbit, plantain, shepherd's purse

If sufficient petri dishes are not available, satisfactory substitute containers include: lids of large peanut-butter jars, small aluminum dishes from frozen potpies, cardboard milk cartons cut down to a depth of about 1.5 cm. Or dishes and covers may be made by molding circles of heavy aluminum foil around a glass petri dish.

The strips of cardboard used as dividers should be as wide as the petri dishes (or other containers) are deep. A good grade is that used in shirt boxes. The tabs at the ends of the dividers may be fastened to the dishes with rubber cement.

The plastic of which the bags are made should be thin (1 or 2 mils), to allow free diffusion of gases. The plastic sheeting used by cleaners to protect clothing is ideal for this purpose and can be used in place of bags. The dishes should be wrapped in the plastic and the loose ends fastened with string or a rubber band.

For covering the seeds to be grown in darkness, coffee cans may be used in place of cardboard boxes, or the dishes may be wrapped in aluminum foil.

A conventional refrigerator may be used to establish the cold environment. However, because the refrigerator light normally goes off when the door is closed, modification is necessary to insure continuous light. Such light can be provided quite simply by running an extension cord, with lamp attached, into the refrigerator. With this cord in place, the rubber gasket around the door will still permit normal opening and closing and at the same time prevent loss of cold air. An alternate method is to run a bypass wire across the light switch in the door frame. This will allow the regular refrigerator light to burn continuously. It may be necessary to remove part of the frame in order to gain access to the switch. Because it produces heat, an incandescent lamp should not be used as the

light source. Small fluorescent lamps (8 to 15 watts) and fix-
tures for them are available commercially. Even fluorescent
lamps generate small amounts of heat, so it is wise to check
the refrigerator a few days prior to the experiment to see that
a temperature of 10-12°C is maintained.

Teachers who have access to a commercial incubator need
only make provision for a continuous source of light to provide
the proper environment for Dishes 3 and 4. Use an extension
cord, as in the case of the refrigerator. If the incubator door
will not close when the cord is in place, it may be necessary to
remove the thermometer and run the extension cord through
the thermometer hole. As a safety measure, wrap tape around
the cord at the point where it enters the incubator.

If an incubator is not available, a simple heat box can be
made from the following materials:
   Corrugated cardboard box or metal box of suitable size
   Fluorescent light tube (same wattage as that used in
         refrigerator)
   100-watt incandescent bulb
   Small brooder thermostat rated at 23-50°C
   Thermometer
   The equipment is to be assembled as shown in Figure T-8.1.

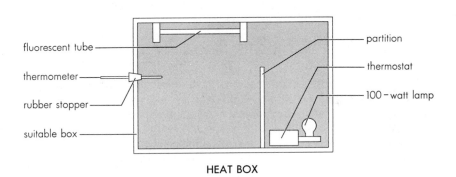

HEAT BOX

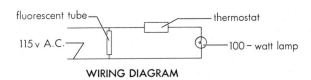

WIRING DIAGRAM

Figure T-8.1

A cardboard or metal partition separates the heat source from the petri dishes. Since the incandescent lamp serves as the heat source, it should be wired in series with the thermostat; the fluorescent light should be wired parallel. It might be necessary to experiment with a slightly higher or lower wattage to obtain the desired temperature.

Homemade or modified equipment is often better than none, but schools should be encouraged to provide standard laboratory equipment obtained from commercial supply houses. Care should be exercised in building or modifying equipment. Before constructing new electrical equipment or modifying existing equipment, check with the school principal concerning local fire codes and regulations.

Discussion. Tomato seeds germinate most rapidly in complete darkness at about 26°C. Lettuce (especially the Great Lakes variety) germinates best in light. Vetch requires a cool environment. Radish germinates well under a wide range of conditions.

Students may have difficulty separating the influence of individual factors from combinations of factors. However, this is a very common experimental design, and the teacher should lend assistance when necessary.

Exercise 8.2
Temperature, Rainfall, and Biome Distribution

After some of the climatograms in the textbook have been studied, the graph-making phase of Exercise 8.2 may be assigned as homework. The number of graphs to be prepared by any one student is a matter of choice. The minimum would seem to be three: one based on local data, one based on a set of data from Group 1 (manual page 143), and one based on a set from Group 2 (manual page 144).

Climatograms are common means of summarizing the two most important climatic variables; they are used especially by geographers. The representation of precipitation by vertical bars is a violation of the general principle that a continuous variable is best shown by a line, but it is justified by the need to distinguish easily between temperature and precipitation. This point is worth making in class discussion because even those students who are familiar with the mechanics of graph-making often do not know how to select a form suitable for a given set of data.

If the graphs are drawn on a variety of grids, comparisons are difficult. Therefore it is well to furnish all students with graph paper of the same kind. The best practice is to duplicate grids that are exactly like those in the textbook—12 blocks wide and 18 high, with the zero of the temperature scale halfway up the vertical axis.

Local climatic data can be obtained from the nearest United States Weather Bureau office. Conversion of Fahrenheit temperatures to centigrade can be done easily with the scale on page 374 of the manual. Precipitation data in inches are converted to centimeters by multiplying by 2.54. Two or three students can be assigned the task of conversion; they should check each other's work before releasing the converted data for class use.

When added to the six graphs in the textbook, the four graphs drawn from the data in Group 1 provide the student with representative climatic data from ten major biomes. Each graph should be discussed from the viewpoint of possible relationships between the climatic data and the characteristic features of the biome. Enlarged copies of the ten climatograms may be posted in the room, where they will be visible to all students. These and the discussion based on them may then serve as a background for making predictions from data in Group 2.

Students should be kept constantly aware of the limitations of the data with which they are working. Some significant variables not indicated in the climatograms are mentioned under "Discussion" (manual page 145). It may also be well to discuss the way in which the data have been derived. The temperature data are means derived from "daily means," which are not really means in the usual statistical sense but, instead, are the midpoints in the range of hourly readings over a twenty-four hour period. The precipitation data, on the other hand, are true means for monthly precipitation over a period of years. The number of years of observation varies from station to station, of course. These data do not indicate the monthly range in precipitation and temperature. And the range of these variables is a significant factor for organisms, as are the extremes.

Having noted limitations in the climatic data, students must realize that a climatogram does not summarize precipitation and temperature for a biome as a whole. Any one climatogram merely shows the data for these variables at one station within a biome. The stations have, of course, been chosen as carefully as possible to provide data that are representative—"typical"—for each biome.

The stations from which the data in Group 2 were obtained are as follows:

a. Washington, D.C. (middle-latitude deciduous forest)
b. Lisbon, Portugal (chaparral)
c. Iquitos, Peru (tropical rain forest)
d. Yuma, Arizona (desert)

e. Odessa, U. S. S. R. (middle-latitude grassland: steppe)
f. Valparaíso, Chile (chaparral)
g. Upernavik, Greenland (tundra)
h. San Antonio, Texas (middle-latitude grassland: mesquite-grass savannah)
i. Bahía Blanca, Argentina (middle-latitude grassland)
j. Oaxaca, Mexico (tropical deciduous forest)
k. Moose Factory, Ontario, Canada (taiga)
l. Fallon, Nevada (middle-latitude desert)

Exercise 8.3
Effects of Fire on Biomes

This exercise can be worked through in a class session, without previous assignment. Or it can be assigned as homework and then discussed briefly in class. Or it can be assigned to certain of the better students for independent work.

It is advantageous, though not essential, for the teacher to read the article on which the exercise is based: "The Ecology of Fire," by C. F. Cooper, Scientific American, April, 1961. Most of the illustrations used in the exercise are taken directly from the article through the courtesy of Gerard Piel, publisher of Scientific American.

To some degree, fire is used as a management tool in all regions. Indeed, it is perhaps the most ancient tool that man has employed to change the landscape. What is not stated in either the exercise or the article is that today there are many other such means—fertilization, herbicides, the saw and ax, disking, and bulldozing—and that these usually can be used more selectively than fire. Thus, though fire may have played a major part in shaping grasslands and forests in the past, ecologists are by no means agreed that fire should continue to have a large role in land management today. It would be well to draw out these points during class discussion.

A field trip to a burned-over area will, of course, provide an excellent opportunity for the class to study the effects of fire.

SUPPLEMENTARY MATERIALS

Materials on Climate

As mentioned on page 127, a discussion of climate was included in experimental editions of the Green Version textbook; it has been omitted from the present edition. This material is presented below and may be used in any way the teacher wishes. Two suggestions: Use it as background for a lecture illustrated with a globe and maps and with charts presented on an overhead projector. Or duplicate the material and distribute it to students for reading.

CLIMATES

Because climate has such an overwhelming effect upon the organisms in any landscape, we should understand something of the way in which it varies from place to place on the surface of the earth. If you already understand the distribution of climates, you may treat this topic as a review. If the topic is new to you, it forms a necessary background in physical science for your biological study.

DISTRIBUTION OF RADIANT ENERGY

Energy enters the biosphere in the form of radiation from the sun. This energy is changed into chemical form through the process of photosynthesis. From the organic substances thus produced, the energy for all the activities of living things is derived. The amount of solar energy received on any particular part of the earth's surface is therefore a most important environmental factor for organisms.

The shape of the earth and its position in relation to the solar system affect the distribution of solar radiation on the earth's surface. Different places receive different amounts of radiation. Through the year the regions near the equator receive most; the polar regions—north and south—receive least.

This situation results from two factors. (As you read on, refer to Figure T-8a.) First, to reach the earth's surface, solar energy must, of course, pass through the earth's atmosphere. The atmosphere absorbs some of the solar energy. The greater the thickness of the atmospheric blanket that the

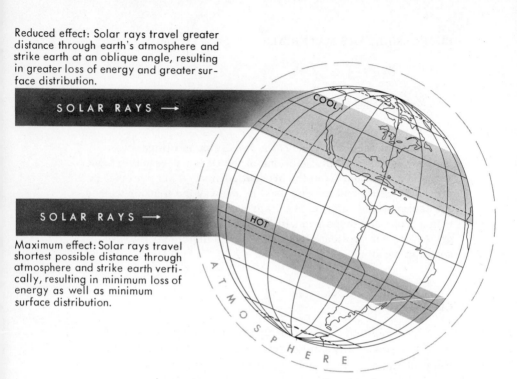

Reduced effect: Solar rays travel greater distance through earth's atmosphere and strike earth at an oblique angle, resulting in greater loss of energy and greater surface distribution.

SOLAR RAYS →

COOL

SOLAR RAYS →

HOT

Maximum effect: Solar rays travel shortest possible distance through atmosphere and strike earth vertically, resulting in minimum loss of energy as well as minimum surface distribution.

ATMOSPHERE

Figure T-8a. Showing how the earth's atmosphere and the angle of contact affect the amount of solar radiation received on the earth's surface—here, during a period of seasonal extremes

energy passes through, the greater the amount of energy absorbed. Rays striking the earth at a right angle (vertically) travel through less atmosphere than do those striking the earth at an acute angle. Hence parts of the earth on which light falls vertically will receive more energy than other parts.

Second, radiation striking the earth's surface at an acute angle is "stretched out." A flashlight may be used to show this. When its light falls vertically on a surface, we see a bright circle. When its light falls at a slant, we see a dimmer oval; the light is dimmer because it is spread over a greater area.

If we look at the matter from the viewpoint of an observer on earth (where the organisms are) instead of from outer space, we can see that the higher the sun is above the horizon, the greater the amount of energy received. In any

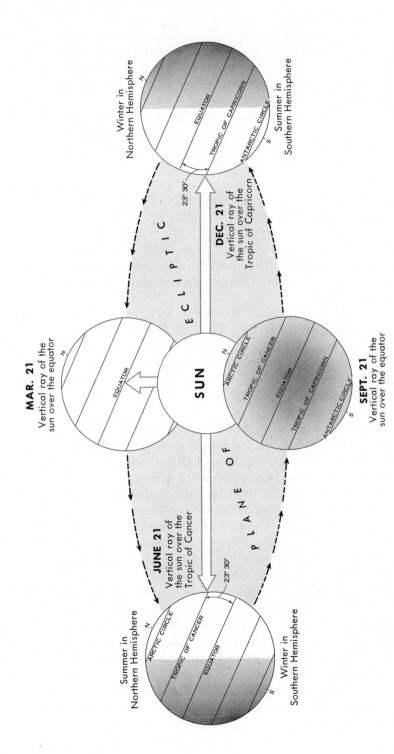

Figure T-8b.   Showing relation between the earth and the sun during the annual cycle

one day at any one place, the sun is highest above the horizon at noon (noon local time, not "zone time" or "daylight saving time"). And any place where the sun is *directly* overhead at noon will receive the maximum possible amount of solar radiation.

As the earth revolves around the sun, the tilt of its axis causes a shift in the latitude at which a ray falls vertically at noon (Figure T-8b). At noon on June 21 the vertical ray will strike the earth 23°30′ (23 degrees and 30 minutes, or 23.5 degrees) north of the equator (along a line called the *Tropic of Cancer*), and on December 21, 23°30′ south of the equator (along the *Tropic of Capricorn*). The sun is never directly overhead at any point north or south of these latitudes; at the poles it is never more than 23°30′ above the horizon. In general, then, the solar radiation received by the earth is greatest between the tropics and decreases rapidly toward the poles.

Thus far we have been considering solar radiation received in an "instant" of time—the *intensity* of radiation. But the time unit most important from the point of view of a photosynthesizing plant is probably twenty-four hours—a day. Thus we must consider not only the intensity of the solar radiation but also its *duration* on the basis of a twenty-four hour period.

Duration is another result of the tilt of the earth in relation to the sun. By examining Figure T-8c carefully, we can see that the parts of the earth beyond 66°30′ north or south will have at least one twenty-four hour period during the year without any sunlight. We also can see that the period between sunrise and sunset is always twelve hours long at the equator, and it does not vary greatly within the tropics. On the other hand, at the poles the sun shines for six months at a stretch; twilight is measured in weeks, and night lasts until dawning begins, about five months later.

Thus there is great variation over the earth's surface both in the duration of daily solar radiation and in its intensity. At the poles the sun shines for six months, but the intensity is always low; within the tropics days are never greatly prolonged, but the intensity of radiation is high. We can conclude that the rate of photosynthesis over the surface of the earth will vary according to geographical position and time of year, with corresponding effects on the whole biotic community.

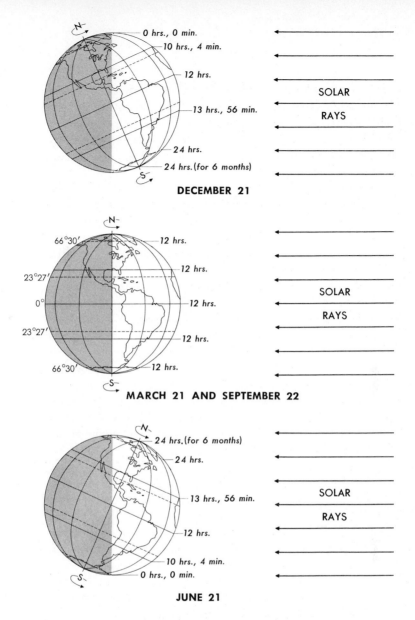

Figure T-8c. Showing distribution of daily solar radiation in the annual cycle

DISTRIBUTION OF HEAT

Up to this point we have discussed solar radiation as if it were only light. Actually it contains many wave lengths besides those we see (textbook Figure 1·4). But it does not contain the energy we call heat. The warmth of the sun's rays, which we feel on a summer's day, is solar radiation transformed into heat as the light strikes our bodies, the air around us, or other material things. (Thus, in interplanetary space, where radiation is plentiful but matter is not, there is very little heat.) Light is the source of energy for photosynthesis, but heat—some degree of it—is important for *all* biochemical processes.

The fact that the sun's "warmth" comes only from the interaction of solar energy with matter leads to a remarkable conclusion: The earth's atmosphere is heated mainly from *below*. When solar radiation strikes the upper atmosphere, very little heat results, because the molecules that compose the upper atmosphere are few and far apart. At lower levels, where the air is denser, more solar energy is changed to heat. But the greatest change occurs when the light hits the lithosphere and hydrosphere (see textbook pages 13 and 14). Therefore, despite the fact that the sun shines above us, its heating effect comes from below.

When a fluid (liquid or gas) is heated from below, the warmer molecules rise. The warmer fluid spreads up and over the cooler portion. In this way heat is distributed throughout a container of water over a fire. Air is a fluid, and over the year it receives more heat in the region of the equator than anywhere else. A basic pattern of atmospheric circulation results.

This massive circulation is brought about by the unequal distribution of solar radiation; it transports heated air over the earth's surface, as shown in Figure T-8d. Solar energy supplies the force, but gravity also plays a part. Cool air is denser—that is, heavier per unit of volume—than warm air. As a result air descends over cooler regions and rises over warmer regions. Since the air near the equator is, in general, warmer and lighter than elsewhere on the globe, the air movement there is upward. As the warm air rises, it is replaced by cooler air from both the Northern and Southern hemispheres. This horizontal movement of air results in constant winds, the *trade winds*. The entire wind pattern shifts with the seasonal movement of the vertical ray of the sun—northward in the period from January to June, southward from July to December.

Another factor affects winds—the rotation of the earth. Because of this rotation, cooler air moving into the region of the *equatorial low* (the "doldrums" of mariners) does not move directly from the north in the Northern Hemisphere or from the south in the Southern Hemisphere (see Figure

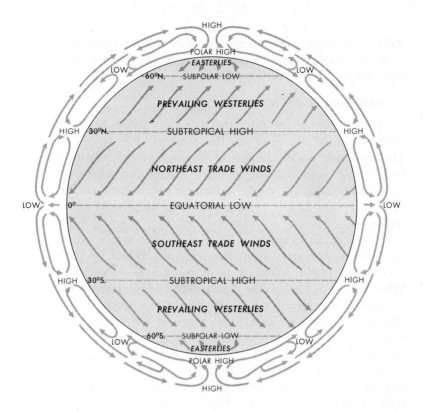

Figure T-8d. Showing basic pattern of atmospheric circulation on the earth's surface

T-8d). Instead, in the Northern Hemisphere the currents flowing toward the equator are turned to the right, resulting in winds that blow from the northeast; in the Southern Hemisphere there is an opposite deflection, to the left, resulting in winds from the southeast.

The circulation of warm air is away from the tropics; cooler air from the *subtropical highs* (the "horse latitudes" of mariners), two regions of descending air, is constantly being brought back for reheating. This means that the equatorial regions of the earth are cooler and the middle latitudes warmer than they would be otherwise. In other words, the region between the tropics exports heat. The air that sinks in the regions of the subtropical highs does not lose all its heat there, however. Some of it swirls out into the higher latitudes—northward in the Northern Hemisphere, southward in the Southern—and mixes with cold air moving toward the equator from the poles. These movements spread heat still farther toward the poles, so that even those extreme regions are warmer than would be expected from the small amount of radiation they receive.

DISTRIBUTION OF MOISTURE

The oceans are the principal sources of moisture for the land. Moisture is carried to the land by circulating air. Therefore our understanding of atmospheric circulation is basic to our understanding of both temperature and moisture conditions on the earth—and these are, in turn, the two most important factors in understanding the distribution of organisms.

Warm water evaporates faster than cold water. Warm air holds more water vapor than cold air. When air passes over warm ocean water, it picks up much water vapor. When the air is cooled, the water vapor precipitates as rain or snow. It may precipitate by passing from a warmer ocean area to a cooler land area. This accounts for the relatively humid (moist) climate of western Europe and for the winter rains in California. Water vapor may precipitate if it meets a cooler air mass. This accounts for the summer rains in the eastern United States. Although warm, moist air from the Gulf of Mexico passes over land that is even warmer, it often meets cool air from Canada, and precipitation results.

On the other hand, along the northern coast of Chile air passes from a cool ocean, where it picks up rather little water, to a warm land, where there are no cool air masses. The result is one of the driest deserts in the world (textbook Figure 8 · 4). But there is another way that air may lose its moisture. We have already seen that the higher atmosphere is cooler. An air mass that is blown against a mountain will rise and, becoming cooler, lose its moisture. In this way the high Andes in Chile receive the moisture that fails to precipitate on the coast.

(The discussion continues with the heading "Distribution of Climates," textbook page 215.)

Audiovisual Materials

There is an abundance of visual materials generally related
to the content of this chapter, but by and large they tend to be
quite elementary. A great need exists for new materials pitched
on the senior high school level, materials that feature biological
principles rather than a mere succession of interesting animal
shots and that avoid anthropomorphism, teleology, and moral-
izing. The items cited below are among the better ones now
available.

Phonograph records: "Sounds of the South American Rain
Forest." (Folkways Records). Produced for the American
Museum of Natural History, this record provides sounds of
weather, of birds, and of mammals.

"Prairie Spring." (Houghton Mifflin Co.). Principally bird
voices of the Canadian prairie.

"Sounds of the American Southwest." (Folkways Records).
Sounds of weather, insects, reptiles, birds, and mammals of
the desert.

"A Day in Algonquin Park." (Houghton Mifflin Co.). Birds,
animals, and wilderness sounds in taiga.

"A Field Guide to Bird Songs" and "A Field Guide to Western
Bird Songs." (Houghton Mifflin Co.). Together these two sets
of records contain voices of virtually all species of North American birds north of Mexico. By selecting characteristic species
of each biome, the teacher can construct an aural image that
should do much to vivify the study of Chapter 8.

Filmstrips: "The World We Live In: The Tundra." (LIFE
Filmstrips). Color. Excellent pictures, a good organization,
some attention to ecological principles—and an unfortunate
abundance of anthropomorphism and teleology.

"The World We Live In: The Woods of Home." (LIFE Filmstrips). The title refers to "middle-latitude deciduous forest."
See comments for the filmstrip above.

"The World We Live In: The Rain Forest." (LIFE Filmstrips). Concentrates on the tropical rain forest of South America.
See comments for first filmstrip, above.

Slides: Perhaps the best method of illustrating this chapter—
at least for the teacher with a good background—is with slides.
These can be placed in any desired sequence, and the "captions"
can be supplied by the teacher—largely in the form of questions
directed to the students. The quantity of good ecological slides
is small compared with the number of taxonomic ones, but all
of the following suppliers have ecological lists: General Biological Supply House, Inc., 8200 S. Hoyne Ave., Chicago, Ill.
60620; Carolina Biological Supply Co., Burlington, N. C. 27216;

and Ward's Natural Science Establishment, P. O. Box 1712, Rochester 3, N. Y. (or Ward's of California, P. O. Box 1749, Monterey, Calif.).

Motion-picture films: "High Arctic: Life on the Land." (National Film Board of Canada). 16 mm. Color. 22 minutes. A film on a specific location in the tundra—Queen Elizabeth Islands, Canada.

"The Spruce Bog." (National Film Board of Canada). 16 mm. Color. 20 minutes. Primarily concerned with pond succession, but provides a good view of the taiga. However, it is short on ecological principles.

"The Boreal Forest." (International Film Bureau). 16 mm. Color. 19 minutes. Community structure in the taiga is based on an analysis of the vegetation. This is followed by a portrayal of insects, birds, and mammals, with particular reference to food sources.

"The Prairie." (International Film Bureau). 16 mm. Color. 18 minutes. The community structure of the middle-latitude grasslands of North America is shown (with special reference to the short-grass plains). This and the preceding film include natural sounds of the biome on the sound track.

"The Grasslands." (Encyclopaedia Britannica). 16 mm. Color. 17 minutes. The theme is the utility of the grasslands to man and their conservation rather than their ecological structure.

"The Temperate Deciduous Forest." (Encyclopaedia Britannica). 16 mm. Color. 17 minutes. The annual cycle of changes in the middle-latitude deciduous forest of North America is well depicted.

"The Desert." (Encyclopaedia Britannica). 16 mm. Color. 22 minutes. Adaptive mechanisms rather than community relationships are featured in this film about deserts in general.

"The Tropical Rain Forest." (Encyclopaedia Britannica). 16 mm. Color. 17 minutes. A good integration of abiotic and biotic factors in this biome.

Teacher's References

AUBERT DE LA RÜE, E., F. BOURLIÈRE, and J. P. HARRAY. The Tropics. New York: Alfred A. Knopf, Inc., 1957. (Magnificently illustrated.)

BATES, M. Animal Worlds. New York: Random House, Inc., 1963. (Reviews the zoological aspects of both terrestrial and aquatic biomes, with a good selection of pictures.)

_____. Where Winter Never Comes. New York: Charles
Scribner's Sons, 1952. (Mostly about the tropical rain forest.
Describes the conditions of tropical life and explores the place
of man in this environment.)

BRAUN, E. L. Deciduous Forests of Eastern North America.
New York: The Blakiston Co., 1950. (Does not describe
an entire biome; devoted exclusively to macroscopic vegetation; covers the subject excellently.)

BURNS, W. A. (ed.). The Natural History of the Southwest.
New York: Franklin Watts, Inc., 1960.

CLEMENTS, F. E., and V. E. SHELFORD. Bio-ecology.
New York: John Wiley and Sons, Inc., 1939. (Now rather
old, but still a good reference for descriptions of biomes
in North America.)

DANSEREAU, P. Biogeography: An Ecological Perspective.
New York: The Ronald Press Co., 1957. (This is not
biogeography in the sense of Green Version Chapter 11.
Concerns the ecological factors in the distribution of life
on earth. Animals are rather slighted.)

FARB, P. The Forest. New York: Time, Inc., Book Division,
1961. (Treats forests in general—as distinguished from
grasslands, deserts, and tundra—and does not describe
biomes specifically. Animals enter the picture only inci-
dentally. Some good illustrations.)

JAEGER, E. C. The North American Deserts. Palo Alto,
Calif.: Stanford University Press, 1957.

LEOPOLD, A. S. The Desert. New York: Time, Inc., Book
Division, 1961. (Similar to Farb, but animals receive more
attention.)

RICHARDS, P. W. The Tropical Rain Forest. London:
Cambridge University Press, 1955. (An excellent description of the tropical rain-forest biome by a perceptive
naturalist.)

THOMAS, W. L. (ed.). Man's Role in Changing the Face of the
Earth. Chicago: University of Chicago Press, 1956. (An
excellent review; historical, contemporary, and projective.)

WEAVER, J. E. North American Prairie. Lincoln, Neb.:
Johnsen Pub. Co., 1954. (For a long time this summary of
results from a lifetime of study will be a source of reference
and inspiration.)

CHAPTER 9

Patterns of Life in the Water

MAJOR IDEAS

1. Because man is a land organism, it has been difficult
for him to comprehend the vastness of the water world. Almost
three-fourths of the total biosphere is encompassed in aquatic
environments—and in the past the proportion was even greater.

2. The ecosystems of inland waters are so closely related
to those of the surrounding land that it is not possible to distinguish separate inland-water biomes.

3. Current, translucency, turnover, and chemical characteristics are the most important abiotic factors in the classification of inland-water ecosystems.

4. In all aquatic communities the greatest proportion of
food production is accomplished by microscopic plants and
protists. The diversity and abundance of aquatic consumers
are an indication of the vast amounts of energy made available
by the aquatic producer system.

5. The chemical characteristics of the sea are to a considerable degree the result of the activities of marine organisms,
just as the chemical characteristics of the atmosphere are to
some extent the result of the activities of terrestrial organisms.

6. Recent explorations have revealed that life occurs even
on the floor of the abyssal depths.

7. Man has influenced inland-water ecosystems almost as
much as he has influenced the surface of the land. However,
except for slight disturbance of the margin, man has as yet had
little effect upon the seas. Indeed, the ocean depths are a
frontier of exploration as rich in possibilities as the depths of
solar space.

TEACHING SUGGESTIONS

Guidelines

In Chapter 8 the principles of tolerance, limiting factors, ecological biogeography, and biomes (and man's influence on them) are treated in the context of terrestrial life. These basic principles are further exemplified in Chapter 9. Additional concepts in Chapter 9 are those pertaining specifically to aquatic life. It is undeniable that aquatic biology is important, but the matters treated in Chapter 10 and Chapters 12 to 20 are probably more basic to a well-rounded course in biology. Therefore, in view of the overlap of concepts in Chapters 8 and 9, the latter might be considered for omission.

Even if a class skips Chapter 9, students who have interests in aquatic biology or who complete their work rapidly might undertake the study of Chapter 9; such individual or small-group efforts might include the setting up of Exercises 9.2, 9.3, and 9.5 as demonstrations for their classes. In any case, if the teacher plans to do Exercise 12.6 the "Background Information" and "Procedure A" of Exercise 9.5 should be brought to the attention of all students.

Some teachers do not want to omit Chapter 9 but find that in the regular sequence of chapters it comes at a season inconvenient for field work. If this problem arises, the whole chapter— textbook and manual—may be shifted to the spring semester. Quite logically it may be inserted as an interlude between Sections Four and Five, where it will serve to focus attention once again upon the individual organism, the species population, and the interaction of both with environment—matters that are fundamental background to Section Five. If this placement is still too early in the spring for field work, Chapter 9 might be taken up between Sections Five and Six.

If the chapter is studied any time after Section Four has been completed, it is possible to introduce many ideas that are unsuitable earlier in the year—for example, osmotic differences between fresh- and salt-water environments.

Even if the chapter is omitted, it may still be desirable to have all students read "The Ocean Environment" (textbook pages 269-273) when the subject of the origin of life arises in Chapter 10. The textbook chapter easily divides into two assignments: pages 251-268 and pages 268-287. The exercises may be done in any sequence.

Some Notes

The photograph at the head of the chapter is a scene on the Pacific coast. Kelp is seen in the water and on the beach.

Figure 9.10: Within the pond the vertical scale is much exaggerated in comparison with the horizontal scale.

Figure 9.15: Rapid and irregular lowering of the water level in such reservoirs fatally exposes shoreline aquatics to the air, and any plants that invade the mud flats are drowned when the level rises again. The band of light rock on the left shore (obscured by shadow on the right) indicates great fluctuation of the water level in this reservoir.

Figure 9.16: In many farm ponds, as in this one, the development of emergent vegetation is prevented by cattle. Farmers who wish to exploit the potentialities of ponds for fish production fence their ponds or allow access for watering of stock at one point only.

Figure 9.17: Many miles of river course are compressed into this diagram.

Page 271: The quantities of water presently locked up in glaciers are estimated differently by different geologists. Recent work in Antarctica suggests that the quantities of ice there would, if melted, result in a much greater rise in sea level than the 18 m given on line 10—perhaps 60 m would be a better estimate.

EXERCISES

9.1   Field and Laboratory Study of a
       Pond Community . . . . Highly Recommended
9.2   Succession in Freshwater Communities:
       A Laboratory Study. . . . . Highly Recommended
9.3   Effects of Salinity on Living
       Organisms . . . . Highly Recommended
9.4   Exploring Marine Communities . . . . Optional
9.5   Measurement of pH in Aquatic Ecosystems . . Optional

Exercise 9.1
Field and Laboratory Study of a Pond Community

Exercise 9.1 parallels Exercise 3.1 and may be substituted for it; both exercises have the same purpose. (No formal statement of purpose is given for Exercise 9.1, but the teacher should refer the student to manual page 47.) When used in the spring, the pond exercise is effective for reviewing community concepts.

This exercise is written primarily for use with a pond of the kind described in the textbook (pages 253-258). It may require modification for use with other kinds of ponds. For example, a pond of the kind shown in textbook Figure 9.16 lacks a zone of emergent plants. The general idea of the exercise (field collection in different habitats, followed by laboratory study of the collected organisms) can be adapted for work in slow-moving streams.

At the Park School, near Baltimore, Maryland, a good artificial pond lies about 20 m from the classroom door. If not unique, this situation is certainly rare. In most places, however, some kind of pond is available at a greater distance from the school. The distance may be so great or the administrative difficulties so complex that trips to the pond by whole classes are impracticable. In such cases it may be possible to organize a small group of volunteers to go to the pond on a weekend and accomplish the collecting phase of the exercise. If the collected material is not crowded, and if it is kept in a refrigerator, it will usually last three or four days. It is less perishable than marine material.

Much of the discussion of field-trip procedure given for Exercise 3.1 (guide pages 75-78) applies to this exercise; the teacher should review it when planning the work. For pond work, safety precautions are essential. Deep ponds should be avoided.

If the field collecting is done by a few students after school or over the weekend, the class should be divided into groups for the laboratory work. Then the collected material can be divided among the groups for identification, observation, and counting. A secretary may be designated for reporting the findings of each team to the class; his notes may be written up on a stencil, duplicated, and a copy distributed to each student.

Exercise 9.2
Succession in Freshwater Communities:
A Laboratory Study

This exercise allows some insight into freshwater biology without a trip outside the classroom; it may be carried on during the winter months. It is particularly concerned with succession and provides good means for deepening understanding of that concept. And it also offers an opportunity to dip back into the levels of individual and population while the mainstream of the work is progressing on the cellular level.

For wide-mouth jars use one-gallon pickle, relish, or mayonnaise jars, obtainable from the school cafeteria or from a restaurant. Clean the jars thoroughly. Rinse them a number of times to remove all traces of soap or detergent; mere traces of these will kill many of the aquatic organisms.

Pond water may be sterilized in an autoclave, but boiling is sufficient. Rainwater may be collected and used in place of pond water. If nothing but tap water is available, condition it before using. This is done by allowing the water to stand for at least forty-eight hours in shallow glass vessels. (Large baking dishes are good.) The distilled water should, if possible, be obtained from a glass still; some organisms are quite sensitive to traces of metallic ions—especially copper.

It is desirable that the setups be replicated. But even one setup for each class may present space problems—especially since the exercise should be continued for six weeks. If laboratory space is inadequate, selected students may set up the jars at home and bring samples of the water to the laboratory for occasional microscopic examination. The teacher must urge caution in the transportation of glass containers.

Additional questions for class discussion: In setting up the jars, why is pond water used rather than distilled water? Why is distilled water used to replace water lost by evaporation? What is the source of energy in the three jars?

Exercise 9.3
Effects of Salinity on Living Organisms

NOTE: The sodium chloride solutions for this exercise should be made up before the class meets to begin the work.

This exercise is concerned with the idea of tolerance, which was first discussed in Chapter 8. Tolerance to salinity is of basic importance to all aquatic organisms. In a more general

view the exercise is concerned with osmoregulation. When osmosis is encountered in Chapter 12, reference to the observations in this exercise will help to make the abstract molecular
process more vivid.

The "Purpose" of Exercise 9.3 can be expanded to include
the following goals: (1) to test the extent to which an organism
tolerates a change in the physical nature of its environment;
(2) to observe in the organism the visible effects produced by
the change in the environment; (3) to discover the degree of
change that the organism can endure; and (4) to determine the
ability of the organism to recover when its normal environment
is restored.

Each pair of students should test the effects of all concen-
trations of sodium chloride on a particular organism. Many
different aquatic organisms may be used. The following are
suggested largely on the basis of availability:

Ameba	elodea (leaf)
Vorticella	Spirogyra or other filamentous algae
Euglena	Daphnia or Cyclops
Hydra	rotifers

Exercise 9.4
Exploring Marine Communities

It is difficult to exaggerate the importance of the sea in any
broad view of biology. And it is also difficult to exaggerate the
difficulties of guiding the great majority of American high school
students to a firsthand acquaintance with marine biology. There
is all the more reason, then, to urge teachers in schools that
are within "striking distance" of the seacoast to bend every effort
toward providing their students with the experience represented
in this exercise. The exercise is suitable for bays and estuaries
as well as for the open seacoast.

The general principles for planning field trips apply to this
exercise; consult the materials for Exercises 3.1 and 9.1 in
this guide. In planning a seashore trip, give particular attention
to safety precautions.

The transportation of living specimens from the field to the
laboratory is likely to result in many disappointments. However,
in recent years the efforts of aquarists to maintain marine organisms have been more and more successful. Some of the
knowledge accrued from these efforts can be obtained through
aquarium hobby shops. These shops also are likely sources
for the "ready-mix salts" needed in formulating artificial

seawater. The teacher can get much help from Turtox Service
Leaflet 20: "Marine Aquaria" (General Biological Supply House,
8200 S. Hoyne Ave., Chicago, Ill. 60620).

Exercise 9.5
Measurement of pH in Aquatic Ecosystems

The basic ideas of acidity and alkalinity were discussed in
textbook Chapter 7. Many teachers regard the extension of these
ideas into the concept of pH as essential in a biology course. Although some use of indicators is possible without development
of the concept (as, for example, in Exercise 1.3), biological
experimentation on any level must remain quite unsophisticated
unless the student learns some method of measuring pH. Therefore, even if Exercise 9.5 is not going to be worked through,
teachers may wish to use the "Background Information" and
"Procedure A."

The ranges of the recommended indicators are as follows:

Methyl red . . . . pH 4.2 (red) to pH 6.2 (yellow)
Bromthymol blue. . . . pH 6.0 (yellow) to pH 7.4 (blue)
Phenolphthalein . . . . pH 8.2 (colorless) to pH 10.0 (red)

Other indicators may be used. A chart of indicators and their
pH ranges may be found in Teaching High School Science: A Sourcebook for the Biological Sciences, E. Morholt, P. F. Brandwein,
and A. Joseph (New York: Harcourt, Brace and Co., 1958), p. 407.

Hydrochloric acid and sodium hydroxide should be 0.1 N
solutions.

The greater the number of water samples, the better. If
many are available, different teams can measure different
samples. However, several teams should measure each sample,
to obtain more than one reading.

The following formulation for artificial seawater is adapted
from Dittmar's composition analysis:[1]

NaCl . . . . . . 27.3 g		K_2SO_4 . . . . . 0.86 g
$MgCl_2$ . . . . . 3.8 g		$CaCO_3$ . . . . . 0.13 g
$MgSO_4$ . . . . . 1.7 g		$MgBr_2$ . . . . . 0.07 g
$CaSO_4$ . . . . . 1.26 g		

Dissolve the salts listed above in 1000 ml of distilled water.

A good brand of wide-range pH test paper is Hydrion. Paper
with a range from pH 3 to pH 9 will cover most needs.

---

[1] W. Dittmar, "Report on Researches into the Composition of
Ocean Water, Collected by H. M. S. Challenger," Physics and
Chemistry, Vol. 1, 1884. See also Sverdrup et al., guide page 155.

SUPPLEMENTARY MATERIALS

Audiovisual Materials

Phonograph record: "Sounds of Sea Animals. " (Folkways Records: FX 6125). Noises made by crustaceans, various fishes, and especially porpoises.

Filmstrips: "The Miracle of the Sea. " ("The World We Live In, " Part II). Color. New York: LIFE Filmstrips, 1954. Contains little about living things, but is useful for establishing the dimensions of the seas and the physical processes that are important factors in the abiotic environment of marine organisms.

"Creatures of the Sea. " ("The World We Live In, " Part VII). Color. New York: LIFE Filmstrips, 1955. Excellent photographs and better-than-average paintings.

"The Coral Reef. " ("The World We Live In, " Part VIII). Color. New York: LIFE Filmstrips, 1955. A good collection of photographs.

"Animal and Plant Communities: the Pond. " ("Interdependence of Living Things" series). Color. New York: McGraw-Hill Book Co. , Inc. , 1961. Descriptive rather than analytical. Good pictures. Text fairly accurate and not marred by excessive teleology.

Motion-picture films: "The Pond. " (International Film Bureau). 16 mm. Color. 20 minutes. Parallels the pond description in the Green Version textbook.

"The Stream. " (International Film Bureau). 16 mm. Color. 15 minutes. An excellent visualization of the "Flowing Waters" section of the Green Version textbook.

"Life in the Ocean. " (Film Associates of California). 16 mm. Color. 13 minutes. Contains little about oceanographic principles, but its beautiful photography will give students far from the sea some close acquaintance with marine animals—and simultaneously it offers a chance to review some animal phyla.

"The Sea. " (Encyclopaedia Britannica Films). 16 mm. Color. 26 minutes. Interrelationships among marine organisms are shown against the background of conditions in the marine environment.

"Plankton and the Open Sea. " (Encyclopaedia Britannica Films). 16 mm. Color. 19 minutes. Uses photomicrography to show many plankton organisms. Also develops the importance of plankton in marine food chains.

"World in a Marsh. " (National Film Board of Canada).
16 mm. Color. 22 minutes. Ecological relationships in a
marsh. The organisms are chiefly those of eastern North
America.

"Survival in the Sea. " (University of Indiana Audiovisual
Center). 16 mm. Color. This is a series of four films, 30
minutes each: (1) "Life Cycle of the Sea. " A general survey
of marine ecology; the basic film in the series. (2) "Life on
the Coral Reef. " Contains some fine underwater photography.
(3) "On the Rocks. " Stresses organisms that are adapted to
life on rocky bottoms and shores. (4) "Where Land and Water
Meet. " Habitats along the sea's margins.

Teacher's References

BATES, M. , and D. P. ABBOTT. Coral Island. New York:
    Charles Scribner's Sons, 1958.
BENNETT, G. W. Management of Artificial Lakes and Ponds.
    New York: Reinhold Publishing Corp. , Book Division,
    1962. (Excellent for relating principles of aquatic ecology
    to the practical techniques of managing impoundments for
    fish production.)
FREY, D. G. (ed.). Limnology in North America. Madison,
    Wis. : University of Wisconsin Press, 1963. (Thirty-two
    contributors survey the limnology of the continent by
    regions.)
HARDY, A. C. The Open Sea, Its Natural History. London:
    William Collins Sons & Co. , Ltd. , 1956. (This British
    book beautifully describes the planktonic world.)
INTERNATIONAL OCEANOGRAPHIC CONGRESS, NEW YORK.
    Oceanography (Publication No. 67), ed. MARY SEARS.
    Washington, D. C. : American Association for the Advance-
    ment of Science, 1961. (A symposium volume that covers
    the whole range of the subject and provides one of the best
    available views of the purposes, requirements, and oppor-
    tunities of the discipline.)
MORGAN, A. H. Field Book of Ponds and Streams. New York:
    G. P. Putnam's Sons, 1930. (Intended as a field guide for
    identification of organisms, but contains a great deal of
    general information on freshwater life.)

NEEDHAM, J. G. , and P. R. NEEDHAM. A Guide to the Study
    of Fresh-water Biology, 5th ed. San Francisco: Holden-
    Day, Inc. , 1962. (Small but of great value to the teacher—
    especially when he is planning Exercise 9.1 or is called
    upon to guide students who have a special interest in aquatic
    biology.)
POPHAM, E. J. Some Aspects of Life in Fresh Water, 2nd ed.
    Cambridge, Mass.: Harvard University Press, 1961. (A
    good, readable introduction for the teacher. Also good for
    the better student.)
REID, G. K. Ecology of Inland Waters and Estuaries. New York:
    Reinhold Publishing Corp. , Book Division, 1961. (Deserves
    a place in this list for its attention to estuaries, much neg-
    lected bodies of water that present some interesting special
    problems.)
SVERDRUP, H. U. , M. W. JOHNSON, and R. H. FLEMING.
    The Oceans; Their Physics, Chemistry, and General Biology.
    New York: Prentice-Hall, Inc. , 1942. (Now becoming rather
    old, but still a mine of information.)
WELCH, P. Limnology, 2nd ed. New York: McGraw-Hill
    Book Co. , Inc. , 1952. (A standard textbook.)

CHAPTER 10

Patterns of Life in the Past

MAJOR IDEAS

1. Fossils comprise the tangible evidence for the existence of organisms in the past.

2. From this evidence paleontologists have been able to piece together a sketchy history of life on earth. This history is more than a mere recital of names and descriptions of extinct organisms; it includes a reconstruction of biotic communities, of climates, and even of whole ecosystems.

3. To reconstruct the past from the scattered and fragmentary fossil evidence, paleontologists begin with a thorough knowledge of the organisms and ecosystems of the present. Then, by inference and logical analysis, they extrapolate this knowledge back into the past—guided by the fossils.

4. Man's understanding of the history of the earth has steadily grown as he has extended his exploration of fossil-bearing rocks. Though this understanding is, and probably always will be, meager, it will increase as more fossils are discovered.

5. In successive layers of rock the presence of certain fossils and the absence of others enable the paleontologist to construct a geological time sequence. In recent years measurements of the products of radioactive decay have begun to tie geological time more firmly to an absolute time scale.

6. While there is little doubt that life on this planet originated in the oceans, paleontologists have no direct evidence of how it originated. Some biologists have been willing to speculate about the origin of complex carbon molecules that could have

been the biochemical forerunners of simple living systems, and recent laboratory experimentation has lent support to some of these speculations.

7. The fossil record indicates that throughout the biological history of the earth, once-abundant kinds of organisms have become extinct and new kinds of organisms have appeared. Where the record is most complete it indicates that this phenomenon is the result of gradual changes in the characteristics of organisms over many generations.

8. No living species can be the ancestor of any other living species; but fossil evidence indicates that some present-day organisms are more like those of various ages in the past than are others. On this basis the taxonomist constructs phylogeny. (This idea is not explicitly stated in the textbook, but it is implicit if the teacher wants to develop it.)

TEACHING SUGGESTIONS

Guidelines

In the textbook this is a long chapter; in the manual, on the other hand, there is but one exercise. Telling the story of our present knowledge of the past requires, by itself, considerable space, and the mere recounting of facts is not enough in a course that attempts to stress the investigative nature of biology. But the very nature of paleontological research makes student laboratory investigations difficult. An attempt must be made to accomplish, by means of the textbook, some goals that might preferably be accomplished through exercises. Hence the disproportion between textbook and manual treatment.

The textbook chapter can be broken up in a number of ways. For short assignments use the following divisions: pages 291-302, pages 302-313, pages 313-322, and pages 322-332. For longer assignments divide the chapter into parts, at page 313. There is also some logic in a short first assignment (pages 291-302) and a long second assignment (pages 302-332). The first contains the basic and important ideas that are most in need of teacher explication; the second is largely narrative and may be read rapidly with the aim of acquiring a panoramic, rather than a detailed, view of fossil history. This plan of assignment is particularly appropriate with students who have had some introduction to life of the past in previous science classes, or when the teacher needs to hurry but does not want to sacrifice the entire chapter.

Exercise 10.1 is best reserved until most of the textbook chapter has been read. Earlier in the study of Chapter 10, students should have some firsthand experience with fossils. If the school is near good fossil-bearing strata, this is pre-eminently an occasion for a field trip; at least, the teacher should lead a Saturday expedition of volunteers. Regardless of the school's location, however, fossils should be in the classroom. The fossil-collector is a breed of hobbyist that may occur any-where, and donations from one can usually be arranged by the teacher. The teacher, in his own journeyings, should always be alert to opportunities for acquiring specimens. Finally, there are the biological supply companies, among which Ward's Natural Science Establishment, Inc. (P. O. Box 1712, Rochester 3, N. Y.) is particularly noted for fossils.

In this chapter—as in the case of Chapters 8 and 9—much stress needs to be placed upon illustrations. Just as we cannot bodily transport students to distant biomes, so we cannot take them to the distant past. But vivid illustration can partially overcome the difficulty. There is, however, a complicating factor in illustrating Chapter 10, a factor often overlooked but crucial to the teaching of biology as a science. When we present a photograph of a scene in a distant biome, we are presenting facts (within narrow tolerances imposed by the limitations of photography). When we present a painting of a scene in the distant past, we are presenting an artifact. It is essential that students perceive this distinction. Both teacher and student must keep in mind that the more vivid and lifelike the portrayal of a scene from the geological past, the further the scene must depart from the strict fossil evidence.

Mindful of the caution in the last paragraph, the authors have tried to balance illustrations of restorations with a goodly number of illustrations showing the fossils themselves. Likewise in the text an attempt has been made to distinguish between statements that are facts concerning the occurrence of fossils and statements that are inferences drawn from such occurrences. The teacher is strongly urged to carry through and strengthen this distinction during class discussions.

Frequent reference should be made to Section Two and to the appendix of the textbook. Neither of these treats extinct groups of organisms, but the task of fitting extinct groups into the assem-blage of modern organisms is instructive. And of course most of the groups on the higher levels of classification have had long histories, so that mention of them recurs frequently in Chapter 10. But perhaps the chief reason for referring to the Appendix is to give the teacher opportunity to show how the arrangement of taxonomic groups reflects the attempts of taxonomists to portray phylogeny—a matter briefly discussed at the end of textbook Chapter 4. After all, Chapter 10 is an exhibit of one major sector of the evidence for evolution.

First impressions to the contrary, the vocabulary burden in this chapter is not great if one keeps in mind the discussion on page 21 of this guide. Much of the vocabulary having to do with taxonomic groups has already been encountered in Section Two. It is true, however, that a large number of generic terms are used both in the text and in the captions of Chapter 10. This is unavoidable. Visual examples must be given, and the examples certainly ought to be identified. Also, some students may wish to investigate certain paleontological topics further, and the names are convenient for this purpose. It is indeed regrettable that paleontologists have had such a Hellenic bias in coining names—and obviously (though this may have to be pointed out to the student) organisms known only from fossils are not likely to have acquired "common" names. But these terms are not a part of the learning burden. What about the terms in the geological time scale? Well, some things any literate person just ought to know.

Some Notes

The photograph at the head of the chapter shows a mounted skeleton of <u>Tyrannosaurus</u> <u>rex</u>.

Figure 10.4: The absolute time scale in the right-hand column (and, in Figure 10.5, the proportions based on it) is recorded in figures that have been widely published. It is perhaps too much to say that they are generally accepted. The student can no doubt find others in various reference works (see note on Figure 1.6, guide page 39). And, as more dating is done by means of radioactive isotopes, still other figures will come into use.

Pages 297-298: For background on methods of dating, see <u>Handbook</u> Chapter 11, "Dating by Radioactive Isotopes."

Page 298: Oparin's <u>Origin of Life</u> is available in paperback (New York: Dover Publications, Inc., 1953).

Figure 10.31: The term "pterosaur" in this figure is equivalent to "pterodactyl," which appears on textbook page 319 in the first and second printings only.

Figure 10.32: Here the artist has obviously used a modern opossum—and, almost certainly, the particular species found in the United States—as a model for his reconstruction. There is no real reason for supposing that <u>Eodelphis</u> had a white face and grizzled fur.

Figures 10.20 and 10.34: Because they are not mentioned in the text, these maps will be overlooked by many students. The teacher, however, may find them useful for relating past geography to present. Consider, too, the question: On what kinds of evidence are such maps based? The geological evidence of evolution in land masses spurred the thinking of Darwin toward the idea of organic evolution.

Figure 10.36: This figure is intended to emphasize the need for caution in accepting restorations. The evidence as found in the rocks (top photograph) clearly requires a great deal of interpretation even to undergo transformation to the mounted skeleton (middle photograph). Still further interpretation is required to arrive at a three-dimensional model—and interpretations may differ (bottom photographs). When only a few fragments are preserved, how much greater must be the distance between fossil and restoration!

Page 324: Both students and teacher may have used "carnivores" in a popular ecological sense, usually as an equivalent to "predator." It may be well, therefore, to note that here it is used in a taxonomic sense, as the English form of "Carnivora" (used in Chapter 4).

Figure 10.38: "<u>Hyracotherium</u>" has priority over the more familiar "<u>Eohippus</u>." It is, however, perfectly permissible to use "eohippus" as a common name. (This note applies to Exercise 10.1 also.)

EXERCISES

10.1 Paleontological Comparison.....Highly Recommended
    Without considerable help from the teacher, the connection between this exercise and the textbook chapter is likely to be rather obscure. Pictures of restorations of the extinct equids will help. The skull or jawbone of a modern horse will make the exercise more "real." Models of fossil teeth and feet can be obtained from Ward's (see address on guide page 91). The

models are quite useful for illustrating some characteristics—
in addition to span of cheek teeth—that have been used in recon-
structing the phylogeny of the Equidae.

Whether illustrative materials are available or not, the
exercise should not be simply assigned for homework. With
most students it is necessary to go over the "Background
Information" and "Procedure" rather carefully; after this the
actual construction of the chart can be done by students outside
of class.

In going over the "Procedure," the following matters should
be emphasized: (1) In Figure 10.1-4 the points are to be plotted
just as they would be plotted on an ordinary line graph, but they
should be placed <u>between</u> the lines dividing the time intervals
rather than on the lines. And of course the line connecting the
points will branch. (2) The directions in the first two paragraphs
on manual page 189 must be followed carefully; the aim is to show
how data on a single characteristic—the span of cheek teeth—fit
the scheme of phylogeny derived from the study of many characteristics. (3) <u>Miohippus</u>, like several other genera, is represented
by two dots, which indicates existence of the genus in two time
levels. It probably will not be obvious to the student that the
genera <u>Anchitherium</u> and <u>Parahippus</u> could not very well have
evolved from species of <u>Miohippus</u> that existed contemporaneously
with them (in the early Miocene). Explain that <u>Anchitherium</u> and
<u>Parahippus</u> were more likely to have arisen from species of
<u>Miohippus</u> living in the late Oligocene.

The work of the students can be facilitated by providing
them with copies of a form similar to Figure 10.1-4. If a
uniform horizontal scale of 4 mm per million years is used,
this form may be conveniently duplicated (lengthwise) on
8-1/2" X 11" paper.

SUPPLEMENTARY MATERIALS

<u>BSCS Pamphlets</u>

AUFFENBERG, W. <u>Present Problems About the Past</u>. Boston:
     D. C. Heath & Co., 1963.
YOUNG, R., and C. PONNAMPERUMA. <u>Early Evolution of Life</u>.
     Boston: D. C. Heath & Co., 1964.

Audiovisual Materials

Phonograph record: "The Scientists Speak: Biology. "
(Harcourt, Brace & World, Inc.). George Gaylord Simpson
talks about his work as a paleontologist.

Filmstrips: "Reptiles Inherit the Earth. " ("The World We
Live In, " Part V). Color. LIFE Filmstrips, 1955. A wonderful
gallery of paintings, with all the familiar and many unfamiliar
Permian and Mesozoic amphibians and reptiles represented. But
there is no mention at all of the fossil evidence on which the
magnificent imagery is based.

"The Age of Mammals. " ("The World We Live In, " Part VI).
Color. LIFE Filmstrips, 1955. Another fine collection of paintings. Includes some introductory matter on stratigraphy, which
links the pictures to the fossil evidence.

Motion-picture films: "Story in the Rocks. " (Shell Oil Co.).
16 mm. Color. 17-1/2 minutes. Deals interestingly with the
more glamorous activities of paleontologists, emphasizing their
skill in interpreting bits and pieces of evidence.

"The Fossil Story. " (Shell Oil Co.). 16 mm. Color. 19
minutes. The practical importance of paleontology in exploring
for oil is the theme. Adds an important facet to Chapter 10.

"How Did Life Begin?" (National Aeronautics and Space
Administration). 16 mm. Color. 20 minutes. Dr. Sidney Fox
discusses the evolutionary relationships of various protein molecules and traces his synthesis of artificial protein.

Teacher's References

AGER, D. V. Principles of Paleoecology. New York: McGraw-
    Hill Book Co. , Inc. , 1963. (An "introduction to the study
    of how and where animals and plants lived in the past. "
    Provides an excellent background for the point of view that
    dominates Chapter 10 of the Green Version.)
ANDREWS, H. N. Studies in Paleobotany. New York: John
    Wiley & Sons, Inc. , 1961. (Not as comprehensive as Darrah,
    but explores in depth some of the most important problems
    of plant evolution.)
DARRAH, W. C. Principles of Paleobotany. New York: The
    Ronald Press Co. , 1960. (A university textbook.)
EASTON, W. H. Invertebrate Paleontology. New York: Harper
    & Brothers, 1960. (A systematic enumeration of fossil
    invertebrates, with numerous illustrations.)

MOORE, R. C. Introduction to Historical Geology, 2nd ed.
New York: McGraw-Hill Book Co. , Inc. , 1958. (A general
text on the history of the earth. The geologist views the
fossil record as a key to earth history rather than as a key
to evolutionary processes; both viewpoints should be in the
teacher's background.)
_____, C. G. LALICKER, and A. G. FISCHER. Invertebrate
Fossils. New York: McGraw-Hill Book Co. , Inc. , 1952.
(Books on invertebrate paleontology are rather specialized;
this one furnishes a good beginning.)
OPARIN, A. I. The Origin of Life. New York: Dover Publications, Inc. , 1953. (The source of much current thinking
on the origin of life; originally published several decades
ago.)
ROMER, A. S. Vertebrate Paleontology, 2nd ed. Chicago:
University of Chicago Press, 1945. (A systematic enu-
meration of fossil vertebrates. Emphasis is on remains
rather than restorations.)
_____. The Vertebrate Story, 4th ed. Chicago: University
of Chicago Press, 1959. (A narrative account of the fossil
history of vertebrate animals.)

CHAPTER 11

The Geography of Life

MAJOR IDEAS

1. The geographical distribution of most species cannot be explained on ecological grounds alone.

2. The present distribution of a species and the distribution of its fossils and of the fossils of its putative ancestors are keys to the distributional history of the species. A similar statement can be made concerning higher levels of classification—genera, families, orders, etc.

3. Organisms vary in ability to disperse; therefore, to explain the distribution of any species, one must consider its structural and physiological characteristics in relation to the nature of the physical barriers that it may have had to cross in spreading from its area of origin.

4. Man has greatly influenced the distribution of many organisms by transporting them—sometimes deliberately, sometimes accidentally—across barriers that they had not themselves been able to surmount.

5. Wallace's realms, derived largely from studies of land vertebrates, illustrate principles of distributional patterns that can be applied, in varying degrees, to other organisms.

TEACHING SUGGESTIONS

Guidelines

Chapter 11 has been designated as the first chapter to be considered for omission if time is insufficient (guide page 19). This does not mean that the authors regard the content of Chapter 11 as unimportant. Obviously, if this had been the case, biogeography would not have gained admittance in the first place; its presence is an indication that it was weighed against other areas of biology and found valuable for the objectives of the course.

The worth of the chapter lies in two directions: First, biogeography helps to orient the student in the world through descriptive organization of the facts of distribution. Thus it contributes to the humanistic aims that the authors of the Green Version maintain to be proper for high school biology (guide page 5). Second, biogeography presents a series of problems that demand an evolutionary explanation. Thus it contributes— and in a way easily visualized by students—to the explication of evolution, the pervading theme of modern biology.

If the chapter is omitted from Section Three, it may be profitably considered—by some students, at least—in connection with Chapter 17, Section Five. At that point the text (particularly textbook pages 339-348 and 366-369) should have a considerably deeper significance than it might have had earlier in the year.

This is another chapter that can very well be started with laboratory work. Exercise 11.1 may even be set up before work on Chapter 10 has been concluded.

The textbook chapter is short; it can be given as a single assignment. If two assignments are preferred, page 348 makes a good dividing point. Pages 336-348 pose problems and deal with theories; pages 348-366 are descriptive; pages 366-370 return to two matters of principle.

Throughout the chapter attention should be directed to the pictures and maps, which have here an especially important function. A large bulletin board can be effectively used to extend the visual materials in the textbook. Students can draw a large outline map of the world and mark off the realm boundaries on it. Pictures of characteristic organisms should be then pasted in proper geographical location. Unfortunately, available pictures are likely to run heavily to mammals, as do those in the textbook. But if an appeal is made to stamp collectors, a surprising amount of zoological—and even considerable botanical—variety can be obtained. In recent years many countries have issued large numbers of beautifully executed stamps illustrating their flora and fauna, often with great accuracy; sometimes the stamps even bear the technical names of the organisms.

Some Notes

The walrus in the photograph at the head of the chapter ties in with the first paragraph on page 337.

Figure 11.5: The subspecies of salamanders and their distinguishing characteristics are as follows: A — P. j. unicoi (white spots on sides); B — P. j. teyahalee (white spots on sides and back); C — P. j. shermani (red legs); D — P. j. rabunensis (white spots on sides, dark belly); E — P. j. jordani (red cheeks); F — P. j. melaventris (all black); G — P. j. metcalfi (light belly).

Page 345: The idea of adaptive radiation was first developed in Chapter 10 (textbook pages 322 ff.).

Figure 11.12: The boundaries of the realms correspond to those usually agreed upon by zoogeographers. And they differ from Wallace's originals only slightly.

Figure 11.13: The numbers of the barriers shown on the map correspond to the numbers used in listing kinds of barriers on textbook page 349.

Figures 11.24 and 11.26: The questions in the captions tie in with the content of Chapter 17, but at this point in the year's work they are rather speculative.

Figures 11.31 and 11.32: The area of origin of a taxonomic group is determined from studies of the distribution in time and space of the fossils representing the group and its probable antecedents. For example, fossils of the Camelidae occur in greatest abundance in rocks of the early Cenozoic of western North America; these fossils represent genera that are more primitive in cameline characteristics than are the living genera of Eurasia and South America.

EXERCISES

11.1   The Effects of Barriers on
         Dispersal . . . . Highly Recommended

11.2   Barriers and Adaptive Radiation . . . . . . Optional
The exercises for Chapter 11 can be used even if the textbook
material is omitted. Exercise 11.1 can be set up as a demonstration by a small group of students; Exercise 11.2 can be assigned
on an individual basis.

Exercise 11.1
The Effects of Barriers on Dispersal

This exercise can arouse considerable interest if the students
clearly understand the way in which the procedure relates to the
purpose. When the apparatus has been set up, the students may
be asked to make some predictions concerning the outcome.
Later these predictions should be checked against the results
of the experiment; comparison of predictions with results is
a good springboard for the concluding discussion.

To obviate the feeling that a "right" result is to be obtained,
some replication of the setup described in the exercise is desirable. However, the setups require considerable space, so replication by teams within a class is usually impractical. In the
majority of schools, where there are at least several biology
classes, one setup per class is sufficient.

A small team can prepare the glassware and, in the presence
of the class, introduce the organisms. In this case only fifteen
to twenty minutes of class time is required initially. Then, after
a few minutes a day for observation, the experiment can be
brought to a conclusion with about thirty minutes of discussion.

The dimensions of the tubing are given on the assumption
that containers about 8 cm high will be used. Height is not
critical, but the dish and beakers (or jars) should all be the
same height so that the tubes will rest horizontally, as indicated
in Figure 11.1-4. Small blocks of wood may be used to correct
differences in container height.

Euglena may be cultured in the laboratory in a modified
Kleb's solution:

KNO_3	0.25 g
$MgSO_4$	0.25 g
KH_2PO	0.25 g
$Ca(NO_3)_2 . 4 H_2O$	1.00 g
Bacto tryptophane broth	0.01 g
Distilled water	1000.00 ml

This stock solution should be diluted 1:10 with distilled water.

Daphnia may be substituted for Planaria.

Evaporation will be about equal in the beakers and the culture
dish; in a week's time it should not be great enough to interfere
with the operation of the setups. In any case, it is not advisable
to add liquid; the addition, unless made equally and simultaneously
to all four containers in each setup, will force liquid and organisms through the tubes.

Exercise 11. 2
Barriers and Adaptive Radiation

This exercise is for assignment on an individual or group
basis. A large museum or zoo furnishes the best material for
the exercise, but where neither is available a really interested
student might be able to accomplish something by using the
numerous fine pictures in Ivan Sanderson's Living Mammals
of the World (New York: Doubleday & Co. , Inc. , 1955) or
François Bourlière's Mammals of the World (New York: Alfred
A. Knopf, Inc. , 1955).

The student's explanation for convergent evolution may be
rather naive at this point. The topic might be brought up again
after Chapter 17 has been studied.

SUPPLEMENTARY MATERIALS

Audiovisual Materials

As in the case of the biomes, the content of this chapter is
best illustrated by means of 2" X 2" slides. Sources are listed
on guide pages 143-144.

Filmstrip: "South American Fossils. " ("Darwin's World
of Nature, " Part IV). Color. New York: LIFE Filmstrips, 1960.
Deals with the development of the South American vertebrate land
fauna after its isolation in the Cretaceous and with the results
of the subsequent rejoining of South America and North America
in the Pleistocene. The pictures are good and the zoogeographical
principles are well presented.

Teacher's References

BEAUFORT, L. F. Zoogeography of the Land and Inland Waters.
    London: Sidgwick & Jackson, Ltd. , 1951.
CAIN, S. A. Foundations of Plant Geography. New York:
    Harper & Brothers, 1944. (Rather old, but it illustrates well
    the synthetic nature of biogeographical study.)
DARLINGTON, P. J. Zoogeography. New York: John Wiley &
    Sons, Inc. , 1957. (The standard current American reference,
    concerned principally with terrestrial vertebrates.)

EKMAN, S. P. Zoogeography of the Sea. Translated by
    ELIZABETH PALMER. London: Sidgwick & Jackson, Ltd.,
    1953. (The biogeography of the seas is entirely omitted from
    the Green Version, but the teacher should have some famil-
    iarity with the subject.)
GEORGE, W. B. Animal Geography. London: William
    Heinemann, Ltd., 1962. (More recent than Darlington.)
GOOD, R. D. The Geography of the Flowering Plants. London:
    Longmans, Green & Co., Ltd., 1953. (As the vertebrates
    have been the principal, though by no means the exclusive,
    source of data for zoogeographers, so the angiosperms have
    been for phytogeographers. This is a standard reference.)
RUNCORN, S. K. (ed.). Continental Drift. New York: Academic
    Press, Inc., 1962. (The geological theory of continental drift
    has a direct bearing on biogeography. It is not mentioned in
    the Green Version, but the teacher may wish to familiarize
    himself with it.)
SIMPSON, G. G. Evolution and Geography. Eugene, Oregon:
    State System of Higher Education, 1953. (An excellent essay
    on the relationship between the fossil record and the present
    distribution of organisms, with special reference to mammals.
    If the teacher wishes to use Green Version Chapter 11 in
    connection with Chapter 17, this book will provide some
    excellent background.)

section *Four*

WITHIN THE INDIVIDUAL ORGANISM

Though the introduction to Section Four occurs almost exactly in the middle of the textbook, it does not represent the halfway point with respect to the learning load. Beginning with Chapter 12 the density of ideas becomes much greater than it was in any of the first eleven chapters; throughout Sections Four and Five, increasing student effort is required. The heavier burden in the second half of the book may in part be balanced by the increasing maturity of the students and by their increasing familiarity with techniques of studying and pondering biological science. But even allowing for greater student efficiency, Sections Four, Five, and Six should be allotted something more than half the year.

Through several generations of biological investigation, heavy emphasis was placed upon the structure and internal functioning of organisms. This emphasis has persisted in high school biology-teaching and in the preparation of teachers long after its decline in biological research. In Section Four of the Green Version is concentrated much of this "traditional" high school biology, the biology that is familiar to the majority of today's biology teachers. Also encountered in Section Four is material from the burgeoning field of biochemistry—a less familiar area and one that is changing with a rapidity likely to make obsolete the factual knowledge of even last year's college graduate.

The blend of the familiar and the unfamiliar in this section may prove challenging to the teacher—or it may be exasperating. To achieve the purposes of the Green Version, the writers found it necessary to reduce what has frequently been the substance of an entire course to less than one section and to abandon much familiar material in the process. It is not possible to explain here the reasoning that led to each reduction or omission. But, in general, it was felt that much of the traditional material could best be placed in junior high school science. For example, many junior high schools already treat effectively the gross anatomy of man; the writers hope this pattern becomes so widespread that even further curtailment of material on human anatomy will be possible—thus allowing space to expand upon the principles of animal physiology through the comparative approach. At present, the teacher must gauge the background of his classes and place stress accordingly.

CHAPTER 12

The Cell

MAJOR IDEAS

    1. Observations and thoughts by men of many nationalities contributed to the development of the cell theory. This theory, though imperfect in details, has been immensely important in the investigation of biological structure and function.

    2. Cell structure varies so greatly that generalizations are inevitably misleading. This applies both to the organelles visible within the cell and to the chemical composition of the living substance.

    3. The biologist aims to explain the functioning of cells in terms of physical principles. Some cell functions are easily understood on this basis, but others require deep understanding of physical sciences, and some have yet to be reduced to a purely physical explanation.

    4. Within the cell some chemical processes are constantly breaking down cell substance, while others are constantly building it up. The net result is energy expenditure—and life.

    5. Chemical reactions in living cells are catalyzed by enzymes, which are proteins manufactured by the cells. Enzymes are highly specific in function.

    6. The release of energy from foods can occur in the absence of oxygen—anaerobic respiration. But to recover the full energy available in food molecules, oxygen is usually required; this aerobic respiration results in the formation of CO_2 and H_2O, the "raw materials" of photosynthesis.

7. To a greater or lesser degree, all cells have the ability to synthesize the complex organic substances that account for almost all the dry weight of cells. For the most part, these cell substances turn out to be the familiar food substances: carbohydrates, fats, and proteins.

8. Among cells that have recognizable nuclei, the process of cell division is remarkably uniform, involving a definite sequence of nuclear events—mitosis.

9. In species that are essentially unicellular, cell division results in the production of new individuals; in colonial and multicellular species, it results in the growth of the individual.

10. The process by which successive generations of cells within a multicellular organism come to differ from each other —the process of cell differentiation—remains one of the major puzzles of biology.

TEACHING SUGGESTIONS

Guidelines

Textbook Chapter 12 is difficult. The writers have undertaken to make it as clear as possible and have ruthlessly pruned away what they considered unessential detail. They have used an unusually spare running vocabulary. But the material remains difficult. Part of the difficulty arises from the large number of unavoidable technical terms; part arises from the abstractness of molecular theory, perhaps here encountered for the first time by some students; and part arises from the forbidding complexity of chemical formulas. Whatever the source of the difficulty, it must be surmounted, for some understanding of cellular structure and function is essential to the student's appreciation of modern biology. And many things in the remainder of the course depend upon that understanding.

The teacher's first response to the difficulty of Chapter 12 should be to reduce the length of assignments; the second should be to increase the time allowed for discussion of each assignment. Five assignments are suggested: pages 376-383, pages 383-388, pages 388-394, pages 394-401, and pages 401-408. The four basic exercises for this chapter should be interspersed with these assignments.

As a term, "cell" is not new to most tenth-grade students. But since their acquaintance with cells is likely to be secondhand, even in school systems that have good junior high school science programs, putting some observational foundation under the term is of first importance.   Therefore Exercise 12.1 should be undertaken early in the work on Chapter 12.   With close teacher guidance it is even possible to do the laboratory work of this exercise before any of the textbook material has been read, leaving the "Summary" of the exercise until later.

The "Cell Physiology" portion of the chapter (pages 383-401) depends heavily on (1) an understanding of cell structure, and (2) acquaintance with the rudiments of the molecular theory and with elements, compounds, and their chemical notation. An adequate understanding of cell structure may be gained from the preceding part of the chapter.   Some acquaintance with molecular theory, elements, and compounds must, however, be expected in the student's background.   To fill in adequately— that is, not merely with words but with a rich observational experience—a totally blank background in physics and chemistry seems a preposterous assignment for a tenth-grade biology course.   And the writers of the Green Version have declined to take on the task.   But the millennium is not yet, and neither writers nor teachers can complacently allow today's student to suffer for lack of a background they hope the future student will possess.

Fortunately, the amount of physics and chemistry needed for an understanding of cell physiology on the level expected in the Green Version is not as great as many persons seem to believe.   The student who reads textbook pages 384-385 thoughtfully will have a sufficient (though certainly neither broad nor profound) view of diffusion.   And a class period or two spent in explaining "element," "compound," "chemical change," "symbol," "formula," and a few other terms will at least curtail student bafflement.   A film such as "A Cell's Chemical Organization" (McGraw-Hill) will also prove helpful.

On the other hand, some teachers may feel that an understanding of cell physiology "on the level expected in the Green Version" is insufficient.   The pertinent arguments in rebuttal are given on guide pages 8-10.   But while the writers see no reason for leading the bulk of tenth graders through the treadmill of the Krebs cycle, they certainly believe the teacher should be well acquainted with modern biochemistry and thus prepared to expand on the text with the occasional interested student or with superior, science-oriented classes.   Section 3 of the Biology Teacher's Handbook provides the teacher with brief expositions of a variety of physicochemical topics, of which "Energy" (Chapter 5), "Molecules and Atomic Weights" (Chapter 7), "Atomic Structure" (Chapter 9), "Chemical Bonds" (Chapter 10), and "Biochemistry" (Chapter 12) are most apropos.

The best presentation of mitosis is, of course, by means of a motion picture. Avoid, however, films that combine mitosis and meiosis (or stop the film before meiosis appears). Meiosis has no relevancy in Chapter 12 and can only confuse. If mitosis is thoroughly understood now, meiosis will be relatively easy when it is encountered in Chapter 15. But the viewing of a film does not assure understanding. The need for Exercise 12.4 remains; the student still needs to link microscopic study with macroscopic reality.

Some Notes

The illustration at the head of the chapter is from a photomicrograph of a young plant cell. The junction of the cell wall with the walls of neighboring cells is quite clear.

Pages 376-378: The history illuminates the development of a biological concept and, as in Chapter 6, it emphasizes the international character of science.

Pages 378-379: The aim here is an understanding of the cell theory—including its limitations—not memorization of a definition of "cell."

Figure 12.4: Note the quotes around "typical" where this figure is referred to on page 379. The cell shown is not typical; it is completely imaginary. (There is no such thing as a typical cell.) Some teachers will miss the endoplasmic reticulum, ribosomes, Golgi bodies, etc. The importance of these is not to be minimized, but a limit to terminology must be drawn somewhere. The September, 1961, issue of Scientific American is an excellent summary of current cytology.

Pages 384-385: To illustrate diffusion, drop a large crystal of copper sulfate or some crystals of potassium permanganate into a small beaker of water, and allow the beaker to sit undisturbed for a few days. A white card behind the beaker will make observation easier.

Page 385: The term "differentially permeable" is preferred to "semi-permeable" (formerly much used); the latter is logically faulty, and the former is more descriptive. The introduction of "differentially" here makes the later "differentiation" (page 405) less strange.

hold the Holy Land, to tread our first steps on it in a difficult battle, the
ttle for peace, the peace of the brave."

Now, as we celebrate the reawakening of creative forces within us
d restore the war-torn home that overlooks the neighbours' where our
ildren shall play together and compete to pick flowers, now, I feel na-
nal and human pride in my Palestinian Arab people whose powers of
ience and giving, of retaining a never-ending bond between homeland,
tory and people, have added a new chapter to the homeland's ancient
ends, that of The Epic of Hope.

To them, to the sons and daughters of that kind enduring nation,
t nation of yew and dew, of fire and sweat, I dedicate this Nobel Prize.
all bear it to those children who have been promised freedom, safety
security in a homeland free of the threats of external occupation or in-
al exploitation.

ow, I know full well, Mr Chairman, that this supreme and greatly sig-
ant prize was not awarded to me and to my partners: Mr.Yitzhak
n, the Israeli Prime Minister, and Mr. Shimon Peres, the Foreign Min-
to crown an achievement: but as an encouragement to pursue a route
greater steps and deeper awareness, with truer intentions so that
ay transform the peace option, the peace of the brave, from words
practice and reality and for us to be worthy of carrying forward the
age entrusted to us by our peoples, as well as humanity and a uni-
l moral duty. The Palestinians, whose national cause guards the
of Arab-Israeli peace, look forward like their Arab brethren, to that
rehensive, just and lasting peace, based on "land for peace" and
iance with international legitimacy and resolutions. Peace, for us, is
et and in our interest. It is an absolute human asset that allows an
dual to freely develop his individuality unbound by any regional,
us or ethnic fetters. It restores to Arab-Israeli relations their inno-
ature, and enables the Arab spirit to reflect through unrestrained
expression its profound understanding of the Jewish-European
, just as it allows the tortured Jewish spirit to express its unfettered
y for the suffering endured by the Palestinian people over their
d history. Only the tortured can understand those who have en-
orture.

ace is in our interest: as only in an atmosphere of just peace shall
estinian people achieve their legitimate ambition for independ-
d sovereignty, and be able to develop their national and cultural
as well as enjoy sound neighbourly relations, mutual respect and
tion with the Israeli people. They, in return, will be able to artic-
ir Middle Eastern identity, and to open up economically and cul-
owards their Arab neighbours. The Arabs are looking forward to
ng their region which the long years of war had prevented from

Photograph 6: Afghan Boys at Play. *Afghan boys play with a balloon in a relatively poor residential area of the old city of Kabul, Afghanistan, damaged during the 1992–1995 civil war. This photograph was taken on Friday, November 12, 2004, the start of the Eid-ul-Fitr holiday weekend that marks the end of the fasting month of Ramadan.*

CONSIDERING THE IMAGE

1. How can these children be enjoying themselves so much in such a war torn setting? Were they even born when war destroyed these buildings? Why wasn't
   the neighborhood rebuilt in the decade following its destruction? To what extent
   do you think these Afghan children are representative of children all over the
   world? Are Western viewers meant to regard them as representative?

2. What is the focal point of this photograph? Where does its energy lie? What
   message(s) does it send, and to what audiences?

Photograph 7: Hmong girl and baby in Binh Lu, Vietnam. *Miguel De Casenave of New York City took this photograph of a Hmong girl and baby during his travels in Vietnam in 2003.*

CONSIDERING THE IMAGE

1. How does your knowledge of the location of this photograph, in Vietnam near the Chinese border, influence the way you interpret the picture? Does it matter whether the young girl is the baby's sister? mother? Or any relation at all? What does this photograph tell Western viewers about the relation of war and peace? What differences in interpretation would there be for viewers who lived through the Vietnam War era and those who didn't? Would the picture have the same meaning for Hmong tribespeople? For other Vietnamese from the North? Or South? How do you account for the fact that the baby's bonnet looks so Western, yet the caretaker is clearly wearing native dress?

2. This photograph won Honorable Mention in "people" category of the Smithsonian Magazine 2004 photography contest. Would you award it a prize? If so, for what reasons? If not, why not?

The Sanctity of Life, in the view of the soldiers of the Forces, will find expression in all their actions; in conside planning; in intelligent and safety-minded training and plementation, in accordance with their mission; in taking ally proper degree of risk and degree of caution; and in th to limit casualties to the scope required to achieve the ob

For many years ahead—even if wars come to an end, aft our land—these words will remain a pillar of fire whic camp, a guiding light for our people. And we take prid
We will pursue the course of peace with determina
We will not let up.
We will not give in.
Peace will triumph over all our enemies, becau grimmer for us all.
And we will prevail.
We will prevail because we regard the buildin blessing for us, and for our children after us. We rega our neighbours on all sides, and for our partners in United States, Russia, Norway, and all mankind. . .
I wish to thank our partners—the Egyptians, Jo and the Chairman of the Palestine Liberation Org Arafat, with whom we share this Nobel Prize—wh of peace and are writing a new page in the annals

Yasser Arafat, The Crescent Moon of Pea

. . . Ever since I was entrusted by my people to u of seeking our lost home, I have been filled v those in exile who bore the keys to their hom their limbs, an inseparable part of them, and th bore their wounds as they bear their names their sacrifices, be granted the rewards of retu
And that the difficult journey on that l end in their own hallways.
Now, as we celebrate together the first s of peace, I stare into the eyes of those marty my consciousness as I stand here on this po the homeland, about their vacant places. I tell them: "How right you were. Your gener

Page 387: The term "osmosis" has been so widely misused that
some biologists have advocated abandoning it. The important
point is that in biological systems osmosis refers to the movement of water molecules only; a plant, for example, does not
obtain nitrate ions from soil water by osmosis. When properly
restricted, "osmosis" seems to be a useful word, since the
diffusion of water through cell membranes is a sufficiently important biological process to warrant a distinctive term.

Page 387—"Difficulties"; page 406—"A Puzzle": The material
under these headings will cause the student who shines by his
memorizing ability to complain that he has nothing to learn.

Page 388: Before beginning "Energy in the Cell," go back to
Chapter 1—not only to review the general flow of energy through
the biosphere but also to review the principal elements found
in living matter (Figure 1. 6).

Page 391: The structural formulas given here and on following
pages are, of course, not to be memorized. They are intended
to show the complexity of even relatively simple organic compounds and to provide a mental image for differentiating large
classes of such compounds. Models will achieve these aims
even more effectively. Such models can be constructed with
toothpicks (or wire) and styrofoam balls. Styrofoam balls of
various sizes and colors may be obtained from Star Band Co. ,
Broad and Commerce Sts. , Portsmouth, Va. Sets of wooden
balls with coil-spring connectors can be obtained from Central
Scientific Co. , 1700 N. Irving Park Rd. , Chicago 13, Ill.

Pages 391 and 392: If students are encountering chemical formulas for the first time, they may easily confuse abbreviations,
such as ATP, with formulas. Even if students have some
familiarity with formulas, it may be well to emphasize this
distinction.

Page 396: With models of glucose and fructose the synthesis of
sucrose can be nicely demonstrated. But the mediation of an
enzyme must be stressed—perhaps by letting the demonstrator
represent the enzyme.

Page 399: Unfortunately the term "base" appears here in
association with nucleic acids. Students must be cautioned
that in this context "base" does not mean "alkali. " It simply
means "that to which something else is attached. "

Pages 402-404: The writers prefer "kinetochore" to "centromere" because the combination centrosome-chromosome-centromere is confusing to the student. The names of the phases of mitosis are omitted because their use tends to belie the uninterrupted continuity of the mitotic process. Moreover, though useful to the cytologist, in this course they would be merely four more terms to be added to an already heavy vocabulary load.

Pages 405-406: The relationship between "The Significance of Mitosis" and "A Puzzle" should be stressed. Here is planted the seed that will give rise to Sutton's hypothesis in Chapter 16.

EXERCISES

12.1	Diversity in Cell Structure	BASIC
12.2	Identifying Some Substances Found in Protoplasm	BASIC
12.3	Diffusion Through a Membrane	BASIC
12.4	Mitosis	BASIC
12.5	Some Characteristics of Living Matter.	Highly Recommended
12.6	A Study of Enzyme Action.	Highly Recommended

Exercise 12.1
Diversity in Cell Structure

This exercise is purely observational and ties in closely with the textbook material on cell structure. The emphasis in the exercise is on living cells that the students can directly associate with whole organisms. This involves more trouble for the teacher than would observation of commercially prepared slides, but, given the BSCS philosophy, the advantage is obvious. Of course only a limited number of cell structures will be seen; if the teacher wants students to see other structures —mitochondria, for example—he may wish to use some commercial slides to supplement the exercise. A few microscopes equipped with oil-immersion lenses would be desirable for such observations.

Materials. The onion can be cut into pieces at the beginning of the day; the pieces will remain usable if kept under water

in finger bowls. In cutting the pieces, take care to avoid slough-
ing off the epidermis.

See guide page 46 for preparation of I_2 KI.

Tradescantia has many uses and is easy to grow. It is a
long-day plant. If the period of illumination is artificially extended, the plant can be kept flowering during the winter months.
The flowers of the closely related Zebrina may also be used.

Elodea (Anacharis) is a common aquarium plant. It is
easy to maintain in an aquarium from which direct sunlight is
excluded. To increase the likelihood of observing cyclosis in
the cells, place some of the material under a bell jar and illu-
minate it for at least twelve hours before using.

Small numbers of toothpicks should be wrapped in aluminum
foil and sterilized in a pressure cooker or autoclave. To avoid
reuse, have each student break his toothpick after use.

To prepare methylene blue solution, add 1.48 g of the dye
to 100 ml of 95-percent ethyl alcohol; let stand for about two days,
stirring frequently; filter and store as stock solution. Before
using, add 10 ml of stock solution to 90 ml of distilled H_2O.

The frog material should be as fresh as possible. One frog
should be used to provide material for morning classes; another
should be used for afternoon classes. Etherize or pith the frog.
With a medicine dropper obtain blood from a large vessel, or
flush an area of bleeding with Ringer's solution. Place the blood
in a small beaker of Ringer's solution. Ingredients of the
solution:

KCl . . . . 0.14 g
NaCl . . . . 6.50 g
$CaCl_2$ . . . . 0.12 g
$NaHCO_2$ . . . . 0.20 g
H_2O (distilled) . . . . . 1000.00 ml

For Procedure F, skin shed in the water in which the frogs
are kept may be used. Or the skin of the freshly killed frog may
be scraped with a sharp scalpel. The materials thus obtained
may be kept in a small beaker of Ringer's solution. Whole skin,
of course, is much too thick for use.

For Procedure G, skin the legs of the frog and dissect out
the large muscles. Separate the bundles and cut them into
pieces about 2 mm square. Place the pieces in a small beaker
of Ringer's solution.

During this exercise a good demonstration to show cilial
action may be set up. Cut away the lower jaw of a frog; then
cut out small pieces from the lining of the upper jaw in the
region between the eye bulges and the throat. Mount a piece
in Ringer's.

Procedure. Two full periods are required for laboratory
work in this exercise. The teacher should demonstrate the

removal of the onion epidermis and the technique of transferring cheek cells to a slide. Even at this late point in the year,
students may need to be cautioned to use <u>small</u> pieces of
material.

If students work in pairs, each pair may be provided with
slides, cover slips, and dissecting tools; but to save time and
trouble, stains and the materials to be observed may be placed
in one or a few centrally located places where students can go
to prepare their mounts. Or this exercise can be conveniently
accomplished by setting up seven stations, one for each part
of the procedure. The class is then divided into seven groups
of students, each to begin at a different station.

Drawings may be made in the students' data books or on
separate sheets, as the teacher desires.

Exercise 12. 2
<u>Identifying Some Substances Found in Protoplasm</u>

Though this exercise seems to be associated most closely
with textbook pages 394-400, and Exercise 12. 3 with textbook
pages 384-388, the idea of chemical tests needs to be established
before the diffusion experiment is undertaken. The introduction
to Exercise 12. 2 can easily be related to textbook pages 382-
383; the exercise may then be referred to again during the discussion of "Syntheses. "

<u>Materials</u>. Some of the solutions to be used in this exer-
cise can be purchased ready-made, or they can be prepared in
the school. The choice depends upon the number of classes and
the availability of assistants. Ready-made solutions are probably most economical in small schools.

Glucose solution: The strength of this solution may be
approximate; roughly 10-percent is good.

Starch solution: Dissolve 1 g of arrowroot starch in a little
cold water. Add this paste to 200 ml of boiling water. Stir
well to avoid lumps, and filter.

Egg-albumen solution: Beat the white of an egg in about
eight volumes of water. Strain through cheesecloth, if necessary.

Benedict's solution: Dissolve 173 g of sodium or potassium
citrate in 700 ml of warm H_2O. Add 200 g of Na_2CO_3 (100 g,
if anhydrous). Filter. Then dissolve 17. 3 g of $CuSO_4$ in 100 ml
of H_2O, and pour the $CuSO_4$ solution slowly into the first solution, stirring continuously. Add enough distilled H_2O to make
1 liter.

Fehling's solution: This consists of two solutions mixed in
equal proportions just before use. Solution 1—Dissolve 34. 6 g

of CuSO$_4$ in 500 ml of distilled water.   Solution 2—Dissolve 125 g of KOH and 173 g of potassium sodium tartrate in 500 ml of distilled H$_2$O.

Iodine solution: Use I$_2$KI (guide page 46).

In the first printing of the student's manual, biuret reagent is listed for testing proteins. This reagent detects proteose and peptones, decomposition products of proteins, which (under the conditions of this exercise) are not likely to be present. In all subsequent printings, therefore, Millon's reagent replaces Biuret reagent.

Millon's reagent: Dissolve 100 g of mercury in 200 ml of concentrated nitric acid under a fume hood. Dilute the solution with twice its volume of distilled water.

Sudan IV is best purchased in solution.

Procedure. If the supply of test tubes is inadequate, the teacher or a team of students may demonstrate the validation of the reagents. But demonstration merely for the sake of saving time is unjustified. In some respects this is the more important part of the exercise, for it involves the basic principle of all specific chemical tests. The identification of the substances in food—the second part of the exercise—is of relatively minor importance instructionally, though essential for rounding out the exercise from the student's point of view.

If the biology laboratory is not equipped with sufficient burners, it may be possible to use the chemistry laboratory for a day. Bunsen burners are not, however, essential; good alcohol lamps provide enough heat.

Both Benedict's and Fehling's solutions, when heated with "reducing sugars" (glucose and maltose, but not sucrose, belong in this class), form yellow, orange, or brick-red precipitates. Danger of hot liquid spouting from the tubes can be reduced by heating the tubes in a water bath. Iodine solution produces a purple-to-black color with starch. Biuret reagent produces a pale pink or violet color with proteose and peptones. Millon's reagent precipitates protein, which, on heating, turns red. When Sudan IV is added to the tubes containing a mixture of oil and water, the dye collects in the oil as the oil separates from the water (after the tubes have been shaken).

Proteins may also be identified by the xanthoproteic test. Add about 3 ml of concentrated nitric acid to the material to be tested. A yellow color indicates protein. (Gentle heating may be needed.) Confirmation is supplied by slowly adding about 8 ml of ammonium hydroxide; the yellow then deepens to orange.

Fats may be more efficiently concentrated by extraction with ether, but NOT in a laboratory containing open flames!!

Each student should have an opportunity to work with a food sample, but the number of different samples need not be large.

Examples of foods: bread, chocolate, hamburger, cake, beans, peanuts, cheese, milk. The solid materials can be ground up in a mortar before being given to the students.

Exercise 12.3
Diffusion Through a Membrane

This exercise may be performed either before or after the students have read the textbook material on "Entry and Exit." It can be done as a demonstration. But the equipment is simple and inexpensive, and when the exercise is done by groups of four students, everyone will be close enough to the material to see the results. Therefore, demonstration is inadvisable.

Materials. Cellulose tubing with a diameter of 3/8" is convenient, but larger tubing may be used. Collodion sacks may also be used. (For construction of these, see E. Morholt, P. F. Brandwein, and A. Joseph, Teaching High School Science: A Sourcebook for the Biological Sciences, New York: Harcourt, Brace and Co., 1958, page 35.)

Prepare soluble starch solution by adding about 10 g of soluble starch to about 500 ml of water. Stir or shake, and then filter. If you cannot obtain soluble starch, try laundry starch. Filter it through a cloth fabric and then through filter paper. It is desirable, but not essential, that the starch mixture be clear. Some brands of soluble starch are reported to diffuse through cellulose membranes, so the starch should be tested before being used by the students.

The glucose solution should be strong—close to saturation— but the exact concentration is not critical.

For preparation of the iodine solution, see guide page 46.

Wide-mouth jars may be used in place of beakers. "Junior" baby-food jars are suitable.

Tes-tape and Clinitest tablets can usually be purchased at a drugstore. They are used by diabetics to test for sugar in urine. They do not require heating. If their reactions with glucose were not demonstrated during work on Exercise 12.2, such a demonstration should be conducted before Exercise 12.3 is started.

Procedure. The exercise should be set up as quickly as possible at the beginning of the period. About twenty minutes is required for diffusion before the glucose test is made. The reaction of the iodine with starch should be visible by the end of the period, but it will be more striking if the tube is allowed to sit for twenty-four hours.

Two setups are employed because iodine in the water sometimes interferes with the use of Tes-tape or Clinitest tablets.
If burners are available, Benedict's or Fehling's solution may
be used. In this case only one setup is necessary, and both
starch and glucose solutions are placed in one tube.

Discussion. It is important that the results of this exercise,
which involves purely physical systems, be related to living
things. Therefore the questions on manual page 208 must be
given special attention. Glucose and starch are both common
materials in living things; the free diffusion of the former and
the lack of diffusion of the latter can be linked to storage of
starch in plant cells, the need to digest starch, the possibility
of feeding glucose by direct injection, and other biological
matters.

The turgidity of the glucose tube after twenty-four hours
not only indicates the diffusion of water (osmosis) but also
demonstrates diffusion pressure. For a further demonstration.
place a piece of fresh carrot or potato in a 10-percent salt
solution for fifteen minutes. Then have students feel it for
comparison with the feel of another fresh piece. How is this
observation related to the observation in the exercise? (Refer
to results of Exercise 9.3.) What makes plant tissues rigid?
Can we say that all plant rigidity is due to turgor?

Turgor is the most important biological effect of diffusion
pressure, but the teacher may wish to demonstrate another
effect by showing how diffusion pressure can support a column
of liquid against the force of gravity. The apparatus in Figure
T-12.3 can be used for this. A more difficult setup, but one
that has a closer connection with biology, may be provided as
follows: Using the technique shown in the lefthand illustration
of manual Figure 12.4-1, suspend a raw egg in hydrochloric
acid until the lower half of the shell is dissolved away. Make
a small hole through the shell and membrane at the opposite
(top) end, and insert a glass tube in the hole, sealing the connection with paraffin. Support this setup with the bare half of
the egg in a beaker of water.

Compare the diffusion rates in the two setups.

Exercise 12.4
Mitosis

To many students examining prepared slides is little more
than a difficult way of looking at pictures. This exercise allows
the student to associate a familiar macroscopic organism directly

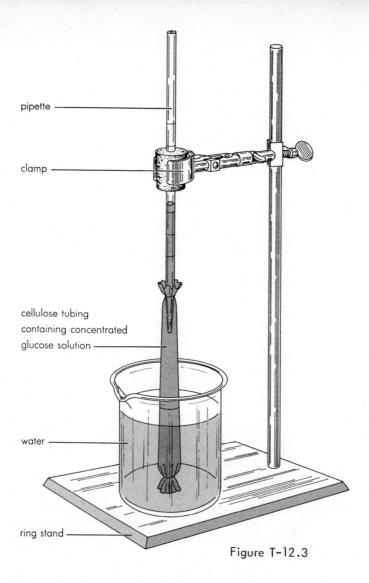

pipette

clamp

cellulose tubing
containing concentrated
glucose solution

water

ring stand

Figure T-12.3

with the somewhat unconvincing story of mitosis told in the textbook. This exercise may also further the student's appreciation
for the techniques of slide preparation.

Materials. Root tips from garlic apparently provide somewhat larger and clearer chromosomes than do those from onion.
Normally, root tips appear within four to six days. Some mar-
keters treat onion bulbs to retard root growth; it may be well to
test the rooting of bulbs a couple weeks before they are to be used.

Fixative solution: One part glacial acetic acid, three parts
absolute alcohol.

Carnoy's fluid: Three parts chloroform, one part glacial
acetic acid, two parts absolute alcohol.

If absolute alcohol is not available for making up the two
preceding reagents, add one part anhydrous $CuSO_4$ to ten parts

95-percent alcohol; shake well and allow to stand for three or four hours, until all CuSO₄ has settled out; decant clear alcohol and keep in tightly stoppered bottle.

Iron-acetocarmin solution: 90 ml of glacial acetic acid and 110 ml of distilled water. Heat mixture to boiling; remove from heat and immediately add 1 g certified carmin dye. Cool solution in refrigerator, then decant. Add a few drops of an aqueous solution of ferric acetate until the color is a dark wine red. (CAUTION: Do not add too much ferric acetate, or the carmin will be precipitated.)

Procedure. For the teacher who is unfamiliar with the "squash" technique the BSCS film "Smear and Squash Techniques" may be useful (Thorne Films, 1229 University Ave., Boulder, Colo. 5-1/2 minutes).

Preliminary preparation of the material (through treatment in Carnoy's fluid) may be done by a small team. But all students should observe the setup of the onion or garlic bulbs and the growth of the roots; this will allow them to clearly associate the small pieces of root (used later) with a real, living organism.

If burners are in short supply, two or three large Erlenmeyer flasks containing boiling water may be set up at strategic places in the laboratory. Students may then bring their slides to these stations for final clearing.

Exercise 12.5
Some Characteristics of Living Matter

NOTE: Preparations for this exercise must be started fourteen days ahead of its use.

Cultures of Physarum polycephalum should be started from sclerotia, which may be purchased from most biological supply houses. The directions in the following paragraph will be clarified by the BSCS Technique Film "Culturing Slime Mold Plasmodium" (Thorne Films, 1229 University Ave., Boulder, Colo. 6-1/2 minutes).

Sterilize a large culture dish (about 8" in diameter) with sodium hypochlorite and rinse thoroughly. Cut two circular pieces of muslin (old sheeting is fine); the diameter of each piece should be about 5 cm greater than the diameter of a petri dish. Boil them. Cover the outer surface of one half of a petri dish with the double thickness of muslin, and fold the edges tightly under the rim of the dish (see Figure T-12.5). Place this muslin "table" in the culture dish, and add water to a depth of about 5 mm. Place the paper bearing the

Physarum sclerotium in the middle of this "table," colored side (the sclerotium side) up. Cover the culture dish with a sheet of glass or a larger dish. The paper towel (Figure T-12.5) helps maintain a humidity gradient in the chamber and, in addition, prevents condensed moisture from dropping onto the slime mold. Store the setup in indirect light at a temperature of about 20°C. When the slime mold has "crawled" onto the muslin, remove the paper. Then feed daily by sprinkling on the surface of the plasmodium a small quantity of oatmeal that has been pushed through a wire kitchen strainer. Avoid dropping oatmeal in the water. Change the water daily. If contaminating molds appear in the culture, they should be cut out with a sterile scalpel. Always cut outside the apparent margin of the mold.

When the slime mold has spread over the entire muslin "table," transfer small bits of the plasmodium to a petri dish containing a thin layer of nonnutrient agar. (Prepare by dissolving 1.5 g of agar in 100 ml of hot water.) It is not necessary to autoclave the dishes or the agar, since slime molds live on bacteria and mold spores. Maintain these cultures for two days under the same light and temperature conditions as above. If necessary the petri dishes containing agar and bits of plasmodium may then be stored for a few days in the refrigerator. Several hours before use, they should be removed from the refrigerator and allowed to warm to room temperature.

The remainder of the plasmodium in the humidity chamber may be sclerotized and stored for later use, as follows: Spread a piece of moistened absorbent paper on the walls of the culture

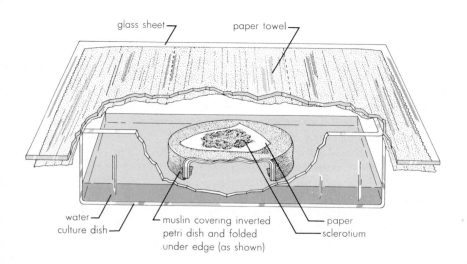

Figure T-12.5

chamber. Move the muslin "table" to the edge of the culture
chamber so that it is in contact with the vertical layer of paper.
Discontinue feeding. In a short time the plasmodium will "crawl"
onto the paper. Remove the paper, place it in a loosely covered
container, and allow it to dry slowly. After several days the
paper containing the sclerotium may be removed, cut into pieces
of convenient size, and stored in an envelope for later use. The
dormant organism will remain viable for one to two years.

Exercise 12.6
A Study of Enzyme Action

This exercise might be deferred until digestion is discussed
in Chapter 14. But there is some advantage in demonstrating
enzyme action at the time it is first discussed (textbook page 389);
furthermore, Chapter 14 is already rather crowded with laboratory
work. Too often, enzymes become associated exclusively with
digestion; by using Exercise 12.6 now, this notion is less likely
to be formed—though there would be no harm in recalling this
work during study of Chapter 14.

Procedure A can be done as a demonstration, following
which seven teams may each perform one of the operations in
Procedure B. If students providing the saliva have been chew-
ing gum, their saliva will produce a positive sugar reaction.
The use of sweetened crackers in the exercise will also produce
a positive sugar reaction.

Though the use of saliva may be considered messy, it has
the advantage of clearly relating enzyme action to a living organism. In the minds of students, diastase (which might be substituted) is divorced from life; if it were used, the exercise would
become a purely chemical—not a biochemical—one. Of course
some attention must be given to establishing a proper investiga-
tory attitude, and good psychological judgment must be used in
selecting the students who will contribute saliva.

For iodine solution and Benedict's or Fehling's solution,
see guide pages 178-179. Hydrion is a good brand of wide-
range pH test paper. The exact pH's of the hydrochloric acid
and sodium hydroxide solutions are not critical.

SUPPLEMENTARY MATERIALS

Mitosis Model

In Exercise 15.2 meiosis is illustrated by means of a model.
A similar model illustrating mitosis may be used in Chapter 12
if time permits—especially if a good film showing mitosis in
living cells is not available. In the meiosis model, strands of
poppit beads represent chromatids; for mitosis, pipe cleaners
will serve just as well, since it is not necessary to show crossing-
over and, therefore, the "chromosomes" do not need to be broken.
Students can make the "chromosomes" by threading two pipe
cleaners through a small bead representing a kinetochore. If
poppit beads are used, they can make the "chromosomes" by
fastening two strands together with a piece of pipe cleaner
representing a kinetochore.

In the procedure given below, maternal and paternal chromosomes are differentiated by color. At this point the distinction
is not necessary, and therefore a single color can be used. But
there is something to be said for the pedagogical value of antici-
pating future developments (if such action does not obscure the
present point), so the teacher may wish to use two colors and
briefly answer the inevitable questions. He must be sure to
emphasize that the colors are symbolic rather than actual.
Procedure:

Make up 6 "chromosomes"—2 long with the kinetochore
in the middle, 2 medium-sized with the kinetochore one-
fourth of the way from one end, and 2 short with the kinetochore in the middle. In each pair, make one "chromosome"
of one color, one of another (see Figure T-12a).

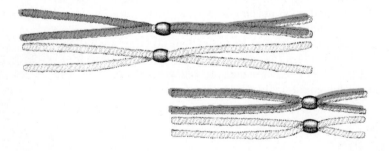

Figure T-12a

Using a crayon, draw a spindle on a large piece of wrapping paper spread out on a table. The spindle should be large enough to accomodate the 6 "chromosomes" when they are arrayed on its equator.

Begin with the "chromosomes" lying at random on the spindle. Bring them from this position into line at the equator. To represent the splitting of the kinetochore, uncouple the "chromatids" and provide each pipe cleaner with a separate bead (or provide each strand of beads with a piece of pipe cleaner).

Now move one pipe cleaner of each pair toward one pole of the spindle and the other toward the other pole of the spindle. If six students are lined up on one side of the table and six on the other side, all the pipe cleaners can be moved simultaneously, just as the chromosomes move in mitosis. The pipe cleaners should be bent at the bead to represent the shape of chromosomes as they migrate to the poles of the spindle (Figure T-12b). Finally, compare the makeup of the set of "chromosomes" at each pole with the makeup of the original set of "chromosomes. "

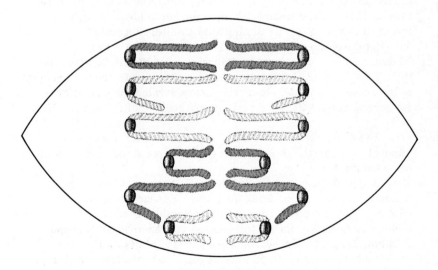

Figure T-12b

BSCS Pamphlet

MAZIA, DANIEL. Cell Differentiation. Boston: D. C. Heath & Co. In press.

Invitations to Enquiry

Invitations 1 and 2 (pp. 53-56 of the Handbook). These invitations involve interpretation of data on the cell nucleus.

Invitation 26 (pp. 141-148 of the Handbook). The ratio of oxygen consumption to carbon dioxide production in the respiration of germinating seeds is used to develop the concept of a linear relation. A fine invitation for students who have had a little algebra.

Invitation 28 (pp. 154-161 of the Handbook). A rather advanced invitation that concerns changes in fermentation rate and the interaction of several variables. Mathematical.

Audiovisual Materials

Filmstrips: "Classification of Matter" (Introduction to Chemistry 1) and "Molecules, Atoms, and Simple Reactions" (Introduction to Chemistry 2). Color. Encyclopaedia Britannica Films, 1960. Excellent review of some basic ideas in physics and chemistry. Expertly arranged to tie ideas together.

Motion-picture films: "The Life and Death of a Cell."
16 mm. Color. 26 minutes. Department of Visual Communication, University of California. Significant content: the importance of the nucleus to the life of a cell, demonstrated through microsurgery mitosis; effects of various environmental factors on living cells.

"The Cell, Structural Unit of Life." 16 mm. Color. 10 minutes. Coronet Films. A short and simple film, useful as an introduction.

"A Cell's Chemical Organization." 16 mm. Color. 28 minutes. McGraw-Hill Book Co., Inc. Essentially a "canned lecture," but has good organization and makes good use of molecular models. Useful for classes that have no background in chemistry and a teacher who is uncertain of his own.

"Cell Respiration." 16 mm. Color. 30 minutes. McGraw-Hill Book Co., Inc. Follows "A Cell's Chemical Organization," and the remarks above apply to it. Supplements the Green Version textbook with a good demonstration of the theory of enzyme action.

"Cells and Their Function." 16 mm. Black & White. 14 minutes. Contemporary Films, Inc., 614 Davis St., Evanston, Ill. The study of cells by means of tissue culture is emphasized. Time-lapse photomicrography shows cells in mitosis.

"Mitosis. " 16 mm. Color. 24 minutes. Encyclopaedia Britannica Films. Includes the effects of chemicals and radiation on mitosis.

Teacher's References

CHAMBERS, R. and E. L. CHAMBERS. Explorations into the Nature of the Living Cell. Cambridge, Mass. : Harvard University Press, 1961. (Summary of a lifetime of investigations into the functioning cell by means of microdissection. Excellent background to more recent biochemical work on fractionated cell constituents.)

CONN, E. E. , and P. K. STUMPF. Outlines of Biochemistry. New York: John Wiley and Sons, Inc. , 1963. (A short textbook.)

GIESE, A. C. Cell Physiology, 2nd ed. Philadelphia: W. B. Saunders Co. , 1962. (An excellent textbook that sticks closely to the fundamental physiology of the isolated cell. The best single reference for this chapter.)

HARRISON, K. A Guide-book to Biochemistry. London: Cambridge University Press, 1959. (According to the publisher, this is "the bare bones of biochemistry"; but it is a very useful skeleton for the teacher who needs to organize knowledge that he has picked up here and there without benefit of formal course work.)

PORTER, K. R. , and M. A. BONNEVILLE. An Introduction to the Fine Structure of Cells and Tissues. Philadelphia: Lea & Febiger, Publishers, 1963. (Primarily a book of illustrations, mostly from electronmicrographs of moderate magnification. Man is the subject of the work.)

ROBERTS, E. D. , W. NOWINSKI, and F. A. SAEZ. General Cytology, 3rd ed. Philadelphia: W. B. Saunders Co. , 1960. (A good standard textbook.)

SCHRADER, F. Mitosis, 2nd ed. New York: Columbia University Press, 1953.

WHITE, P. R. The Cultivation of Animal and Plant Cells, 2nd ed. New York: The Ronald Press Co. , 1963. (The techniques of in vitro cultivation of cells are not likely to be of everyday use to the high school teacher, but he should make himself familiar with their history.)

The Functioning Plant

MAJOR IDEAS

    1.   Man's understanding of photosynthesis began with experiments on plant growth, advanced greatly in the chemical revolution that brought about the downfall of the phlogiston theory, and reached a basic formulation in the first half of the nineteenth century. In the twentieth century new methods—especially chromatography and isotope techniques—have revealed the enormous physicochemical complexity behind the simple term "photosynthesis."

    2.   The present understanding of photosynthesis may be summarized in three sets of reactions: two involve the transfer of light energy into chemical energy; the third—the "dark reaction"—incorporates carbon dioxide into organic compounds. It appears that only "light capture" is unique to chlorophyll-bearing organisms.

    3.   As specialized organs of photosynthesis, leaves exhibit (both externally and internally) close correlation of form and function. In addition, structures that, on the basis of their morphogenesis, must be regarded as leaves carry on various nonphotosynthetic functions and have forms corresponding to such functions. Complementarity of form and function is as conspicuous in roots as in leaves and is only a little less so in stems.

    4.   In the majority of land plants, water is constantly being lost (principally through leaves) and is constantly being absorbed from soil (through roots). In addition to performing the function of absorption, roots usually furnish plants with anchorage and with a site for the storage of food.

5.   The complex microscopic structure of stems is primarily associated with conduction of liquids in the plant body. As yet, biophysical explanations of conduction do not completely account for all observations.

6.   In contrast to animal growth, the growth of multicellular plants is a result of mitotic activity in persistently undifferentiated tissues—meristems.

7.   After plant cells have been formed by mitosis, their increase in size is in many cases under the control of auxin. Auxin distribution is influenced by light; differential distribution of auxin results in changes in the direction of stem elongation.

8.   Because they are the most conspicuous plants and the most important ones to man, tracheophytes receive the major emphasis in studies of plant structure and function. But all plants have wide synthetic powers—even the fungi, which lack photosynthesis—and they all exchange substances with their environment.

TEACHING SUGGESTIONS

Guidelines

The talk by Rabinowitch on the record "The Scientists Speak" (see guide page 202) makes an excellent beginning to the study of plants. From this, work can turn to the textbook, though Exercise 13.1 should not be long delayed. Textbook pages 412-423 obviously form a coherent assignment. The remainder of the textbook chapter can be divided in several ways. The authors suggest three more assignments: pages 423-433, pages 433-442, and pages 442-448.

The process of photosynthesis is placed at the beginning of the chapter for a number of reasons. First, since flow of energy through the biosphere is a principal theme of the course, the most significant activity of plants—even considering all the exceptions—is photosynthesis. Second, after the diversion for mitosis and differentiation, it seems wise to get back as quickly as possible to some biochemical matters before their faint impressions dim irrecoverably. Third, photosynthesis is a function that brings into focus the details of tracheophyte anatomy and physiology.

Students (and perhaps some teachers) must be reminded that in the <u>Green</u> <u>Version</u> course the term "textbook" has shed connotations appropriate to twelfth-century scholasticism. It is <u>not</u> intended that the student memorize the details of biochemistry involved in the description of photosynthesis. At the least, however, presentation in the text and in the diagrams (Figures 13.5, 13.6, and 13.8) should add up to some appreciation for the complexity of apparently simple processes and for the work of biochemists who have used great ingenuity in unraveling the tangled threads of evidence. In addition, most students should carry away the knowledge that photosynthesis— as usually defined—consists of an initial light-trapping stage and a subsequent light-independent synthesis, that research in photosynthesis uses chromatography and analytical methods involving isotopes, and that knowledge has not yet proceeded to the point where man is independent of plants. Even to accomplish these minimum aims, however, some details must be given; it is not enough merely to <u>state</u> that photosynthesis is complex.

After the excursion into biochemistry, the portion of the chapter dealing with vascular plants returns students and teachers to more familiar matters. Insofar as material is familiar, no learning occurs, of course; the teacher must beware that nostalgia does not induce unprofitable lingering. In many school systems students are already well acquainted with at least the external and macroscopic morphology of vascular plants—and the authors hope that this will be even more true in the future. If this is the case, attention should be focused on microscopic anatomy and, especially, on physiology. Although morphology and physiology are complementary, it is possible to approach the systems level of biology either by way of structure, which is then elucidated in terms of function, or by way of function, which is then explored in the light of available structure. On the high school level the second approach seems preferable wherever a happy compromise between the two extremes cannot be arranged.

Depending upon the background of students and the extent of their need for concrete referents for their thinking, the teacher may introduce illustrative laboratory work. Collections of living plants to show variations in leaf, stem, and root structure ought to be maintained. A session or two with microscopes to observe the microstructure of plant organs may be desirable—preferably beginning with hand-sectioned materials (see filmstrip reference on guide page 202).

Some Notes

Pages 412-418: Again history is used as a springboard for launching a chapter—and as an additional illustration of the way in which scientific ideas grow from scientific investigation.

Figure 13.1: Recall the chloroplasts of elodea leaf cells seen in Exercise 12.1.

Figure 13.4: Point out that the horizontal axis of this graph represents a segment of Figure 1.4. As noted in the text, the figure gives a partial answer to the question "Why are plants green?" It does not, of course, give any clue to the reason chlorophyll fails to utilize energy in the green portion of the spectrum.

Pages 418-422: Remind students that ATP, ADP, PGAL, TPN, and RuDP are abbreviations, not formulas. Unfortunately, the matter is complicated by $TPN \cdot H_2$.

Page 418: Emphasize that the "light reaction" is a whole series of reactions; likewise the "dark reaction."

Page 419: In the chemical reaction (and also in Figures 13.5 and 13.6), the P represents a phosphate group, not phosphorus. In Chapter 12 the symbol Ⓟ was used to represent a phosphate group. This inconsistency in symbolism appears in early printings of the textbook.

Figure 13.6: In the first and second printings "CO_2"—instead of "O_2"—mistakenly appears in the lower right corner. How many students are sufficiently alert to note that CO_2 cannot be derived from OH radicals?

Figure 13.7: Compare the soil with Figure 7.1 and the plant tissues with Figure 13.18.

Figure 13.18: Some of the labeled structures are not mentioned in the text. The teacher may want to employ the names of several of these—as, for example, pericycle and endodermis—when explaining the origin of secondary roots. Or the unlabeled structures may raise student questions that can be the basis for reference to more advanced books.

Page 422: Note that the term "meristem" has no relationship to the word "stem."

Figure 13.32: In biology, causation is usually assumed to be complex. It is difficult to control all possible factors, especially genetic ones. Conclusions, therefore, are not based on results from a single setup; data from many replications of an experiment are required.

EXERCISES

13.1   Separation of the Pigments That Occur
        in Leaves . . . . BASIC
13.2   Loss of Water by Plants . . . . BASIC
13.3   Chemical Action in a Plant . . . .   BASIC
13.4   Chemical Control of Plant Growth . . . . BASIC
13.5   Photosynthetic Reserves . . . . Highly
                                                Recommended
13.6   Rate of Growth: Leaves . . . . Optional
13.7   Transport of Phosphates in Plants . . . . . . Optional

Two exercises in later chapters—15.4 and 18.2—are concerned with plant physiology. Both require several weeks of growing time between setup and conclusion; if they are started during the work on Chapter 13, they can be concluded during study of the chapters for which they are designated. Whether or not this plan is adopted, Exercise 18.2 must be set up several weeks before Chapter 18 is studied; otherwise—on a normal schedule—it will not be ready for conclusion by the end of the school year.

Exercise 13.1
Separation of the Pigments That Occur in Leaves

Though more sophisticated separation methods are now widely employed by biochemists, paper chromatography remains useful. And as a demonstration of the basic principle of chromatography, the separation of leaf pigments is highly effective and meaningful to high school students.

The materials and equipment required for this exercise are easily obtained in quantity, the manipulations are simple, and the students' satisfaction with their results is great; therefore it is desirable to have very small teams—preferably pairs.

The assembling of the apparatus, as described in the first paragraph of the "Procedure," may be done the day before the chromatogram is to be run. This allows time for the atmo-

sphere in the tube to become saturated with the vapor of the
solvent. If the laboratory period is less than fifty minutes long,
this preliminary step is essential. (CAUTION: It is the atmosphere, not the filter-paper strip, that is to be saturated; after
being fitted to the tube, the strip should be laid aside until the
leaf extract is prepared.)

The specified mixture of acetone and petroleum ether produces best separation, though other proportions may be used.
Pure acetone, used in the extraction, is poor as a solvent in the
chromatography tube. Theoretically, any leaves containing
chlorophyll are usable, but some kinds are better than others.
Pelargonium (household geranium) is good; but the pigments in
spinach leaves are especially rich and easy to extract—and
spinach is easily obtained at all seasons. Pipettes with suit-
ably fine tips may be made by heating a piece of tubing, pulling
it out to a small diameter, allowing it to cool, and cutting it
in two at the middle of the constriction. The large end of each
piece can be made to fit the rubber bulb from an ordinary medicine dropper by heating to softness and enlarging with the shank
of a triangular file.

While the chromatogram is developing, the red fluorescence
of chlorophyll may be demonstrated: In a piece of black paper
cut a hole with a diameter about one-third the circumference of
a test tube. Wrap the paper around the tube, and pour chlorophyll
extract into the tube to a point above the top of the hole. Using
a strong light source—a microscope spotlight, for example—
shine a beam of light on the tube about 45 degrees from the
normal.

In well-developed chromatograms a band of yellow pigment
will be found close to the leading edge of the solvent. This band
contains carotenes and has an R_f of almost 1.00. (R_f = distance
of band from origin divided by distance of leading edge of solvent
from origin.) Much lower on the paper, starting at about R_f 0.4,
there will be, first, another yellow band (sometimes distinguish-
able as two separate bands) containing xanthophylls; second, a
band of bluish-green chlorophyll a; and third, a band of yellowish-
green chlorophyll b. (If the pigment extract has been allowed to
stand for some time, a gray band may be seen above the xanthophylls; this is pheophytin, a decomposition product of chlorophyll.)

For well-known mixtures, such as leaf extract, the identification of the major groups of substances (carotenes and xanthophylls are still mixtures) is sufficient on the basis of color and
R_f. Positive identification is made by cutting the bands apart,
separately redissolving the substances, running absorption spectra
in a spectrophotometer, and then comparing the curves with curves
obtained from the pure substances.

SAINT MARY'S COLLEGE, CALIF.

The separation of the pigments by differential solution can be shown through the use of variegated leaves, such as those of coleus. Boiling in water removes the red anthocyanins, but not the chlorophylls, carotenes, and xanthophylls.

Exercise 13.2
Loss of Water by Plants

This exercise can be done as a demonstration. But if the rather simple apparatus is obtainable in sufficient quantity, work by teams is much to be preferred. If the exercise is done in a reasonably uniform manner by several teams, the teacher has another opportunity to point out the effect of pooling results from replication.

Teams of four students should be able to work efficiently. Some students are disappointed by negative data; try to avoid them when picking the team for the control setup.

Materials. The leafy stems should be woody so that they can be forced through the stopper holes without damage. If leafy, woody plants are not available at the time the exercise is appropriate, tomato or sunflower plants grown indoors can be used. The stems must be selected to fit the holes in the rubber stoppers and inserted with care. When the stems are cut, their ends should immediately be submerged in water; they should not be allowed to become dry at any time thereafter. For distribution to teams they may be transferred to separate containers of water.

The bore of both glass and rubber tubing should be as small as can be obtained.

The water in the flasks must be at room temperature; otherwise, expansion caused by warming will make the water column move upward. The flasks may be filled before class time and allowed to come to room temperature, or containers of water at room temperature may be provided. The flasks must be completely filled with water so that the insertion of the stoppers will force the water out, leaving no air space.

Vacuum-pump compound has been found to be a good sealer. Vaseline is unsatisfactory.

Procedure. If students are unfamiliar with pipettes, practice in reading them should be given. Students may also have to be shown how to fill pipettes. Some teachers have found 5-ml pipettes more satisfactory than the 1-ml size, but 5-ml pipettes require a longer time between successive readings. If pipettes are not available, lengths of small-bore glass tubing may be used. With a rubber band fasten a metric rule behind each piece of tubing. The volume of the tubing per centimeter of length may be de-

termined by filling a piece with water and emptying this water
into a small graduated cylinder. (The last of the water may need
to be blown out.) Then divide the volume of the water (in milliliters) by the length of the tube (in centimeters) to find the
milliliters per centimeter.

If the leafy shoots are taken from a shrub on or near the
school grounds, an estimate of water loss from the whole plant
may be made. Estimate the number of leaves on the shrub,
divide by the number of leaves on the experimental shoot, and
multiply by the volume of water lost in the pipette during the
first ten minutes. This figure can be multiplied by 6 to obtain
the water loss per hour. Use of the data for the second ten
minutes gives an estimate of water loss from the plant on a
windy day. This procedure provides an experience that helps
to explain how data such as those given on textbook page 428
are obtained.

If shoots are taken from different kinds of trees or shrubs,
some comparisons can be made among species, but the values
of replication will be lost.

Some questions that may be used in discussion:

1.   What other environmental factors might influence the
rate of transpiration?

2.   What variations in the structure of the plant might
influence the rate of transpiration?

3.   When a plant is transplanted, its ability to obtain water
may be impaired by the destruction of roots. On the basis of
the results from this exercise, what suggestions might be made
for treating a transplant to reduce dangers of wilting through
excessive loss of water?

Exercise 13.3
Chemical Action in a Plant

The scalpels must be quite sharp. To conserve corn—and
fingers—it would be well for the teacher to demonstrate the
proper technique for cutting the corn grains. The procedure
allows for extra corn grains in case some are cut poorly. Those
cut at odd angles will still serve for the iodine test.

Molds are sometimes troublesome. Treatment of the corn
grains with a fungicide (see guide page 42) may be advisable.
Careful attention to proper technique in handling petri dishes will
also help.

To prepare FAA, mix 500 ml of 95-percent ethyl alcohol,
20 ml of glacial acetic acid, 100 ml of 40-percent formaldehyde
solution, and 400 ml of water.

To prepare starch agar, mix 10 g of powdered starch and 10 g of agar in 980 ml of water and heat until agar is dissolved.

To prepare plain agar, mix 20 g of agar in 980 ml of water and heat until agar is dissolved. Approximately 15 ml of agar will make a thin layer in a 100-mm petri dish. Avoid making the layer of agar too thick.

If Tes-tape is not available, cut small pieces of agar from the plates and heat in a test tube with Benedict's or Fehling's solution.

Some questions that may be used in discussion:

1.   What advantage lies in the storage of foods in the form of substances insoluble in water?

2.   Why must such substances be changed to soluble forms before they can be transported?

3.   As it ripens, a banana becomes increasingly sweet. How might this be explained in the light of the exercise? Can you show that an unripe banana contains starch?

4.   Can the chemical change investigated in this exercise proceed in the opposite direction? Why is young corn sweet?

Exercise 13.4
Chemical Control of Plant Growth

NOTE: Preparations for this exercise must begin several weeks before it is set up. If bean plants are used, allow three or four weeks from the time the seeds are planted.

Plants other than beans may be used—for example, tomato, begonia, or coleus. To obtain the value of replication, it is suggested that most teams use the same species of plant; a few teams might use other species for comparison.

It is convenient to have each plant in a separate container, but this requires a large number of pots. Cardboard milk cartons of the half-pint size, with holes punched in the bottom for drainage, serve very well. Be sure to allow for less than 100-percent germination when planting seeds—excess plants can be thinned out. Sticks used in ice-cream bars and popsicles are useful if commercial pot labels are unavailable.

Indoleacetic acid in lanolin paste may be purchased. Or it may be made from the powdered chemical and lanolin (for directions, see E. Morholt et al., Teaching High School Science: A Sourcebook for the Biological Sciences, Harcourt, Brace and Co., 1958, pages 116-118). If the teacher has several classes, indolebutyric acid or alpha-naphthalene acetic acid may be used in some, indoleacetic acid in others.

Exercise 13.5
Photosynthetic Reserves

NOTE: Preparations for this exercise must begin about six weeks before it is expected that the experiment will be run.

Sunflower and zinnia are very satisfactory plants for this experiment. Coleus has such great reserves that its chief use is to provide a contrast with other plants. Geranium slips grow too slowly. Beans, with their compound leaves, present problems. And corn, of course, is unsuitable.

Grow the seedlings in strong light to avoid spindly plants, which may not support the weight of the foil.

Use the thinnest aluminum foil obtainable.

If the teacher wishes to raise questions concerning the effect of injury and the nutritional requirements for healing, one team might remove the leaves from one of its plants.

Exercise 13.6
Rate of Growth: Leaves

If this exercise is started on a Monday (with planting to be done on Tuesday), the days scheduled for measuring will be school days. Of course, adjustments can be made in the schedule, but the intervals between measurements ought to be approximately equal.

Kidney beans have proved useful; they are fairly large and usually have a rather high percentage of germination. Lima beans have large embryos but often have a poor germination rate.

See guide page 42 for notes on fungicides.

Used flats can be obtained cheaply from nurseries. Almost any kind of loosely constructed wooden box 8 to 15 cm deep may be substituted. Cardboard boxes are likely to disintegrate.

This exercise is an approach to the sigmoid growth curve. Many factors alter or obscure this curve. In Exercise 2.1 the curve does not flatten out; in Exercise 2.2 the curve usually declines; in Exercise 2.3 the curve approaches a fluctuating equilibrium. None of these patterns is likely to occur in the growth curve of an individual or in a part of an individual. However, all these curves have the general characteristic of beginning with a gentle slope that steadily steepens.

Exercise 13.7
Transport of Phosphates in Plants

CAUTION: Teachers intending to use this exercise should become thoroughly familiar with the techniques for insuring safety in the handling of radioactive materials.

This exercise is best done as a demonstration. With proper supervision, however, the demonstration can be carried out by a team of students. When classes are small, the exercise is feasible for class use.

Band-aids are excellent ready-made gauze pads, complete with a good adhesive tape.

P^{32} has a half-life of two weeks. Specify a delivery date when ordering, and place the order well in advance of that date. For maximum effectiveness, the material should be used as soon as it arrives.

Raise tomato plants in small pots or paper cups filled with vermiculite. Water with a solution of one of the soluble ferti-lizers, such as Hyponex or Ortho-gro. If the plants get plenty of light, they will be about the right height when they have four or five leaves.

Use X-ray film or high-speed cut film such as Tri-X or Royal Pan (Kodak) or Super Pan Press or Triple S (Ansco).

The blotters used in plant presses are suitable. One such blotter can be cut into four pieces of a size sufficient for use in this exercise.

The "Radioactive Waste" jar should not be used for any other purpose. It should be plainly marked.

The film must not be exposed to any kind of light. If the school does not have a darkroom, a totally dark closet will do. Ordinary doors are not lightproof, but at night a windowless closet or storeroom can be made totally dark if there are no lights in the adjacent room or hall.

The film holder shown on manual page 235 is made from a printing frame used by amateur photographers. It is convenient but not essential. Any arrangement that will hold the plant, the plastic sheets, and the photographic film in firm contact will serve.

Any standard developer may be used. Or the films may be taken in a lighttight container to a commercial photographer. However, most schools have a number of amateur photographers.

The following references may be useful in connection with this exercise:

CHASE, G. D., S. RITUPER, and J. W. SULCOSKI. Experiments in Nuclear Science: The Teacher's Guide. Minneapolis: Burgess Publishing Co., 1964. (Not especially oriented to biology, but contains much up-to-date information on ordering, handling, and disposing of radioisotopes.)

SCHENBERG, S. (ed.). Laboratory Experiments with Radioisotopes for High School Science Demonstrations. Washington, D. C.: U.S. Government Printing Office, 1958.

TYSON, J. W. Atomic Radiation in the High School Science Class. 4923 Strass Drive, Austin 3, Texas: Oldfriends' Books, 1961.

SUPPLEMENTARY MATERIALS

Invitations to Enquiry

Invitation 4 (pp. 59-60 of the Handbook). A paraphrasing of Priestley's mouse-plant experiment is used to illustrate the interpretation of complex data.

Invitation 6 (pp. 67-69 of the Handbook). Van Helmont's problem is posed as the basis for an experiment—to be designed by the student. If the student has read the textbook, this may be more a matter of recall than of design.

Invitation 7 (pp. 69-71 of the Handbook). An extension of Invitation 6; the role of a control in experimentation is explored.

Invitation 14 (pp. 93-96 of the Handbook). The role of hypothesis in experimentation, with some attention to teleological thinking. This invitation on phototropism makes a good introduction to textbook pages 444-447.

Invitation 19 (pp. 113-115 of the Handbook). Part of a series of invitations on causation, this one deals with serial causation as illustrated by investigation of photosynthesis.

Invitation 27 (pp. 148-153 of the Handbook). Using data on the relation of light intensity to photosynthesis, this invitation stresses the linear relationship between variables.

Invitation 29 (pp. 161-164 of the Handbook). Dealing with growth regulation in leaves through application of 2-4-D, this invitation provides a good review of the logarithmic growth curve, which the student encountered in Exercise 2.1.

Invitation 30   (pp. 165-167 of the Handbook).   The relationship between light and auxin formation is used to develop a second
type of nonlinear curve.

Audiovisual Materials

Models: Large-scale models are excellent teaching devices.
Perhaps the most useful models for this course are those showing
the microscopic structure of leaves, stems, and roots. Models
give a three-dimensional impression that cannot be obtained from
Figure 13.18. On the other hand, models are misleading in some
respects—especially as to relative size of microscopic and macroscopic structures—and they must emphasize the "typical."
Therefore, students should have an opportunity to see a variety
of real plant materials both macroscopically and microscopically.
But good models are useful in summarizing. No particular
brand of models can be recommended; before purchasing, the
teacher should (if possible) examine the many items available
or at least study the well-illustrated brochures that most makers
or dealers supply.

Phonograph record: "Photosynthesis and You." ("The
Scientists Speak: Biology"). Harcourt, Brace and Co., 1959.
Dr. Eugene Rabinowitch emphasizes the physicochemical basis
of research on photosynthesis. The textbook account is more
detailed and more up-to-date, but the purpose of the record is
inspirational rather than informational.

Filmstrip: "Introduction to Stem Sectioning and Staining."
Color. Society for Visual Education, 1962. Useful for showing
techniques.

Motion-picture films: "Colour of Life." 16 mm. Color.
24 minutes. National Film Board of Canada. Illustrates the
development of the maple seedling (by time-lapse photography);
also shows seasonal changes and the process of photosynthesis
in leaves.

"Rhythmic Motions in Growing Plants." 16 mm. Color.
11 minutes. William Harlow, Syracuse 10, N. Y. Excellent
on plant movements—both those that represent responses to
external stimuli and those that are intrinsic.

Teacher's References

CRONQUIST, A. Introductory Botany. New York: Harper &
   Row, Publishers, 1961. (A recent college textbook of a
   somewhat encyclopedic nature.)
FOSTER, A. F., and E. M. GIFFORD, JR. Comparative
   Morphology of Vascular Plants. San Francisco: W. H.
   Freeman & Co., Publishers, 1959. (A somewhat
   advanced textbook on the structure of vascular plants;
   good background for the middle section of Green Version
   Chapter 13.)
JAMES, W. O. An Introduction to Plant Physiology, 6th ed.
   New York: Oxford University Press, 1963. (A good,
   brief treatment of general plant physiology.)
JENSEN, W. A., and L. G. KAVALJIAN (eds.). Plant
   Biology Today; Advances and Challenges. Belmont,
   Calif.: Wadsworth Publishing Co., Inc., 1963.
   (Devoted to papers presented at a symposium sponsored
   by the AAAS and the Botanical Society of America; a
   good survey of the growing points in modern botany.)
LEE, A. E. A Laboratory Block: Plant Growth and Development.
   (A BSCS publication.) Boston: D. C. Heath & Co., 1963.
   (Contains much valuable information on techniques for plant
   experimentation.)
_____, and C. HEIMSCH. Development and Structure of
   Plants. New York: Holt, Rinehart & Winston, Inc., 1962.
   (A booklet of 64 large-size pages devoted entirely to photo-
   graphs of the macro- and microstructure of tracheophytes.)
SINNOTT, E. W., and K. S. WILSON. Botany: Principles and
   Problems, 6th ed. New York: McGraw-Hill Book Co., Inc.,
   1963. (The most recent edition of a venerable, conservative
   college textbook.)
WEISZ, P. B., and M. S. FULLER. The Science of Botany.
   New York: McGraw-Hill Book Co., Inc., 1962. (A new
   college textbook that stresses biochemical aspects of botany.)
WENT, F. W. The Plants. New York: Time, Inc., 1963. (One
   of the volumes in the LIFE Nature Library. A wide-gauge
   view of the plant kingdom, with some excellent photographs.)

The Functioning Animal

MAJOR IDEAS

1. Animals depend directly or indirectly upon plants as their source of energy.

2. To obtain this energy, animals capture or otherwise secure food and ingest it.

3. In animals digestion always occurs in a cavity of the body (unlike digestion performed by plants and many protists). From the cavity the digested foods—that is, foods changed to a diffusible form—are absorbed into the cells.

4. Since cellular respiration is basically aerobic in animals, oxygen is required sooner or later; hence animals have various structures by which oxygen may be obtained from the environment.

5. Most animals have a transport system by which substances are carried through the body. In larger animals this is a vascular system—containing a fluid that is pumped by muscular movements of a heart. Some such systems are "open," others "closed."

6. Metabolic activities result in the accumulation of substances that are either useless or poisonous. In macroscopic freshwater and terrestrial animals, special organs or organ systems excrete these substances into the environment.

7. Every animal maintains a dynamic equilibrium both internally, between cells and their "internal environment," and externally, between the whole organism and its external environment. By means of homeostatic mechanisms involving the endocrine and nervous systems, the animal maintains internal coördination and copes with the vagaries of the external environment.

8. Nervous systems range from a very simple network of nerve cells to a complex system of highly specialized neurons coördinated by a brain.

9. Animals move by means of muscles that are, in most cases, attached either to the inside of an external skeleton or to the outside of an internal skeleton.

TEACHING SUGGESTIONS

Guidelines

A good approach to this chapter is through laboratory work. Part A of Exercise 14.1 is certain to stimulate interest in the living animal—which, more than anything else, is the purpose of Chapter 14. Before proceeding with Parts B and C, however, an assignment in the textbook chapter should be made: pages 452-461. A convenient and logical division of the remainder of the chapter is pages 461-476 and pages 476-492.

Before proceeding very far it would be well to review textbook Chapter 4 and appropriate portions of the Appendix, where the animals used as examples in Chapter 14 may be placed in their taxonomic relationships.

As a result of his experiences in the college biology courses of yesteryear, the teacher may feel a frustrating sense of incompleteness throughout this chapter. Here one might expect the venerable crayfish with his exopodites and endopodites, the clam, the starfish, the dogfish, and the perch; or one might expect human anatomy and physiology in a setting of hygienic and wholesome living. All these are important. But if the many other aspects of biology that occupy so much space in the Green Version are conceded to have value for the tenth-grade student, then much that has been part and parcel of biology courses in the past must be omitted. For the omission of "type animals" the authors submit no apology: depth studies of selected forms are important in the training of zoologists, but this is not our purpose. As for the omission of much human anatomy and physiology, the authors believe that a great deal of such material is repetitious at the tenth-grade level: excellent heart models recur in science fairs from the fourth grade upward. In the opinion of the writers, the near future will see even more descriptive human anatomy taught in Grades 7-9.

Chapter 14 is a survey of the ways in which animal structure is correlated with the requirements of "the animal way of life":

the intake of materials, the distribution of materials, the release of energy from foods, the disposal of excess and poisonous substances, the internal coördination of all metabolic activities, and the means of coping with the environment. Such a view of animal structure and function seems consistent with the ecological orientation of the <u>Green</u> <u>Version</u>. While somewhat abstract, this view has been successfully grasped by both ninth- and tenth-grade students. The teacher must, however, do whatever he can to reduce the abstractness by constantly providing examples of live animals, preserved specimens, and pictures. The textbook aids in this effort by using the physiology of man as the terminal and most completely developed example for each major life function. The skillful teacher will use his students as laboratory subjects wherever possible—some possible uses are given in Exercises 14.4 and 14.8 (and 12.6). In addition, students can serve as their own experimental animals when investigating breathing rate, reaction of iris to light, fatigue of a muscle, levers in the skeletal system, and many other matters.

At this stage in the course, students should have improved their abilities to read, to study, and to think. "Guide Questions" demanding something more than mere repetition of text material are now being occasionally introduced. But some students may still be struggling merely to obtain ideas from the printed page. Therefore the teacher should discriminate in assigning "Guide Questions" as well as in assigning "Problems."

<u>Some Notes</u>

In the picture at the head of the chapter, a squirrel is eating the fruit of osage orange.

Pages 455-456: The teacher may wish to discuss hydrolysis and its role in digestion, emphasizing that it is the opposite of dehydration synthesis.

Figures 14.3 and 14.4: Here and in subsequent systems, stress the connections between successive levels of organizational complexity. And point out that all existing levels of organization have been "successful" from the viewpoint of the survival of the species.

Figure 14.5: Urge students not to memorize the chart, but rather to consider the structures that produce specific enzymes and to note the major steps in digestion of the "basic" foods (carbohydrates, fats, proteins).

Figure 14.11: This figure requires some interpretation. The circulatory system of the earthworm appears to be "open" because the connections between vessels in the dorsal and ventral body walls cannot be shown in a longitudinal diagram.

Figure 14.16: Note that the Mg bonding differs from that shown in Figure 13.3. This is because porphyrin bonds are constantly shifting. The striking similarity of heme and chlorophyll with respect to chemical structure is worthy of discussion and speculation.

Pages 468-469: To most of us, blood clotting appears to be a simple process; upon investigation it turns out to be a complicated biological phenomenon. A chalkboard diagram will help to explain the process. Some students should seek information on phlebitis and internal blood clotting.

Figure 14.18: Make certain that students understand why whole blood does not enter the lymphatics.

Figure 14.21: Note relationship of structures to functions.

Pages 478-481: Students frequently confuse the functions of enzymes, animal hormones, and plant hormones. This is a good place to discuss their similarities and differences.

Pages 476-486: The textbook does not use the term "homeostasis," but the teacher may wish to do so. It is a fashionable word that has other virtues as well. Better than "dynamic equilibrium," it implies self-correcting mechanisms—such as the CO_2 mechanism of breathing (page 481) and the atrial-pressure mechanism of heartbeat rate (pages 485-486).

Figure 14.24: Some biologists believe the nerve network of coelenterates to be a staining artifact. See H. M. Lenhoff and W. F. Loomis, The Biology of Hydra and of Some Other Coelenterates, Miami, Fla.: University of Miami Press, 1961.

Figure 14.25: Neuroanatomists do not seem to agree on axon terminology. The labeling in this figure follows one system of nomenclature for the sensory neuron, but others reverse the axon-dendrite terminology.

EXERCISES

Exercise 14.1

Animal Structure and Function: The Frog

This exercise has been limited to material that can readily be covered in three laboratory periods, one part per period. Every teacher will probably think of additional observations he would like his students to make. It is suggested that these—and questions relating to them—be inserted at appropriate places in the present exercise. Any new questions may be accommodated by adding letters to the numbers already in use (e.g., 1a, 1b, 2a, 2b, etc.).

If "grass frogs" (Rana pipiens and relatives) are to be used, an order for "medium" frogs will usually provide approximately equal numbers of both sexes; an order for "large" frogs will usually provide a preponderance of females.

If Exercise 14.5 is to be omitted, consider setting it up as a demonstration during work on Exercise 14.1.

Part A. This part of the exercise enlarges upon some aspects of Exercise 4.4. If that exercise was done by the class, it should be reviewed before work is started on Exercise 14.1.

Encourage a calm atmosphere for Part A—but do not expect too much. Chances are that about half of the frogs will escape temporarily sometime during the day. Frogs may be covered with a battery jar to hamper mobility, but this also hampers visibility.

If frogs have been kept in a refrigerator, they should be removed from it at least two hours (preferably two days) before the laboratory period. The teacher or lab assistants should tie the cords to the frogs' legs before the animals are distributed to teams. The frogs should be distributed in containers. Students should never be allowed to dangle the frogs on the cords! Otherwise the cords, when used for one period at a time, do not seem to injure the animals.

| 1. Locating base of skull | 2. Inserting needle into foramen magnum | 3. Moving needle to destroy brain | 4. Pithing the spine |

Figure T-14.1. Steps in pithing anesthetized frog.
The head is to the left in all pictures.

Do not expect to get results from all parts of this exercise. Frogs that have been handled may not attempt to feed, even if hungry. Some teachers who have kept a few frogs apart in a quiet, undisturbed terrarium have been able to demonstrate feeding to small groups of students when the frogs used by the teams have failed to coöperate.

Part B. Anesthetize the frogs with ether, with chloroform, with a solution of 2-percent urethane in water, or with a solution of 0.1-percent chlorotone in water. Frogs should be pithed before being distributed to teams (see Figure T-14.1). If student assistants are employed to aid in pithing, be careful to select very stable and reliable ones with a serious interest in biology. It is important to stress the results of pithing, so that students are not led to the mistaken belief that a cruel vivisection is being practiced.

Observations recommended in Part B are rather few because a considerable amount of time will be required for carrying out dissection procedure.

A 1-ml pipette should be used for inflating the lungs. If the frogs are small, students may not be able to find the glottis. Some teachers order one large bullfrog for each class so that this operation and a few others requiring large size may be demonstrated.

Success in all operations should not be expected in all teams. It will probably be necessary to have the successes of some teams shared with members of unsuccessful teams.

Item 27: It is thought that the distilled water removes calcium ions. Lack of calcium ions in the intercellular fluids is known to cause convulsive muscular contractions. This is referred to obliquely on textbook page 480.

If a refrigerator is not available and the weather is warm, it may be necessary to place the frogs in a preservative solution consisting of one part commercial formalin mixed with seven parts tap water. If this is done, each team should attach an identification tag to its frog.

Part C. If frogs have been stored in formalin, they should be washed for at least one hour in running water before the laboratory period. Exposure to formalin will have changed the colors of some organs.

If possible, a dissectible manikin should be used during this part of the exercise, to bring out comparisons with human structure. This procedure is not only instructive in itself; it also carries along the comparative approach adopted in the textbook chapter.

Exercise 14.2
Digestion of Fats

This exercise can be done as a demonstration, but students will obtain greater satisfaction by doing it in teams. The procedure is somewhat delicate, and different teams may get different results. This provides an opportunity to emphasize the need for care in procedure; the teacher can assist the students in developing team pride in workmanship.

If heat sources are in short supply, water baths can be made larger, and each one can be used by several teams. If this is done, tubes must be labeled with team symbols as well as numbers. Sometimes the wax of a glass-marking pencil has a tendency to melt when the tubes are placed in the water bath. If this happens, Label-on tape can be used to mark the tubes.

It may be necessary to point out that cream contains fats. Some students might wish to try the exercise with the vegetable oil used in Exercise 12.2.

The litmus should be a saturated solution prepared with distilled water.

The pancreatin solution is prepared by dissolving 5 g of powdered pancreatin in 100 ml of distilled water. The solution should be fresh—preferably made just before the experiment.

At this stage in the year's work, students should be developing the ability to draw conclusions from a simple experiment without being led step by step through an examination of the data. Exercise 14.2 gives the teacher an opportunity to find out if such an ability has been developed. However, if a slow class is involved, it may be well to discuss the results, casting the lettered points (under "Conclusions") in the form of questions before asking students to write up their statements.

Exercise 14.3
A Heart at Work

It is important that the counts in this exercise be made
quickly. Therefore the students should be familiarized with
Daphnia before the period in which the exercise is to be done.
It would be well to assign temperatures to teams and to have
teams decide which members are to perform each task during
the laboratory period. Some practice in counting rapidly by
making pencil dots on paper might be given.

Assuming that room temperature is about 20°C, suggested
temperatures are: 15°, 10°, and 5°C with ice water; and 25°,
30°, and 35°C with hot water.

It is not necessary to have a separate hot-water supply for
each team. One large container can be maintained at about 90°.
If one laboratory assistant is made responsible for distribution
of the hot water, movement about the room can be reduced, and
safety enhanced.

Daphnia may be collected from ponds and lakes during most
months of the year. They can be ordered from biological supply
houses and quite often may be obtained at aquarium supply stores
or at fish hatcheries. Daphnia magna is the largest and, therefore, the species of choice. D. pulex and D. longispina, though
smaller than D. magna, will prove satisfactory in this exercise.

The Daphnia culture can be maintained for one to two weeks
in pond water at 22° to 26°C. The culture should be kept out of
direct sunlight. If the culture is to be maintained for a longer
period, a culture medium must be provided. Perhaps one of
the simplest methods is the following: Place Daphnia in tap water
that has stood for several hours. Feed the Daphnia a yeast suspension in water, adding enough suspension to make the water
milky. The water should be changed once a month. An aerator
may be used, or the culture may be stirred once a day. Many
types of media are suggested in literature, particularly in
Galtsoff et al., Culture Methods for Invertebrate Animals—New
York: Dover Publications, Inc., 1959.

The normal heartbeat of Daphnia is approximately 300 to
350 per minute. Students can obtain an approximate beat by tapping with a pencil in rhythm with the heartbeat. The dots should
be made in a continuous line, back and forth, in this manner:

A 50-ml beaker is a good container for the Daphnia. It must
be made of heat-resistant glass, since it will be transferred from
ice water to hot water. A 250-ml beaker provides a good water
jacket.

If depression slides are not available, place small pieces of a broken cover slip (using forceps!) around the drop of water containing the Daphnia; this will prevent the animal from being crushed when the cover slip is added.

If stereomicroscopes are not available, the low power of the monocular scope may be used, but considerable difficulty in keeping the specimen within the field of view will be encountered.

In addition to snails, mosquito larvae and Tubifex worms may be used for comparisons.

A comparison between the heartbeat rate of Daphnia at room temperature and that of man can be made by having students count their own pulses. These data, assembled on the chalkboard, will not only provide a comparison with Daphnia but will emphasize the variability of data and lead to a better understanding of the many "normal" values found in textbooks of human physiology.

Besides the drugs suggested in the manual, other substances that might be tried are aspirin, tea, phenobarbital, carbonated beverages, coffee, and tobacco.

Exercise 14.4

Chemoreceptors in Man

Though this exercise is regarded as basic, one or more parts of it may be omitted if time is pressing. If all materials are ready, Parts A and B of the procedure can be accomplished in one period. If the teacher wishes to combine Parts B and C in a second laboratory session, then Part A can be repeated in the first, with students of each pair alternating, thus giving each student experience with all four tastes. Another alternative is to assign Part C as homework.

In all parts of this exercise, the power of suggestion is great. Students should be warned about it. Most will try to be objective if they are cautioned. This may be a good time to discuss the difficulties of experimentation that involves a report from a subject. The topic may be reviewed during discussion of textbook pages 614-617 in Chapter 18.

Student assistants are very useful in this exercise. In Part A, for example, only one or two stock bottles of the solutions are required if student assistants are available to deliver the solutions as needed.

A simple method for assigning solutions in Part B is to have all students who were designated "A" (in Part A) work with the sugar solutions and all students who were designated "B" work with the salt solutions.

In Part C a system for labeling the "unknowns" must be devised, so that the discussion following the experiment will be meaningful.

All solutions should be made up before the laboratory period. The sucrose and salt solutions for Part B are made up by dilution, as follows: Make up one of the 0.5-percent solutions. Pour 20 ml of this solution into 80 ml of distilled water to make the 0.1-percent solution; pour 10 ml of this solution into 90 ml of water to make the 0.05-percent solution; pour 2 ml of this solution into 98 ml of water to make the 0.01-percent solution; and so on. Follow the same procedure to make up the second series of solutions.

The toothpick swabs should be prepared before the laboratory period, because students tend to make them too large and loose. The pledgets of cotton should be wrapped very tightly and should not be more than 3 mm in diameter. The prepared swabs may be wrapped in paper and sterilized in an autoclave if the teacher wishes.

Small battery jars or 1-gallon pickle or mayonnaise jars (available from restaurants or cafeterias) make convenient waste jars. If plenty of sinks are available, waste jars may not be needed.

Suggestions for additional solutions in Part C: grapefruit juice, garlic salt. All of the solutions should be dilute.

Exercise 14.5
Capillary Circulation

Observation of capillary circulation can be accomplished through demonstration. If this is all that time will permit, it might be well to set up the demonstration while Exercise 14.1 is being done. However, the experimental work with drugs is a very desirable part of the exercise.

Materials. If the frogs have been refrigerated, they must be removed at least two hours before use, to establish normal circulation.

Goldfish may be substituted for frogs. The method for handling a goldfish is shown in Figure T-14.5. Goldfish have some advantages: they are cheap, more expendable, somewhat more easily handled, and less likely to offend the sensibilities of students. On the other hand, they cannot be kept out of water for very long, and taxonomically they are more remote from man.

Large rubber bands may be substituted for the cord. Corrugated cardboard may be used in place of the pine board, but

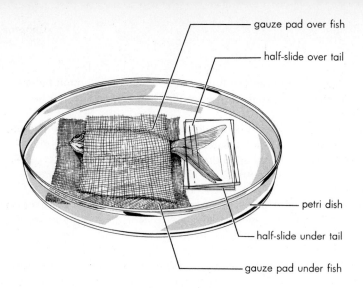

gauze pad over fish

half-slide over tail

petri dish

half-slide under tail

gauze pad under fish

Figure T-14.5

it is likely to soften after much exposure to moisture. A pile of books may be used to supplement the microscope stage in supporting the board. Or a team member may be assigned the job of supporting the board.

See guide page 177 for preparation of Ringer's solution.

It is better to have considerable repetition with few drugs than to test many drugs a few times. The teacher should assign the drugs so that five or more teams will report on the same drug. Lactic acid, alcohol, and sodium nitrite are readily available from the usual suppliers of chemicals; the others may be obtained from pharmacies with the aid of a physician. Good results have been obtained with nicotine extracted from cigarette filters. Lactic acid, histamine, acetylcholine, alcohol, and sodium nitrite are vasodilators; nicotine and adrenalin are vasoconstrictors.

Discussion. Concerning the "Introduction" (manual page 257), it may be instructive to point out other cases where scientific reasoning preceded observation—for example, the prediction of the existence of the outer planets from perturbations in the orbits of known planets, and Maxwell's prediction of electromagnetic waves from mathematical considerations.

During muscular exercise, lactic acid, produced by incomplete oxidation of glucose, accumulates in muscles. How would this accumulation, acting on the capillaries, affect muscle action? A feedback (homeostatic) mechanism is involved here.

Discuss alcohol as a treatment for exposure to cold. This involves considerations of mechanisms by which heat is radiated from the body.

Why would the drugs applied to frog skin be likely to produce little effect when applied to human skin?

Exercise 14.6
Testing for Vitamin C

This exercise provides an opportunity to develop some ideas concerning vitamins, which are treated lightly in the textbook.

The size of the test tubes is not critical, but a small size is preferable, since small quantities of materials are being used.

Use the sodium salt of indophenol, which is soluble in water, to make the 0.1-percent solution (1 g in 100 ml of water).

If graduated cylinders are used, select a 10-ml or 25-ml size.

Vitamin C tablets contain fillers; therefore it is difficult to compute the percentage of vitamin C in any solution made from them. A 10-percent solution of ascorbic acid can be purchased in drugstores under the trade name Cecon. A preliminary test of the 10-percent solution against the 0.1-percent indophenol solution will indicate the further dilution necessary to prepare a stock solution for the class. The strength should be such that at least two drops of the solution is required to render the indophenol colorless.

Fresh fruit juices should be diluted 1:9. Frozen juices should be diluted as directed for reconstitution—and then further diluted 1:9. In addition to solutions mentioned in the manual, many others may be used. Teams may test about five solutions. The assignment of solutions may be staggered among teams so that a number of results from each solution will be available for comparison.

Exercise 14.7
Maintaining Water Balance

This exercise could just as well go with Chapter 18, where correlation of physiology and behavior is developed briefly (textbook page 611). If it is used with Chapter 14, it should certainly be reviewed when the class considers behavior.

The test of water loss (the part of the procedure involving cobalt chloride assemblies) may be carried out for the whole class by one team. The entire exercise could be done as a demonstration by one team, but direct observation by all students would then be difficult. Furthermore, there are distinct advantages to replication of the moisture-gradient dishes, since there is likely to be considerable variation of behavior among individual organisms.

Materials. The amounts of materials given in the manual are for use with three species of organisms. More may be used; two, of course, is a minimum.

In preparation of the filter-paper assemblies, two steps are critical: first, the cobalt chloride solution must be saturated so that the dry paper will have a deep-blue color; second, the corks must be placed quickly and firmly into the tubes when they are removed from the drying oven so that no water is taken up from the atmosphere. The second step is especially difficult in humid climates.

Rectangular plastic dishes are available through standard laboratory suppliers. Other suitable containers may be improvised. Cardboard boxes lined with aluminum foil have been used successfully. The dimensions given are not critical, but they are close to minimum.

Various substitutes can be used for the animals listed. Pill bugs (Oniscus) and termites are likely to seek wet conditions; grain beetles (Ptinus) and cockroaches are likely to seek dry environments.

Discussion. Past experience indicates that the wireworm requires about seven hours to produce moisture sufficient to turn all the filter-paper squares pink; in this length of time there is no change of color in the filter-paper squares in the tube containing the mealworm.

The directions do not explicitly state that the control tube should be opened for the length of time required to insert the animals into the other tubes. After several months of laboratory work, it is hoped that some students will raise this point. If they do not, the teacher should.

Each team may consider the questions separately, or the data may be pooled and the questions taken up in class discussion.

Does this exercise have implications for control of the arthropod species used?

Exercise 14.8

Rate of Heartbeat in a Mammal

Thus far in the course, exercises have been rather rigidly structured. For the most part this is necessary in classroom situations where space is limited, where students vary greatly in abilities, and where logistical problems are complex. Individual students who wish to obtain practice in the planning of experiments have had the opportunity to do so in many of the items listed "For Further Investigation." It seems desirable, however, to provide an opportunity for all students to participate in the designing of an experiment.

The hints in the manual should be sufficient for most students. The teacher need only set reasonable limits on the activities proposed by the students. If the class is divided into teams, each may have different ideas about procedure. Such differences can be of value when results are discussed.

Pairs or teams of students should put their data into a form suitable for presentation to the class. The data should be accompanied by an interpretation of meaning or by a conclusion.

The exercise should not be allowed to end without class discussion. Emphasis should be placed on evaluation of the ways in which the teams formulated the problem and the suitability of their procedures. Consider the role of controls, influence of sex, variability of data, and meaning of "normal" heartbeat rate. In the course of such a discussion, most of the ideas relevant to heart physiology will be developed.

SUPPLEMENTARY MATERIALS

BSCS Pamphlets

DU BRUL, E. L. Biomechanics of the Body. Boston: D. C. Heath & Co., 1963. (An aspect of biophysics that emphasizes the human body and gross structure; suitable for students who would be repelled by the kind of biophysics featured in Suckling's work, below.)

GORDON, A. S. Blood Cell Physiology. Boston: D. C. Heath & Co., 1963. (Somewhat more closely related to the materials in Chapter 14 than are the other two pamphlets.)

SUCKLING, E. E. Bioelectricity. Boston: D. C. Heath & Co., 1962. (An excellent example of biophysics for the high school student; builds on the material in Green Version Chapter 14, but goes far beyond it.)

Invitations to Enquiry

Invitation 12 (pp. 84-86 of the Handbook). Through the investigation of vitamin deficiency, this invitation develops the role of hypothesis in experimentation and the difficulty of achieving control.

Invitation 15 (pp. 96-103 of the Handbook). A long invitation that uses neurohormones as a means of exploring the origin of scientific problems.

Invitation 17 (pp. 108-112 of the Handbook). Thyroid function is used to introduce the concept of causation in biological inquiry.

Invitations 21-24 (pp. 116-130 of the Handbook). A series of invitations, dealing with various aspects of causation and all concerned with the endocrine system of mammals.

Invitations 32-36 (pp. 173-184 of the Handbook). This series of invitations makes use of animal structure—chiefly muscle structure—to develop reasoning about function.

Audiovisual Materials

Models: Just as models are very useful in developing ideas of plant structure, they are also useful in developing ideas of animal structure. Of course, experience with models is not as good as firsthand acquaintance with the structures of living or recently deceased specimens. But if Exercise 14.1 is done thoroughly and proper emphasis is placed upon physiology, time will seldom permit detailed anatomical investigations of other animals. Nor will other considerations permit much anatomical investigation of the most interesting of animals—man. Therefore, a good manikin should at least be available—preferably one with interchangeable reproductive systems, so that it also may be used in connection with Chapter 15.

Phonograph records: "Heart Recordings," Columbia Records, KL 4976; and "Stethoscopic Heart Sounds," Columbia Records, KL 4240. The sounds of normal human heartbeat and of abnormalities such as arrhythmias, murmurs, etc.

Filmstrips: "William Harvey." Color. Encyclopaedia Britannica Filmstrips. For the most part, historical content has been crowded out of Chapter 14. This filmstrip may help to restore the balance; it is especially recommended if Exercise 14.5 is performed.

"Metamorphosis." Color. LIFE Filmstrips. Too often endocrine control is taught exclusively from a mammalian or (at most) a vertebrate viewpoint. This filmstrip deals with the hormones of insect metamorphosis; furthermore, it is a beautiful example of the way in which experimental procedure can be explicated on a filmstrip.

There are many filmstrips on human anatomy and physiology. On the whole their quality is poor and the level of presentation far below that proper for senior high school. One of the better series is the "High School Biology Series" (Color. McGraw-Hill Text Films, 1963), which includes the following filmstrips:

"Digestion. " Good for review, but overloaded with terminology.

"Circulation. " Ties other systems to the circulatory and has good summarizations of clotting.

"Respiration. " Rather routine except for a brief treatment of feedback control of breathing.

"How the Nervous System Works. " Good supplement to Chapter 14: all-or-none principle, acetylcholine at synapse, proprioceptors and enteroceptors.

"The Endocrine System. " Abundant facts, but fails to produce a whole impression; wordy.

Motion-picture films: "Frog Skeletal Muscle Response. " 16 mm. Color. 8 minutes. Thorne Films, Boulder, Colo. Shows use of the kymograph in studying normal muscle response, tetany, and fatigue.

"Human Body: Skeleton. " 16 mm. Color. 10 minutes. Coronet Films. A good supplement to Chapter 14; shows (by fluorography) human skeleton in action.

"The Blood. " 16 mm. Color. 20 minutes. Encyclopaedia Britannica Films. Probably too much, but has good sequences that can be selected: blood-cell types and counting procedure, illustrations of capillary circulation, clotting.

"Digestion, Part I (Mechanical). " 16 mm. Color. 17 minutes. United World Films, Inc. The mechanical processes, absorption, function of the liver.

"Digestion, Part 2 (Chemical). " 16 mm. Color. 19 minutes. United World Films, Inc. Structure and function of digestive glands, distribution of digested foods.

"Circulation. " 16 mm. Color. 28 minutes. McGraw-Hill. Essentially a "canned lecture, " but contains good description of the early experimental work on mammalian circulation as well as the usual topics.

"The Animal and the Environment. " 16 mm. Color. 28 minutes. McGraw-Hill. The self-regulating mechanisms (homeostasis) involved in breathing, heartbeat, and kidney function are described and illustrated.

"The Senses. " 16 mm. Color. 28 minutes. McGraw-Hill. Sight, hearing, and taste, and the nervous and chemical processes involved in these processes. Includes a good sequence on the experimental determination of taste in houseflies. May serve well as a link with Chapter 18.

Teacher's References

BEST, C. H., and N. B. TAYLOR. The Human Body. New
York: Henry Holt & Co., Inc., 1956. (A good reference
for quickly locating information on human anatomy and
physiology.)

PROSSER, C. L., and F. A. BROWN, JR. Comparative
Animal Physiology, 2nd ed. Philadelphia: W. B. Saunders
Co., 1961. (Perhaps the basic reference for Chapter 14;
rich in detail and broad in its coverage of the animal
kingdom.)

SMITH, H. W. From Fish to Philosopher. New York: Doubleday
& Co., Inc., 1961. (The problems of water balance in
vertebrates, presented in an informal way.)

STORER, T. L., and R. L. USINGER. General Zoology, 3rd ed.
New York: McGraw-Hill Book Co., Inc., 1957. (An encyclopedic college text; very useful for a quick check of anatomical
and physiological facts on all phyla.)

TURNER, C. D. General Endocrinology. Philadelphia: W. B.
Saunders Co., 1960. (Unlike many books in its field, this
one gives some consideration to the hormones of invertebrates.)

CHAPTER 15

Reproduction

MAJOR IDEAS

1.   Reproduction (here considered a process involving whole organisms as opposed to replication of molecules within individuals) is characteristic of living things, but not essential for the existence of any individual. Yet, because individuals die, it is a process essential for the survival of species and, ultimately, for the continued existence of the biosphere.

2.   Contrary to common impressions based largely on familiar vertebrate animals, asexual reproduction is widespread in all three kingdoms, though only among protists and a relatively few species of plants is it the sole method of reproduction.

3.   Sexuality is less significant as a feature distinguishing one kind of reproductive process than as a feature resulting in great variability of genotypes. Thus sexuality is an important cog in the mechanism of evolution. [This idea can be developed only in a rudimentary way in Chapter 15.]

4.   Sex is fundamentally a biochemical characteristic that determines which gametes in a given species will unite to form zygotes and which will not. When morphological differences are correlated with biochemical differences, it is possible to distinguish male gametes (sperms) from female gametes (eggs). Likewise, organs or individuals that produce sperms are male, and organs or individuals that produce eggs are female.

5.   Meiosis is a process that results in the halving of the chromosome number in cells. Since it occurs regularly at

some point in the life cycle of sexually reproducing organisms, it reverses the doubling of the chromosome number, which results from zygote formation.

6.   Alternation of sexually and asexually reproducing generations is characteristic of a large part of the plant kingdom, but it is exceptional in the animal kingdom.

7.   In animals and multicellular plants, an adult organism develops from a zygote, not merely by a proliferation of cells through mitosis, but by a more or less orderly process of differentiation that accompanies the increase of cell numbers. The study of the earlier parts of this development is the province of embryology.

8.   Among multicellular species there is a rough correlation between (a) the number of gametes and (b) the probability of fertilization and the amount of protection afforded the developing embryos.

9.   In many land plants and animals, the embryo develops and is nourished within the parental body, with the result that a relatively large proportion of eggs reach at least a late embryonic stage.

TEACHING SUGGESTIONS

Guidelines

The best approach to this chapter is probably through the textbook. The introductory "Why Reproduction?" provides good material for class discussion. At this stage in the year's work, some students should have built up a background from which they can draw facts significant for the discussion. If Flask 7 from Exercise 6.2 has been saved (as was suggested), it should be brought out as a silent witness against abiogenesis.

A second logical approach is through Exercise 15.5. This approach is especially effective if pairs of frogs in amplexus can be secured—a distinct possibility in many parts of the country at the season in which this chapter is likely to be undertaken. (The artificial techniques described in Parts A and B of the "Procedure" are then unnecessary.) When embryological development of eggs has begun, attention can be directed back to the textbook for the broader significance of the events witnessed in the laboratory.

For assignment purposes the textbook chapter may be divided as follows: pages 496-508, pages 508-516, pages 516-530. The primary aim of the chapter is to establish a rational, objective, and integrated view of reproduction as a basic (perhaps the basic) process in biology. Secondarily, Chapter 15 provides a background for later development of concepts of heredity and evolution. In pursuing these aims the student will undoubtedly gain perspective on his own personal interests in reproductive processes. And the teacher may, if he wishes, substitute man for rat as the example of mammalian reproduction—or, better, compare and contrast man with rat. But this is a biology course: Just as the authors have stressed ecology rather than conservation, nutrition rather than dieting, and the dynamics of host-parasite relationships rather than "health habits," so they insist that the biology of reproduction—not sex education—is the proper emphasis for the biology course.

Some Notes

Page 498: Asexual reproduction in the potato is easy to demonstrate. But watch out for potatoes that have been chemically or radioactively treated to inhibit sprouting.

Page 499: Bryophyllum can be grown in the laboratory. Another genus that has the same habit is Kalanchoe, which is also easy to grow.

Page 499: The apple-tree example may raise a question concerning the source of diversity in apple seedlings. The mechanism is of basic importance to topics in Chapters 16 and 17. At this point, however, only an analogy can be given—the diversity of characteristics among brothers and sisters, offspring of a single pair of human parents.

Pages 500-501: If "fruiting" plants of such species of Lycopodium as L. obscurum or L. complanatum are collected in the autumn and dried in a plant press, the specimens will release a visible shower of spores when tapped lightly. The spores can then be observed under the microscope. Or bread mold (Rhizopus) may be used to demonstrate sporangia and spores (see Exercise 6.1, Bowl 8).

Figure 15.11: Crossing-over has little significance at this point. But, since it occurs regularly in meiosis, it deserves to be men-

tioned as part of the process. Throughout the course students
have encountered facts that were not immediately explainable.
And if they are getting the spirit of the course, they may quickly
ask, "Why does crossing-over occur?" Put in that very common
form (and better students may no longer be using such a form) the
question is, of course, basically unanswerable. Historically,
crossing-over was at first merely a cytological curiosity—as it
must be here to the students. But it did turn out to have significance; and it will have significance for the student in the next
chapter.

Figures 15.15, 15.18, 15.23: The teacher should not expect
the details of these figures to be memorized. But the figures
should be compared and used to establish the evolutionary decline
of the gametophyte generation (see also guide pages 236-238).

Page 511: Selaginella is not likely to be familiar to students. But
it is fairly easily cultured in a terrarium or greenhouse, so living
material should be available in the classroom. Biological supply
houses provide stocks of some species.

Pages 514-515: Refer to Figure 5.10. The diversity of sculpturing
found among pollen grains may provide an interested student with
a fine topic for microscopic investigation. This can be started now
with house or greenhouse plants; it can be extended to wild flowers
as they appear later in the spring. (In the Gulf states and southern
California, much out-of-doors material will no doubt be available
when Chapter 15 is studied.)

Pages 518-521: To most students hermaphroditism and partheno-
genesis are highly abnormal. The teacher has an opportunity to
broaden understanding here: What is abnormal in one group of
organisms may be normal in another. A definition of "normal"
may be necessary.

Figure 15.33: If the teacher wishes to present the reproductive
structure of man, the Frohse Anatomical Charts (A. J. Nystrom
& Co., 3333 Elston Ave., Chicago, Ill. 60618) are excellent.
Better still is the Nystrom manikin with interchangeable inserts
of reproductive parts.

EXERCISES

The number of basic exercises for this chapter is three.
Exercises 15.1 and 15.4 are alternates to each other, and so are
Exercises 15.3 and 15.5. In each pair of alternates, both exercises depend upon the same principles, and neither has any great
superiority over the other. Availability of materials and teacher
familiarity with techniques should be the guides in making choices.
Of course all four exercises may be undertaken, but a certain
amount of repetition will result, and the extra time might be better
spent on other exercises.

<u>Exercise 15.1</u>
<u>Vegetative Reproduction: Regeneration (Animal)</u>

For various reasons some teachers may not wish to use
this exercise. The general principle involved in it can just as
well be studied in Exercise 15.4, though experience has shown
that students have a rather higher level of interest in animal
materials than in plant materials. If Exercise 15.1 is carried
out by a class, then Exercise 15.4 might be used as a demonstration or as a special project to be worked out by individuals
at home. If Exercise 15.4 is chosen as the basic one, then
Exercise 15.1 could be done as a demonstration. In this case
a microprojector will be useful for showing the planarians to
the class.

In Exercise 15.1 it is desirable to have at least two teams
working on each procedure. The number of worms per team
may be increased. However, if a choice must be made between more teams and more worms per team, the former is
preferable; it allows for greater participation and better
averaging of inequalities resulting from faulty technique.

Materials. Planarians can be purchased from supply houses
or collected in the field. The animals live in ponds or slow-moving
streams, where they may be found on the undersurfaces of stones
or submerged logs. In the laboratory they should be kept in glass
or dark-enameled pans. Keep them dark and cool (but not refrigerated) in springwater, pond water, or conditioned tap water. To
condition tap water, draw it into containers and let stand in the
laboratory for two days or more. This allows chlorine to diffuse
into the air. Use shallow containers that provide a large surface
area—not bottles. Feed planarians twice a week on small strips
of liver. After two or three hours of feeding, remove the uneaten
meat, rinse out the dish, and fill it with clean water. Do not feed
the animals for one week before they are to be used.

Small camel's hair brushes (used by artists for water color)
are best for handling planarians without injuring them.

The best instruments for cutting planarians are razor blades
or scalpels with small, detachable blades. An effective knife may
be made by splitting a double-edged razor blade in two and break-
ing off pieces of the sharp edge. These razor chips are then
mounted on wooden handles or glued to pieces of glass rod with
waterproof cement; the glass should be heated and flattened at
the place where the blade is to be attached.

Hand lenses may be substituted for stereomicroscopes.

Notes on results. "Procedure A" should yield well-
proportioned worms, the heads appearing first. The regenerating
parts can be distinguished clearly by their lack of pigment.

"Procedure B" should result in regeneration that begins at
right angles to the plane of cut; later the whole body usually
straightens out. This experiment and the preceding one demonstrate the power of "regulation" in developing systems—that is,
the ability to attain the normal form even when some distortion
is introduced into the system.

"Procedure C" should yield regenerates in which the heads
are disproportionately large. In some cases the heads may be
malformed; in particular, the eyes may tend to fuse together.
If a sufficient number of planarians have been cut, it may be
found that head abnormalities or failures of the head to form
are most frequent in the more posterior pieces. Despite early
disproportion, the worms should gradually assume normal
proportions. Occasionally a very short piece will regenerate
a head at each end.

"Procedure D" indicates that planarians can reorganize
along a lateral edge as well as along an anterior or posterior
edge. By making a large number of longitudinal cuts at the
anterior ends of planarians, it is possible to produce 10-
headed monsters! In such cases the posterior ends never
attempt to regularize the situation by dividing, so the abnormal
form persists. It is thought that the occasional production of

double-headed monsters among vertebrates, including mammals,
results from an accidental splitting of the anterior end of the
very young embryo.

The procedures in this exercise have been adapted from
the BSCS Laboratory Block Animal Growth and Development,
by Florence Moog (Boston: D. C. Heath & Co. , 1963).

Exercise 15. 2
Meiosis

If the teacher has used the model technique in connection
with mitosis in Chapter 12 (see guide pages 186-187), the
general scheme of the procedure will already be familiar to the
student. Otherwise some time will be required to establish the
identity of the model materials.

In Exercise 15. 2 pipe cleaners may be used as substitutes
for poppit beads, but they are not as suitable as in the case of
mitosis; at the point where crossing-over is simulated, they will
have to be cut and the pieces twisted together. Further, when the
"chromosomes" are grasped at the "kinetochores" and pulled
toward the poles, the pipe cleaners will not assume characteristic
shapes. Pipe cleaners may be dyed to obtain two colors.

If enough materials are available, three pairs of homologous
"chromosomes" may be constructed. A very short pair will
clearly show the relationship between chromosome length and the
probability that crossing-over will occur.

In this exercise the manipulation of the materials achieves
the purpose; therefore no attempt has been made to drag in a
summary or other form of written work. But a number of points
can be made in discussion, either during the procedure or afterwards. One worth considering (because of its bearing on matters
in Chapter 16) is the random distribution of paternal and maternal
chromosomes during synapsis. Since no directions are given for
arranging the colors, there is likely to be considerable variation
among teams when the "chromosomes" are placed in homologous
pairs. The consequent separation of paternal and maternal
chromosomes may be pointed out—without necessarily developing
any genetic implications at this time.

This exercise may be repeated when recombinations are dealt
with (Chapter 16). The beads then represent genes. If the beads
are marked with washable ink, the genetic effects of crossing-
over can readily be seen. For example, the events shown in textbook Figure 16. 14 can be duplicated; or crossing-over can be
demonstrated at different distances from the kinetochore; or, with
strands of 15 or more beads, double crossing-over can be shown.

Exercise 15.3
Development of an Embryo: Chick

NOTE: Preparations for this exercise must begin at least
four weeks prior to class use.

Exercise 15.5 is an alternate to this one. Both have been
designated as basic, but it is expected that time will permit only
one to be attempted.

This exercise is a good test of the extent to which (1) a class
has developed team coördination, and (2) individuals have developed
manual dexterity and the habit of careful attention to directions.
The exercise requires a considerable degree of skill, and it is to
be expected that some teams will be unsuccessful.

Part A can be done as a demonstration. Two or three eggs,
set up around the room, can be observed by small groups of
students while other work is in progress. Parts B and C each
require a full laboratory period. Or both can be done in one
period if Part B is assigned to some teams and Part C to others;
the materials are then exchanged between teams for observation
by all. The teacher should become familiar with the techniques
before attempting to lead a class through them.

Preparations. Fertile eggs may be obtained from hatcheries
or from poultry farmers who keep roosters in their flocks. In
ordering, make some allowance for infertile eggs.

To secure embryos that correspond in development to the
standard illustrations of chick embryos at 24 hours, 33 hours,
48 hours, etc., keep the eggs cool (but not below 10°C) until they
are incubated. When eggs are stored for more than a week after
they are laid, viability of the embryos is greatly reduced. During
incubation of the eggs, temperature should be kept between 37°
and 39°C, and the relative humidity of the incubator should be 50
percent or more. Because sufficient oxygen must pass through
the shells to the embryos, the eggs should be arranged so that
some air space surrounds each. Using a soft pencil, mark each
egg with the date and the time at which incubation is started. To
prevent the embryos from sticking to the shells, rotate the eggs
daily. The marks will enable you to keep track of the rotation.

Set up a schedule for incubating the eggs. In the case of the
two-day eggs, variations of a few hours' incubation can produce
considerable differences in the appearance of the embryos. Therefore, when putting eggs for this stage into the incubator, the hour
when each class meets must be considered. The exact hour at
which incubation starts is not as important for the five-day eggs,
however. The same is true for the eggs used to show later stages.
Note that incubation of some eggs must begin twenty-one days
before use.

Suggestions for improving an incubator may be found in
R. E. Barthelemy, J. R. Dawson, Jr., and A. E. Lee, Equipment and Techniques for the Biology Teaching Laboratory
(Boulder, Colo.: BSCS, 1962). Before use, the incubator
(whether improvised or purchased) should be thoroughly tested for
its ability to maintain a steady temperature over the required time.

Materials. To prepare physiological saline solution, dissolve
9 g of sodium chloride in 1 liter of distilled water. The solution
must be kept at a temperature of 37°C when in use. A student
laboratory assistant may be assigned to maintain the solution at
proper temperature and deliver it to teams as needed.

Plastic refrigerator dishes may be substituted for finger
bowls.

For the opening of early-stage eggs, cotton batting forms a
better nest than paper towels, but it is more expensive.

Scissors must have fine points. The ordinary dissecting
scissors are not satisfactory.

Petri dishes may be substituted for Syracuse watch glasses.

Students frequently wish to preserve their specimens. This
can be done in 70-percent alcohol. The small embryos on the
filter-paper rings can be preserved in vials. Larger embryos
should be preserved in wide-mouth jars. Because water in the
specimens dilutes the preservative, drain out the alcohol after
two days and replace it.

The techniques in this exercise are adapted from the BSCS
Laboratory Block Animal Growth and Development, by Florence
Moog (Boston: D. C. Heath & Co., 1963).

Exercise 15.4
Vegetative Reproduction: Regeneration (Plant)

This exercise is optional if Exercise 15.1 is done by the
entire class; however, it may still be done as a demonstration
or as an individual project to be carried out at home.

Coleus is a common plant, easily obtained and likely to give
good results. The household geranium (Pelargonium) may be
used, but results appear more slowly and there is likely to be
more difficulty with molds. The directions must be modified
slightly when plants with alternate leaves are used.

Good comparisons can be made if different species of plants
are used by different teams, but replication should also be provided. One scheme is to have all teams in a class use the same
species but have different classes use different species.

If teams must be large, each pair of students on a team may
be made responsible for setting up one of the cuttings.

Materials. Almost any container that allows good drainage may be used. The saucer permits watering from below, so that the plastic bag need not be disturbed.

Vermiculite may be substituted for sand. If possible the medium should be heat-sterilized in an oven before use.

The plants from which cuttings are taken should be young and vigorous, with several branches.

Discussion. Some students may think that the original plant is the control in this experiment. Why isn't it? Does every experiment require a control? (Cutting A is the closest thing to a control in this experiment.)

Point out that the healing of a wound (callus formation) on the injured surface of a plant involves regeneration. So does the healing of wounds in animals.

Present the following statement to students for discussion:

Vegetative reproduction as a result of accidental fragmentation is probably not important to the coleus population, but it is of some importance to streamside willows and to many plants that grow in shallow water.

Exercise 15.5
Development of an Embryo: Frog

This exercise is basic only if Exercise 15.3 is not done.

The teacher is urged to read the BSCS Laboratory Block Animal Growth and Development, by Florence Moog (Boston: D. C. Heath & Co., 1963). This exercise has been adapted from procedures described in that book.

In the normal teaching schedule, this exercise is likely to occur at a time when frog eggs are naturally available in many parts of the country. If this is the case, Parts A and B may be omitted. Keep a pond under observation each morning; try to collect only the freshest eggs. Eggs that were not present on the previous day were probably laid during the night. Or collect pairs of frogs in amplexus and bring them into the laboratory. The species of frog is not important; but be sure to keep in mind that Figure 15.5-1 applies to Rana pipiens, and considerable deviation can be expected with the use of other species of Rana.

Omission of Parts A and B greatly simplifies the exercise— but it also bypasses some excellent experiences with hormonal control. If the exercise is scheduled after the normal egg-laying season and the teacher still wishes to have Parts A and B done, this may be accomplished by keeping a few frogs in a refrigerator, thus delaying ovulation and mating by several weeks.

Part A. The teams for this part may be larger than for the other two. However, some allowance should be made for treated frogs that may die or that may, for one reason or another, fail to respond to the treatment. (Immaturity is a common cause of failure; be sure the frogs equal or exceed the minimum size.)

The simplest method of getting equipment to demonstrate ovulation and fertilization in the frog is to purchase from a biological supply house a kit that contains the necessary male frogs, a female frog, and a bottle containing a suspension of pituitaries. To cover the possibility of failure, order several kits. However, a better learning experience can be arranged by dissecting out whole pituitaries and injecting these between the skin and body wall of the abdomen, using a #18 hypodermic needle. This procedure emphasizes the fact that gonadotrophins are not just present or absent but vary in quantity. The number of pituitaries required to induce ovulation in a female varies with the sex of the donors and the season. Pituitaries from female frogs are approximately twice as potent as those from males. The suggested dosage of female pituitaries from September to January is 5; January to March, 4; March, 3; April, 2.

Dissecting out the frog pituitary is a difficult procedure. A BSCS Technique Film ("Removing the Frog Pituitary." 16 mm. Color. 1 minute. Thorne Films, Boulder, Colo.) shows the complete procedure. This may be shown to the class at the teacher's discretion, but the procedure itself should be attempted only by students especially adept and interested in biological techniques.

In lieu of the film, Figure T-15.5a and the following directions may be used: Anesthetize a frog with ether, chloroform, a solution of 2-percent urethane in water, or a solution of 0.1-percent chlorotone in water. Insert the blade of a pair of strong, sharp-pointed scissors into the mouth at the angle of the jaw (Figure T-15.5a, top), cutting back on each side to extend the width of the mouth, and making a transverse cut just posterior to the tympanic membranes.

You have now cut off the upper jaw and skull as far back as the rear of the tympanum. Pith the body by inserting a dissecting needle into the spinal column and moving it about to destroy the spinal cord. Discard the carcass. Wash the head and place it, ventral side up, on a dissecting pan. Cut away the skin on the roof of the mouth and expose the bones of the skull.

Carefully insert the scissors in the opening at the base of the brain, and cut down one side of the bony floor of the cranium to a point even with the posterior margin of the eye socket; do the same on the other side (Figure T-15.5a, bottom left). Both cuts should be approximately 2.5 mm from the midline. Using forceps, carefully turn back the resulting flap of bone to expose the under-

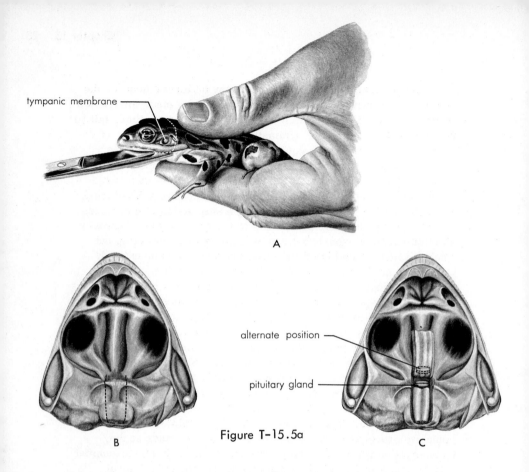

tympanic membrane

alternate position

pituitary gland

Figure T-15.5a

B

A

C

side of the brain (Figure T-15.5a, bottom right). The pinkish
pituitary gland is attached to the brain just posterior to the crossed
optic nerves (optic chiasma) and is about three times the size of a
common pinhead. Usually the pituitary adheres to the bony flap.
Remove it with fine forceps, and place it in a small amount of
amphibian saline solution (0.65-percent NaCl) in a watch glass.

Part A should be done on a Friday, if possible. The female
frogs should be ovulating by Monday; development of the embryos
can then be followed through the 96-hour stage before the next
weekend.

Part B. This part of the "Procedure" is long. With good
students it can be accomplished in a 55-minute laboratory period.
If the period is shorter and the students are inept, it is well to
dissect out the testes in one period and complete the procedure
the next day. This may be done by stopping the procedure at the
point of removal and continuing as follows: Rinse the testes in
amphibian saline and gently blot with a paper towel. Fit a thin
layer of cotton into a petri dish. Then remove the cotton, dip it in
saline, squeeze firmly, and replace in the dish. There must be
no standing water in the dish! Place the testes on the cotton,
cover with a second layer of moist cotton, put the cover on the
dish, and store overnight in a refrigerator.

Pond water is the best medium for the eggs and developing embryos. Tap water, even when aged, is unsatisfactory. If pond water is not available, use a 10-percent Holtfreter's solution. First, prepare a stock solution by dissolving 3.5 g of NaCl, 0.05 g of KCl, and 0.2 g of NaHCO₃ in 1 liter of distilled water. To make 10-percent Holtfreter's, combine one part of the stock solution and nine parts of distilled water.

Frog embryos pass rapidly through the early stages of development. Students will have an opportunity to observe at least a few of these stages if the teacher fertilizes some frog eggs early in the morning, before classes begin. These can be observed by the first class of the day. Then if a few dishes of fertilized eggs are saved from each class, later classes will be able to observe additional stages of development.

If stereomicroscopes are not available, some worthwhile observations can be made with hand lenses. In either case, a strong light source is important. Use a microscope lamp or the following improvisation: Place an incandescent bulb in a simple socket mounted on a board. Obtain a square piece of thin aluminum sheeting (such as that used in offset printing); the height of the square should be somewhat greater than the height of the bulb and socket. Bend the square so that two adjacent corners come together, and staple shut the folded edge between these corners. Open the free edges somewhat, and stand the resulting reflector on the board so that the stapled edge extends over the bulb. But take care that this device does not overheat the dish being observed.

The Temperature Gradient Box was discussed in connection with Exercise 2.4 (see Figure T-2.4a). If such a box is not available, some dishes should be kept at room temperature; others should be kept at a higher temperature by being placed in a box that contains a lighted bulb (a thermostat is desirable but not essential if frequent checks are made); still others should be kept below room temperature in a refrigerator.

Part C. The daily observations should take no more than ten minutes of each period.

The principal object in this exercise is the observation of embryonic development; the experimental aspect is incidental. Therefore relatively little time need be devoted to the study of the data. However, if the data are obtained, they may be plotted on a grid such as that shown in Figure T-15.5b. On this grid the standard rate of development (shown in manual Figure 15.5-1) produces a straight line, which facilitates comparison of graph lines from experimental data.

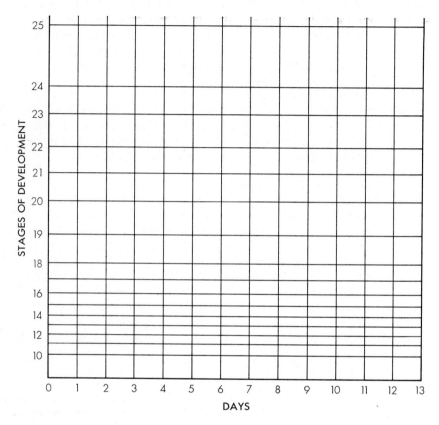

Figure T-15.5b

Exercise 15.6
Effects of X-Irradiation upon Seeds

This exercise is adapted from work by Robert C. Nims, which is described in Laboratory Experiments with Radioisotopes for High School Science Demonstrations, edited by Samuel Schenberg (Washington, D. C.: U. S. Government Printing Office, 1958).

The design of the exercise lends itself well to teams of four or eight, with one or two students being responsible for each step. Several teams may use the same kind of seed, thus increasing the amount of data.

If a local source of irradiation (a hospital or a dentist's office) is not available, seeds already irradiated at various

intensities may be purchased. But such a procedure has a
tendency to reduce student interest. Even if students do not
see the irradiation performed, taking seeds to the X-ray source
lends some immediacy that is lacking when irradiated seeds are
purchased.

If the dosages of radiation can be measured, Vial 1 should
receive 7000 roentgens, Vial 2 should receive 14,000 r, and
Vial 3 should receive 28,000 r.

Preparations. The kinds of seeds suggested have been
found to work well, but other kinds could be substituted.

Pill vials or the plastic tubes in which toothbrushes, cigars,
and some other products are sold make suitable containers for
the seeds.

Standard greenhouse flats are quite satisfactory for growing
the plants. They have the advantage of not needing to be lined.
One such flat will be large enough to accommodate all the seeds
to be planted by one team (60)—but the four groups of seeds
must be clearly separated and their arrangement marked on a
chart.

If the long-term study ("For Further Investigation," manual
page 297) is to be carried out, the seeds should be planted in soil
or vermiculite. If vermiculite is used, it should be watered with
a solution of a commercial plant-nutrient mixture—for example,
Hyponex.

Discussion. A useful form for summarizing the data on the
chalkboard follows:

	AVERAGE GERMINATION			AVERAGE HEIGHT		
	Oats	Corn	Sunflower	Oats	Corn	Sunflower
Nonirradiated seeds						
Irradiated, vial 1						
Irradiated, vial 2						
Irradiated, vial 3						

The teacher should be able to bring out many points not
included in the manual. At this time the emphasis should be on
development. But the results should be referred to during work
on Chapters 16 and 17 to bring out the significance of mutational
effects, the connection of irradiation with "lethals," and the role
of radiation exposure in evolution—the last operating through
population principles that hark back to Chapter 2.

SUPPLEMENTARY MATERIALS

Additional Exercise

For teachers who wish to include some observational work
for Chapter 15, the exercise that follows is provided as a model.
Similar work could be done with mosses, liverworts, gymnosperms, and angiosperms, using a combination of fresh plant
materials and prepared microscope slides.

Alternation of Generations in Ferns

Introduction. Ferns are of no great economic importance.
But the importance of an organism is not established on the basis
of its economic value alone. Regardless of how small or apparently
useless a plant or animal may seem, it is of value if we can learn
from it something that extends our understanding and enriches
our appreciation of life.
Some forms of life may be more worthy of study than others,
but all are products of a long, slow process of change and evolution; each form presents unanswered questions of ancestry, biochemical processes, and behavior. When you look at a fern, it
may be a good idea to remind yourself that before you is a modern
descendant of plants that dominated the earth for millions of years
before man arrived to appreciate—or ignore—them (textbook pages
309-310).
Purpose. In this exercise the life cycle of a fern is studied for
comparison with that of other plants.
Materials and equipment. The following items are needed by
each team:
1. Intact specimen of fern sporophyte, fresh or dried
2. Living fern sporophytes in pots, 2 or 3 per class
3. Hand lens
4. Scalpel
5. Microscope slide
6. Medicine dropper
7. Cover slip
8. Monocular microscope
9. Fern gametophyte
10. Stereomicroscope

Procedure. Examine your specimen of a fern sporophyte, comparing it with a living plant growing in a pot. Where is the stem located in the growing plant?(1) With a hand lens observe the leaves (fronds). The veins are neither netted nor parallel, but are said to be dichotomous (refer to manual page 68). What does this term mean?(2) Notice that some of the leaves have small, brown, dotlike or elongated structures, called sori (singular, sorus). On which surface of the leaves do they occur— upper or lower?(3) Do the leaves that bear sori look like those that do not?(4)

With a scalpel, scrape off a few of the sori. Deposit them in the middle of a clean slide; add a drop of water and a cover slip. Examine with a microscope, using low power. Small, stalked structures you may see are spore cases. If you find cases, examine one closely and notice the row of thick-walled cells across the top and around one side of a case. Some of the cases may have been broken in handling. Draw a whole spore case. Spores from broken cases may be scattered on the slide; other spores may be observed inside the broken cases. Using high power, draw two or three spores.

As a spore case reaches maturity, its cells begin to dry out. The row of thick-walled cells straightens, tearing the case open and exposing the spores. As the case continues to dry out, the row of thick-walled cells acts as a spring and snaps back into position, throwing the spores into the air. This remarkable mechanism results in one of the fastest movements found anywhere in the plant kingdom. Spores are so small that they may float in the air for a long time. Volcanic islands and lava flows are frequently populated by ferns and mosses well in advance of the appearance of seed plants. Explain.(5)

Spores that settle from the air in favorable locations germinate and develop gametophytes. Examine a fern gametophyte under the stereomicroscope. Describe the size and shape of the gametophyte.(6) Observe the threadlike structures on the lower surface; these are not vascular, so they are called rhizoids rather than roots. Although it is small and relatively inconspicuous, the gametophyte is important in the fern reproductive cycle, for it produces both male and female gametes. The male organs (antheridia) appear as small, dome-shaped, multicellular structures among the rhizoids on the undersurface of the gametophyte. Antheridia generally develop before the female organs (archegonia) appear. The archegonia are also produced on the undersurface of the gametophyte—but near the notch. They are flask-shaped, with enlarged basal portions buried in the tissues of the gametophytes and necks projecting above the surface. Each basal portion of an archegonium contains an egg.

Remove an antheridium and crush it in a drop of water on a clean slide. Add a cover slip and examine under low power of the monocular microscope. Can you see any released sperms? What kind of movement, if any, do they show?(7) Sperms liberated from the antheridia swim to the archegonia; fertilization takes place in the archegonia. .In what kind of habitat must gametophytes grow for fertilization to occur?(8) In most ferns both antheridia and archegonia are produced on the same gametophyte, though sperms and eggs do not ordinarily mature at the same time. How is this likely to affect the parentage of the offspring?(9)

The zygote divides repeatedly to form a young sporophyte, which generally grows several years before it begins to produce spores. Soon after the roots and leaves of the young sporophyte are well developed, the parent gametophyte dies and decays—in other words, the sporophyte remains dependent upon the gametophyte for a very short time. How does this compare with the relationship between gametophyte and sporophyte in mosses?(10)

Notes for teachers. The exercise is written for use with a species of fern that has moderately dimorphic fronds— Polystichum acrostichoides or Polypodium virginianum, for example. But almost any fern of a convenient size can be used. The specimens for each team should be of the same species as the potted plants, which are included so that the position of the rhizome (underground stem) can be shown.

Ejection of spores from sporangia may be demonstrated if mature sporangia are available. Test sporangia from different individuals until some are found at the proper stage; keep these plants in a plastic bag until class time. Place a sorus under a stereomicroscope and focus a bright light on it. Heat from the lamp will cause the sporangia to dry out. They will first dehisce; then, as drying continues, the annuli will snap back, ejecting the spores.

Fern gametophytes may be grown by several methods. One involves planting spores on blocks of plaster of Paris. Mix plaster of Paris with water until it attains a viscous, but easily stirred, consistency. Pour it into a small aluminum pie pan (smaller than the diameter of the dish you will use). When it hardens, wash it thoroughly with a nutrient solution. The solution may be made from a commercial fertilizer such as Hyponex (1 g dissolved in 1 liter of water) or from the materials supplied for hydroponics experiments (General Biological Supply House or Carolina Biological Supply Co. —addresses on guide page 91). Set up the apparatus shown in Figure T-15a. Lay fern fronds bearing mature sporangia on a piece of white paper, and place under a lamp to dry. The spores that collect on the paper may then be blown gently onto the moist surface of the plaster block. Place the apparatus in indirect but not dim light. Young gameto-phytes should appear in about ten days; mature antheridia and archegonia should develop in about two months.

A similar method of growing fern gametophytes involves use of a clean, preferably new flowerpot stuffed tightly with fibrous (not granulated) peat moss (Figure T-15b). Spores should be collected and sown on the surface of the pot in the manner described above for the plaster block.

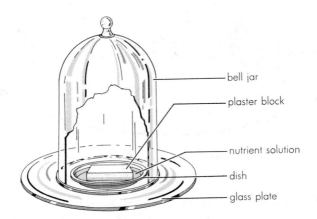

bell jar
plaster block
nutrient solution
dish
glass plate

Figure T-15a

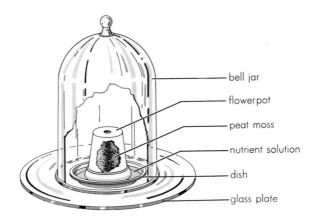

bell jar
flowerpot
peat moss
nutrient solution
dish
glass plate

Figure T-15b

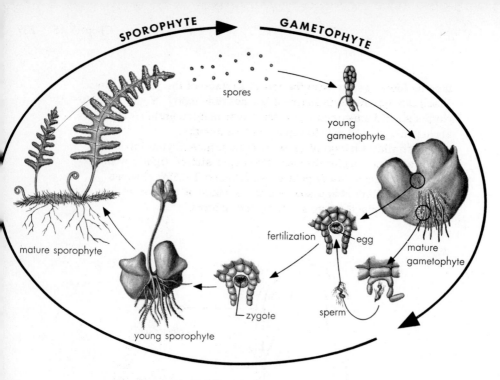

Figure T-15c. Reproductive cycle of a fern

Figure T-15c is designed along the same lines as textbook Figures 15.15, 15.18, and 15.23. Teachers may wish to reproduce these figures for use with an overhead projector.

Invitations to Enquiry

Invitation 37 (pp. 184–187 of the Handbook). Changes in the pattern of circulation in the human infant just prior to birth are used to elicit reasoning about structural changes as evidence of function.

Audiovisual Materials

Filmstrips: "Reproduction Among Mammals." Black & White. Encyclopaedia Britannica Films. Simple and direct presentation (except for omission of copulation); uses a good combination of drawings and photographs. The species used is the domestic pig.

"The Reproductive Systems." ("High School Biology Series"). Color. McGraw-Hill Text-Film Division, 1963. Uses man as the example. Good drawings of male system; rather poor of female system. Embryology and birth are depicted but are poorly related to female physiology.

Motion-picture films: "Mitosis and Meiosis. " 16 mm. Color. 16-1/2 minutes. Indiana University Films. Very good for recalling mitosis and contrasting meiosis with it.

"Asexual Reproduction. " 16 mm. Color. 10 minutes. Indiana University Films. Includes time-lapse photography of fission, budding, and spore formation.

"Theories of Development. " (AIBS Film Series). 16 mm. Color. 28 minutes. McGraw-Hill Text-Film Division. Outlines history of theories and depicts development of frog.

"The Chick Embryo from Primitive Streak to Hatching. " 16 mm. Color. 13 minutes. Encyclopaedia Britannica Films. Includes time-lapse photography of the formation of the heart, beating of the heart, and circulating blood.

Teacher's References

BULLOUGH, W. S. Vertebrate Reproductive Cycles, 2nd ed. New York: John Wiley & Sons, Inc. , 1961. (Excellent review of the diversity of vertebrate reproductive patterns and their endocrinological basis.)

CORNER, G. W. Ourselves Unborn. New Haven, Conn. : Yale University Press, 1944. (Old, but still an excellent non-technical account of human embryology.)

HAMBURGER, V. A Manual of Experimental Embryology. Chicago: University of Chicago Press, 1960. (Excellent reference; highly desirable as background for Exercises 15.3 and 15.5.)

PATTEN, B. M. Foundations of Embryology, 2nd ed. New York: McGraw-Hill Book Co. , Inc. , 1964. (New edition of a standard work devoted primarily to the standard vertebrate examples. Many other vertebrate embryology texts are available.)

WARDLAW, C. W. Embryogenesis in Plants. New York: John Wiley & Sons, Inc. , 1955. (Treatise on the early stages of development in the embryophytes—bryophytes plus tracheophytes.)

WILLIER, B. H., and J. M. OPPENHEIMER (eds.). Foundations of Experimental Embryology. Englewood Cliffs, N. J. : Prentice-Hall, Inc. , 1964. (Eleven papers in the field of experimental embryology, originally published between 1888 and 1939, a period in which the foundations of the science were laid.)

CHAPTER 16

Heredity

MAJOR IDEAS

1.   Through a combination of fortunate mathematical background, native astuteness, and considerable luck, Gregor Mendel developed a fruitful inheritance theory that was fundamentally different from all previous theories. While his theory lay unnoticed for more than four decades, the developing biology of the late nineteenth century was building cytological evidence in support of it.

2.   Mendel's experimental results forced him to a particulate theory of inheritance. By assuming that heredity is determined by particles transmitted from generation to generation through the gametes, he was able to explain the phenomena of dominance, segregation, and independent assortment.

3.   Soon after their rediscovery, Mendel's principles were linked with nineteenth-century advances in cytology to form a chromosome theory of inheritance. Abundant experimental work during the first quarter of the twentieth century substantiated this theory.

4.   Twentieth-century experimental work revealed new principles: linkage, nondominance, multiple alleles, continuously varying traits, etc. All of these phenomena were unknown to Mendel, but they proved to be explainable in terms of the chromosome theory.

5.   The origin of new traits in organisms has been traced to chemical changes in nuclear materials—mutations. In recent years gene mutation has been linked to alterations in the structure of DNA molecules. These alterations occur "naturally," but they can be caused to occur at an increased rate by treatment of cell nuclei with high temperatures, certain chemicals, or (especially) ionizing radiations.

6.   During the last quarter century increasing attention to the genetics of molds, bacteria, and other microorganisms has resulted in an understanding of the way in which genes function in heredity. Genes direct the synthesis of proteins—especially enzymes; this direction is currently supposed to be through the "coding" on DNA molecules of sequences of nucleotide bases that correspond to sequences of amino acids in proteins. [This last idea is developed only sketchily in the textbook.]

7.   Improvements in cytological and statistical techniques during the past fifteen years have greatly increased knowledge of human heredity without resort to breeding experiments: the human chromosomes have been accurately numbered and described; chromosome anomalies have been linked to clinical syndromes; and metabolic defects—traceable to gene defects— have been elucidated. Yet, many human "traits" of great interest still have not yielded to genetic analysis, which points up the close interaction of genetic constitution and environmental situation.

TEACHING SUGGESTIONS

Guidelines

Exercise 16.1 poses a problem that is basic to the proper evaluation of the whole subject of heredity—the relationship between genetic constitution and environmental influences. Though the old heredity-environment argument has been largely resolved in the minds of biologists, their utterances may still betray biases that they do not intend but which easily mislead the layman. Therefore, before the apparently deterministic Mendelian deductions are examined, Exercise 16.1 provides a balanced view that is favorable both for the approach to genetics and for the later consideration of genetics in evolution. To be used most effectively, however, the exercise must be set up about ten days before the textbook chapter is started.

The teacher who dives boldly into Chapter 16, assigning large blocks of material in the textbook, setting up brief discussion periods, and passing quickly from one exercise to another, is doomed to disappointment. Genetics is a difficult subject. To lead students through Mendel's results is easy; to drill students in constructing Punnett squares is not much harder; to get students to memorize the definitions of "allele,"

"nondominance," "mutation," "lethal," etc., requires mere
persistence. But to really learn genetics is difficult; the more
fully the teacher is aware of the difficulty, the greater the likelihood of a reasonable degree of success in teaching it.

The difficulty begins with a large terminology. It is compounded by frequent use of symbols. And it is made hopeless
(in the eyes of some students) by mathematics. The teacher
can alleviate the first difficulty by moving slowly from one set
of terms to the next. He can cope with the second difficulty by
repetition and an abundance of examples. But he cannot expect
to overcome native ineptness and perhaps ten years of mounting
distaste for mathematics in any reasonable time. He must be
satisfied with bringing a degree of understanding to as many
students as possible.

In view of the difficulties, the textbook chapter should be
divided into at least three assignments: pages 534-545,
pages 545-552, and pages 552-566. With many classes it may
be better to go over Mendel's experiments thoroughly (pages
535-540) and then tackle the Mendelian theory separately
(pages 540-545). Before the theory is gone into, however,
Exercise 16.2 should be undertaken. It is not guaranteed to
supply every student with insight, but it will help many. Then,
as work proceeds with Exercise 16.3, mathematical probability
will appear again; before the results of the exercise are analyzed,
some time should be spent on chi-square. The inoculation will
not "take" in all students; but some, at least, will gain a glimpse
of an area that is of central import to all modern science—
statistical inference.

Aside from the general difficulties discussed above, several
specific topics are always troublesome. The inexperienced
teacher should be alert for signs of confusion in the following:
the meaning of "proof" in science; the fact that many allelic
genes may exist in a population, even though an individual
normally carries only two alleles; the idea that most mutations
are harmful. In addition, reasoning from data is difficult for
many students; the following topics in Chapter 16 deserve considerable explication from the teacher: Mendel's reasoning
(at least, as far as it is given in the textbook); Sutton's reasoning;
Morgan's reasoning about the Y chromosome; the reasoning involved in mapping genes; and the reasoning in the Neurospora
experiments.

In chemistry and physics the solution of problems is recognized as an important means by which students gain understanding.
In biology this principle has not been as frequently adopted, but at
least in genetics it is certainly applicable. Most college genetics
texts (see "Teacher's References," guide page 258) contain large
numbers of problems. The teacher must select and adapt to se-

cure series of problems that are commensurate with his students' abilities. It is more desirable to supply many simple problems that illustrate a limited number of principles through the use of different traits in different organisms than to cover a wide range of principles with a limited number of difficult or sophisticated problems.

In discussing the last portion of the chapter, it is easy to bog down in an endless recital of human disorders and in vague speculation concerning the role of heredity in producing them. Students have a natural interest in human genetics. It is well to capitalize on student interests, but they should not be allowed to capsize the course. Although human genetics concludes the chapter, "Source of New Traits" (pages 555-559) is the real bridge to Chapter 17; therefore, brief return to that topic should be the final business for Chapter 16.

Some Notes

The illustration at the head of the chapter depicts two contradictory principles in heredity through sexual reproduction: (1) the sibling offspring all have the characteristics of pigs, but (2) they differ from one another in details—here, coloring.

Page 535: The scientific study of heredity did not begin with Mendel. But so fundamental were the changes he wrought in biological thinking that attention to previous investigators serves no useful purpose in explaining genetics to students and is best left to historians of science.

Figure 16.4: Some books list flower color as a trait studied by Mendel. But this is not an additional trait; Mendel noted that white flowers regularly accompanied white seed coat and that colored flowers (plus a reddish tint on the stem in the axils of the leaves) regularly accompanied colored seed coat.

Figure 16.5: On the basis of later experimental work, some irreverent biologists have declared that Mendel must have "fudged" his figures. More charitable writers have suggested that Mendel intended his figures to be illustrative only. It really doesn't matter. Error in detail does not detract from the discovery of an inclusive principle; on the other hand, no degree of accuracy in figures would have compensated for faulty reasoning that might have led to unsupportable conclusions.

Page 540: "In science the simplest explanation that fits all the facts is always preferred." The teacher should see that this paramount principle of procedure is not overlooked. The Principle of Parsimony actually antedates modern science; perhaps its most famous form is in the words of William of Occam: "Entia non sunt multiplicanda praeter necessitatem" (Occam's razor).

Page 547: "Meaning of 'proof.'" This is another contribution to the student's concept of the scientific enterprise.

Pages 550-551: A review of meiosis (textbook pages 503-508) is needed at this point.

Page 552: Recombination will be encountered again as an important contributor to evolutionary change (textbook page 587).

Figure 16.16: The teacher may wish to use this example to revive the ideas engendered by Exercise 16.1. If hair is plucked from the back of a Himalayan rabbit and the animal is then placed in a low-temperature cage, the regenerated hair is dark; if the plucked rabbit is placed in a high-temperature cage, the regenerated hair is usually white.

Page 554: Human blood types are encountered again in Figure 17.14 and in Exercise 19.2.

Pages 556-557: DNA has become a kind of status symbol. Certainly it is difficult to overemphasize the importance of discoveries in "molecular biology" during the past decade. But an appreciable number of biologists do not subscribe to the full creed, and many more deplore recent journalistic extrapolations of the data. In any case the authors of the Green Version believe that the memorization of the "anatomy" of the DNA molecule is as inexcusable in high school biology today as was the memorization of crayfish appendages and grasshopper mouthparts yesterday.

EXERCISES

16.1 Heredity and Environment . . . . BASIC
16.2 Probability . . . . BASIC
16.3 Mendelian Monohybrid Cross in Drosophila . . . . BASIC
16.4 Human Inheritance . . . . BASIC

The work with <u>Drosophila</u> is highly desirable, but the teacher
may expect many difficulties. <u>Drosophila</u> culture is not easy,
especially if the teacher has only slight experience. But it is
worthwhile for the teacher to gain experience (if he does not already
have it), since the little beasts have many nongenetic uses—for
example, to show insect metamorphosis and to illustrate population
growth under various conditions.

Exercise 16.1
<u>Heredity and Environment</u>

This exercise addresses itself to a matter that receives only
cursory treatment in the textbook—and then toward the end of the
chapter. The exercise may be started before any reading assignment is made. However, since it requires two weeks to carry
through, most classes probably will be discussing Mendel's work
before it is completed. By that time Exercise 16.1 can be used
to illustrate the 3:1 ratio in the F_2 generation.

Seeds of corn or sorghum may be used, but tobacco has the
advantage of requiring very little space for germinating large
numbers of seeds. This is particularly important in providing
for darkness; a single box on a window ledge will do the job for
the petri dishes of several classes. Moreover, it has been
found that the small size of the tobacco seeds arouses a great
deal of interest. And at this stage in the course, many students
have developed considerable pride in their laboratory dexterity—
the small seeds challenge them.

The seeds should be counted out before the laboratory period
and delivered to the teams in small medicine vials.

Eight to ten days will normally be required before counting
begins. If the experiment is set up on a Monday, the first count
usually can be made eight days later (on a Tuesday), and the last
count then occurs on a Friday. If the experiment is set up on a
Friday, the first count can be made on the tenth day (a Monday).
Other schedules involve an inconvenient break for a weekend.

Teams of four are suggested. In counting, one pair of
students can count Dish <u>A</u> and the other pair Dish <u>B</u>, each
student checking the count of his partner. Exchanging dishes
between pairs on alternate days provides a further check and
emphasizes team responsibility.

While counting is in progress, the teacher should check the
counts of Dish <u>B</u> (on Day 1 especially). The "albinos" usually

contain some yellow pigment; because students often expect a
dichotomy of "colored" vs. "uncolored," the yellowish seedlings are sometimes reported as "green." And take care that
the white radicles are not counted as "albino" seedlings.

After conclusions have been reached by each team, data
of all teams may be pooled on the chalkboard in a form similar
to the one on manual page 300. A ratio of green:albino can then
be calculated from all the data and related to Mendel's results.

Suggested questions for class discussion: What must have
been the genotypes of the parent plants? What must have been
their phenotypes? When investigating this trait, could you
follow the Mendelian P_1 -F_1 -F_2 sequence of generations?
(The last question brings up the matter of lethal genes, but the
term need not be used until Figure 16.21 in the textbook clearly
recalls this exercise. Actually, chlorophyll formation is inhibited
in the homozygous recessive only for a time. Some albino seedlings ultimately form chlorophyll and grow to maturity. Thus a
P_1 cross is possible. And this, of course, brings up the relativity
of the term "lethal.")

Exercise 16.2
Probability

The ideas developed in this exercise are needed for understanding Mendel's theory. Therefore it should be done early
in the study of Chapter 16.

Both parts of the "Procedure" can be carried out in one
period. "Studying the Data" requires the pooling of results—and
some discussion—which can best be done coöperatively in class,
after students have worked out Items 1 and 2 at home.

Be sure to point out the relationship between the conclusion
about size of sample (Item 3) and the practice in several past
exercises of combining team data.

Exercise 16.3
Mendelian Monohybrid Cross in Drosophila

This exercise should be preceded by a practice period in
which students learn to distinguish male and female flies and
to etherize and handle flies properly. The 3-minute BSCS
Technique Film "Genetics: Techniques of Handling Drosophila"
is useful; it may be shown to the class two or three times.

Equipment. The following items are needed for culturing Drosophila:

1. Culture bottles (1/2-pint milk bottles, 250-ml wide-mouth collecting bottles, or any wide-mouth jars of similar size), for keeping stocks, about 12 for five or six classes
2. Glass vials (about 80 mm X 23 mm), for individual crosses, 1 gross for each cross
3. Absorbent cotton (cheapest grade), 1 lb
4. Cheesecloth (cheapest grade), for enclosing cotton plugs
5. Pyrex flask (1000 ml or larger) with wicker covering. The cover allows you to pour directly from the flask while the medium is hot.
6. Iron support stand
7. Meeker burner (preferred) or Bunsen burner
8. Wire screen (with asbestos), to prevent the medium from scorching while cooking

(NOTE: A kitchen saucepan and a gas or electric hot plate may be used as substitutes for Items 5 through 8.)

9. Large pyrex funnel with a 6- to 8-inch length of rubber tubing attached and closed with a pinch clamp
10. Paper toweling (1" X 2" strips for each culture bottle and much narrower strips for each vial)
11. Graduated cylinder (100 ml or larger)
12. Trip balance
13. Glass-marking crayon, Labelon tape, or adhesive labels
14. Filter paper (large), for weighing materials on the scale
15. Pressure cooker, for sterilization
16. Measuring cup
17. Ring stand and clamp

Media. Many kinds of media have been used for culturing Drosophila, and it is generally agreed that all are suitable for development of fruit flies if yeast is added. The two formulas given below are recommended—one for its simplicity of measurement and storage and the other for its economical use of agar and its use of a mold inhibitor.

The first medium is prepared from a dry mixture developed by W. F. Hollander, Genetics Department, Iowa State University. It may be kept in dry storage until needed, at which time water is added to make up the desired amount. No mold inhibitor is used by Hollander (though 5 to 6 ml of 0.5-percent propionic acid could be added).

Sugar (sucrose) . . . . 3 parts by volume
Cornmeal . . . . 2 parts by volume
Brewers' yeast . . . . 1 part by volume
Granulated agar . . . . 1 part by volume

Mix these ingredients thoroughly. To make up the medium, add about 400 cc of the dry mix to 1 liter of cold water.

The second medium is a formula prepared by Dr. Bentley Glass at Johns Hopkins University. It is extremely economical in the use of agar, which is, by far, the most expensive ingredient in any medium.

Water . . . . 540 ml
Cornmeal . . . . 50 g
Rolled oats . . . . 25 g
Dextrose . . . . 50 g
Brewers' dry yeast . . . . 5 g
Agar . . . . 3 g
0.5-percent propionic acid . . . 3 ml

A 1/2-pint milk bottle filled to a depth of 1 inch requires about 45 ml of medium; therefore the quantities given above will fill about 12 bottles.

Place the liquid mixture resulting from either the Hollander or the Glass formula over a burner, and bring to a boil. Boil gently for about five minutes or until the foaming stops. After boiling, transfer the mixture from the flask to the glass funnel mounted on the ring stand. Extend the rubber tubing into a culture bottle or vial, and regulate the flow of medium with the clamp. Fill each bottle to a depth of 2.5 cm and each vial to a depth of about 2 cm. With a glass rod or a pencil, push one end of a doubled strip of paper toweling to the bottom of the container while the medium is still soft. It is sometimes necessary to gouge a fermentation vent through the medium to the bottom of the container; otherwise, when live yeasts are introduced, CO_2 may build up rapidly under the medium and push it toward the top of the bottle or vial, trapping the flies. The vents may not be necessary if the paper strip is inserted deeply. The strips also provide additional surface for egg-laying and pupation. Plug containers with cotton stoppers wrapped in cheesecloth. (These stoppers may be used over and over if sterilized each time.)

After the culture containers have been filled and plugged, they must be sterilized in a pressure cooker or autoclave. The standard time for sterilization is fifteen minutes, at about 15 lb of pressure. This procedure will usually kill bacteria and mold spores in the medium. Then the culture containers may be stored for several weeks either in a refrigerator or in a deep-freeze. If a refrigerator or freezer is available, all the containers needed for Exercises 16.3 and 16.7 can be made up at one time.

About twenty-four hours before flies are introduced, inoculate the medium (thawed, if it has been frozen) in each culture container with 6 drops of a milky suspension of living yeast. The dry, packaged yeast obtainable in grocery stores is quite satisfactory.

Drosophila culture. Pure strains of Drosophila may be obtained from biological supply houses or, in some instances, from geneticists in nearby colleges or universities.

The flies from stock centers will be in small vials. Use these to start your own stock cultures. Before transferring the flies from the vials to culture bottles, be sure there is no excess moisture on the medium or the sides of the bottles: flies can get stuck rather easily. Place a funnel in a bottle. Before removing the cotton stopper from a vial, force the flies to the bottom by tapping the vial on a table. When the flies have collected on the bottom of the vial, quickly remove the cotton stopper and invert the vial into the funnel. Holding the vial, funnel, and bottle firmly together, force the flies into the bottle by gently tapping the bottom of the bottle on a rubber pad. At least five to ten pairs of flies should be used as parents in making stock cultures.

Add a little yeast suspension to the stock center vial, and attach the vial to the side of the culture bottle with a rubber band. Eggs and larvae still in the vial will thus be saved to continue development and to provide more stock materials.

Stock and experimental cultures may be kept on shelves or on the desks in the laboratory. They should not be kept in a refrigerator, or near a radiator, or on a window ledge in the sun. If the room is quite warm (25°C), the Drosophila will develop rapidly; if it is cool (15°C), a longer period of time is required to complete the life cycle. If the temperature of Drosophila cultures exceeds 28°C for any period of time, the flies will become sterile.

In the southern states it has been found that some species of ants will crawl through the cotton plugs and chew up the developing flies. This can be prevented by placing culture bottles on blocks in a shallow pan of water.

It is essential that all stock cultures be labeled clearly and accurately.

Cultures should be changed every three or four weeks to avoid contamination by mites (minute parasites that live on flies) and molds. Medium should never be allowed to dry out, and water or yeast suspension should be added when moisture is required. At least two sets of each culture should be maintained in case one fails. Old culture bottles should be sterilized and cleaned soon after they are no longer needed.

Collecting virgin females. After mating, female Drosophila store the sperms they receive and use them to fertilize a large number of eggs over a period of time. Therefore the females used in any experimental cross must be virgin. Flies used in maintaining stock cultures need not be virgin, since the females could only have been fertilized by males from the same genetic stock.

Females usually do not mate until twelve hours after emerging. If all the adult flies are shaken from a culture bottle, the females emerging in that bottle during the next twelve hours are likely to be virgin when collected. Some geneticists recommend collecting the females after a ten-hour period. Virgin females may be collected at intervals over a period of time and kept in a food vial. Two or three collections per day can be made from a culture bottle. Put no more than twenty-five virgin females in a vial.

It is sometimes difficult to distinguish the sex of very young flies. If in doubt, use the sex-comb characteristic in males. One stray male in a vial of (originally) virgin females will make the entire vial worthless in an experiment.

Experimental mating. When an experimental mating between virgin females and males of the desired genetic strain is to be made, the flies are put directly into a vial containing medium. A safe method for introducing etherized flies into a food vial is to invert the vial over the flies; they will crawl up to the food when they recover, and the cotton plug can then be inserted. There should be no excess moisture in the vial.

If a temperature of 20° to 22°C is maintained, mating, egg-laying, and the development of larvae to a good size should take no more than a week. After seven or eight days the parent flies should be shaken out of the container. This will prevent confusion of the parent flies with the offspring when counts are made. Once flies begin to emerge, they may be classified and counted for ten days. Counting longer than this again runs into the danger of overlapping generations. The first F_1 flies may have mated before being counted and, hence, may have left some eggs in the same container.

Many types of etherizers are in use. For simplicity, economy, and ease of handling, the authors recommend the one in Figure 16.3-2 (manual page 311). For each etherizer obtain a shot glass of heavy construction, a small aluminum funnel (6.5 cm), and 15 cm of heavy cotton string. Modify the funnel as follows (see also Figure T-16.3): With a pair of wire cutters, make cuts about 1 cm apart around the bottom edge of the funnel neck. Bend the resulting tabs outward 90 degrees. Lay the string along the neck, with about 5 cm extending beyond the tip. Hold the funnel horizontally in your left hand (if you are right-handed), with the thumb securing the end of the string. With your right hand extend the string along the outside of the funnel neck until it reaches the base of the cone. Wrap the free end of the string around the funnel neck beginning at the cone. Wrap the string in a single layer toward the end of the neck. When the tabs are reached, tie the two ends in a tight knot. Bend the tabs up over the tightly wrapped string. The string will act as absorbent material for the ether.

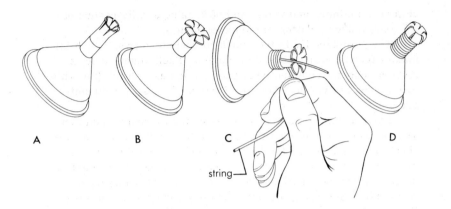

A   B   C   D

string—

Figure T-16.3. Steps in preparing a funnel for a
Drosophila etherizer

The cheapest technical grade of ether is quite adequate.
When students are working with ether, the room should be well
ventilated. A warning about dangerous explosive fumes should
be given by the teacher: No flames of any kind should be allowed
in the room at this time.

After they are etherized, flies can be dumped onto the
examination plates for observation. Care should be taken to
avoid overheating the flies with a strong light. If the light
source must be brought close to the flies, fluorescent lamps
should be used. Or to filter out the heat, light from an incandescent lamp can be passed through a round flask filled with
weak copper sulfate solution.

Do not leave flies in the etherizer more than one minute.
Etherized flies will recover in about five minutes. If the flies
begin to recover before examination is completed, they may be
returned to the etherizer for a second dose. Warn students
that the flies are more easily killed by a second dose of ether
than by the first; therefore, re-etherizing should not exceed
thirty seconds.

Take care that the students do not overetherize their flies
and kill them—thus limiting the supply of flies for the use of subsequent classes. If flies are overetherized, their wings turn up
vertically over their backs. If this happens, you might as well
put them in the morgue.

Keeping records. Adequate records are essential to the
success of an experiment and an understanding of the results.
Impress upon the student the importance of properly labeling

culture containers and vials, and of keeping a daily record of
all observances relating to the experiments.

The wild-type fly is the standard phenotype from which all
mutant types are inherited departures. Each mutant type is
given a descriptive adjective. Such names as "white" (for white
eyes, a recessive) or "Bar" (for "barred" eyes, a dominant)
are used.

For convenience a symbol is assigned to each mutant gene.
The symbol is sometimes the initial letter of the mutant name—
ebony body is represented by the symbol e. But the number of
mutant genes is so large that they cannot all be represented by
single letters; so additional letters are used, such as those
immediately following the initial one (ey for eyeless) or sugges-
tive letters—especially consonants—from the rest of the name
(dp for dumpy). By convention the names and symbols of recessive mutant types begin with small letters, while names and
symbols of dominants begin with capitals. Drosophila geneticists
no longer use the alternative-sized letter for the alternative
member of a pair of alleles. Instead they substitute a plus sign
(+) as a superscript with the gene symbol to represent the wild-
type allele. Example: the dominant wild-type allele of b (black)
is not B, but b^+; and the recessive wild-type allele of B (Bar)
is not b, but B^+.

Exercise 16.4
Human Inheritance

This exercise can be done as a homework assignment and
checked in a class discussion. It is best undertaken when work
on the textbook chapter is nearing completion and just before
work on Chapter 17 is begun.

If charts for testing color blindness are available, a study
may be made of this trait by having each student test his parents
and siblings.

Exercise 16.5
Genetic Differences in Peas

As written, this exercise takes three days to complete.
However, a two-day schedule can be used, as follows: Day 1—
The initial weighing of peas and the observation of the starch
grains. Have the preparation of the extract done out of class

by a special team.   Day 2—The observations of the glucose agar
and (between observations) the weighing of the soaked peas.

On Day 1 the bottles are weighed wet because they will be
wet when the final weighing is done.

Dried peas are very hard, and grinding them with mortar
and pestle is difficult.   It may be necessary to break the peas
with a hammer or squeeze them in a pair of pliers before mortar
and pestle are effective.   Ideally a Waring Blendor should be
used (40 ml of water for each 10 g of peas).   Be sure to clean
the machine thoroughly between grindings.

The extract must be stored in the refrigerator, since the
enzyme deteriorates rapidly at room temperature.   But be
sure to remove the extract from the refrigerator an hour before
use, since action of the enzyme is very slow at low temperatures.

When the test is made on the agar, the warmer the room,
the better.   In standing overnight, most of the solid materials
will settle out of the extract, and the almost clear supernatant
can then be decanted.   However, clear extract entirely free of
starch grains can be obtained quickly with a centrifuge.

Directions for preparing glucose agar: Be sure to use plain
agar.   To 400 ml of distilled water add 8 g of agar and 2 g of
glucose-1-phosphate (the Cori ester).   Boil vigorously until
the foam becomes quite coarse.   Pour into petri dishes.   Cover
and keep in refrigerator until one hour before use.   The
glucose-1-phosphate is expensive, so it is desirable to use
small petri dishes and keep the agar layer thin.   If these directions are followed, the amounts given here are sufficient to
prepare forty dishes.

Be sure students use a separate medicine dropper for each
of the two extracts and for the $I_2 KI$—three droppers altogether.

Exercise 16.6
Inheritance of Two Traits

Of course, fruit flies can be used to illustrate the idea in
this exercise.   But it seems desirable to give students some
insight into the diversity of organisms used in genetics.   The
materials and procedure in the work with corn are simple and
economical of time.   Therefore the exercise is recommended
as written.   If, however, the teacher wishes to use fruit flies
the "dumpy" and "sepia" mutants are suggested.

Though one ear of corn for each pair of students is desirable,
one for every four students will serve.   Students then take turns
doing the counting.

The corn characteristics used are purple and yellow color, and smooth and shrunken texture.

Item 12: In predicting expected ratios in the F_2 generations, students should use the algebraic method (see textbook page 543) rather than the Punnett-square method.

Item 18: The chi-square test merely indicates whether the difference between the observed and expected ratios is significant —that is, whether the difference is greater than that to be expected on the basis of chance. It does not indicate anything about the cause of the difference.

Exercise 16.7

A Test Cross

Exercise 16.3 was rather lengthy, and there are several important matters in addition to genetics to be considered before the year ends. But teachers may wish to exploit the fruit-fly skills that students developed in that exercise. Therefore Exercise 16.7 may be desirable—at least for a team of interested students.

"Dumpy," "ebony," or "sepia" is a good trait to use in this exercise. The mixture of homozygous and heterozygous dominants found in a normal F_2 generation is suitable for supplying the flies to be tested. Of course such a source of test flies is likely to yield twice as many heterozygotes as homozygotes. You can also mix the pure-breeding dominant stock, used in making P_1 crosses, with the F_1 progeny of the cross between pure-breeding dominant and recessive stocks.

The teacher should assign some teams to test female unknowns and some to test male unknowns. Teams can then be supplied with recessives of the proper sex for their cross, eliminating the hunt for flies of the correct sex and avoiding one possible source of error—the introduction of recessives of both sexes into a culture bottle with the fly to be tested.

Directions in the manual call for each team to test two flies. This number can be varied, of course; the limit is set by the number of bottles that can be prepared and cared for.

This is a good exercise for students to attempt as a special project, primarily for the thrill of experimenting.

SUPPLEMENTARY MATERIALS

Invitations to Enquiry

Invitation 5 (pp. 64-67 of the Handbook). This invitation is concerned with measurement in general and has no direct bearing on genetics—but this seems a good time to formalize a topic that has been frequently mentioned before.

Audiovisual Materials

Charts: In teaching the basic ideas of progeny ratios in Mendelian crosses, repetition is valuable. One good way to secure this is through the use of classroom charts that display the ratios. Good charts are available from General Biological Supply House (see Appendix C for address).

Phonograph record: "Genes—the Core of Our Being. " ("The Scientists Speak: Biology"). Harcourt, Brace and Co. Should be used toward the end of Chapter 16. One of the greatest living geneticists, H. J. Muller, speaks directly to the student, emphasizing mutations.

Motion-picture films: "DNA: Molecule of Heredity. " 16 mm. Color. 16 minutes. Encyclopaedia Britannica Films. Good description of the role of DNA molecules in inheritance, adding considerably to the account in Chapter 16.

"Genetics: Improving Plants and Animals. " 16 mm. Color. 13 minutes. Coronet Films. Good for bringing out some of the practical applications of genetics—a topic neglected in the textbook.

"Biochemical Genetics. " (AIBS Film Series). 16 mm. Color. 28 minutes. McGraw-Hill Book Co. , Inc. Useful if the teacher wishes to explore this important topic more deeply than does the Green Version.

"Genes and Chromosomes. " (AIBS Film Series). 16 mm. Color. 28 minutes. McGraw-Hill Book Co. , Inc. Linkage, crossing-over, and gene-mapping are difficult ideas, and this film can help to clarify them.

Teacher's References

KING, R. C. Genetics. New York: Oxford University Press, 1962. (A thoroughly up-to-date approach to genetics, excellently illustrated.)

LEVINE, R. P. Genetics. New York: Holt, Rinehart & Winston, Inc., 1962. (A good, succinct treatment for the teacher who needs a "refresher.")

MOORE, J. A. Heredity and Development. New York: Oxford University Press, 1963. (The relationship of heredity to embryology, with special attention to the role of DNA.)

MULLER, H. J. Studies in Genetics. Bloomington, Ind.: Indiana University Press, 1962. (Papers of the distinguished Nobel laureate, selected by himself and organized around topics to which he has contributed significantly.)

PETERS, J. A. (ed.). Classic Papers in Genetics. Englewood Cliffs, N. J.: Prentice-Hall, Inc., 1959. (A selection of original papers—including Mendel's—that have been land-marks in the development of the science.)

SINNOTT, E. W., L. C. DUNN, and T. DOBZHANSKY. Principles of Genetics, 5th ed. New York: McGraw-Hill Book Co., Inc., 1958. (One of the most widely used college textbooks of genetics; encyclopedic, sound, sober.)

STERN, C. Principles of Human Genetics, 2nd ed. San Francisco: W. H. Freeman & Co., Publishers, 1960.

STRAUSS, B. S. An Outline of Chemical Genetics. Philadelphia: W. B. Saunders Co., 1960. (Rather technical, but good for the teacher whose genetics belongs to the prewar era.)

STRICKBERGER, M. W. Experiments in Genetics with Drosophila. New York: John Wiley & Sons, Inc., 1962. (Excellent guide for the teacher unfamiliar with the handling of the fruit fly.)

section Five

ADAPTATION

If the authors' endeavors have been at all successful, both student and teacher should now be aware of the artificiality of section and chapter boundaries in this course. Chapter 16 belongs as much to Section Five as to Section Four—and heredity is implicit in reproduction. But there must be pauses; some order must be imposed upon nature. So it has seemed best to draw a line between the mechanisms of heredity and the mechanisms of evolution, which depend upon them.

With some propriety the reader might be inclined to see a larger gap between Chapters 17 and 18 than between Chapters 16 and 17. Certainly the coupling of evolution and behavior is no more orthodox than the wide separation of the "story of evolution" (Chapter 10) from the mechanisms of evolution (Chapter 17). But there is justification for both organizational decisions.

Of the nine themes that run through the course (see guide page 6), evolution is one of the most pervasive. Indeed, some biologists see in evolution the grand principle around which all of biology must be organized. But to some biologists there is an even deeper principle: Every unit of life—from most particular to most comprehensive—is an internally organized system that is constantly adjusting to the exigencies of a more or less unorganized environment. Such a view underlies the linking of the mechanisms by which populations adjust through relatively long periods of time to their environments (evolution) with the mechanisms by which individuals adjust in relatively short periods of time to their environments (behavior).

If biology were a suprahuman entity, Section Five would end the course. But in actuality, biology is a human construct. Living things existed long before man—and may persist long after him. Biology is not the biosphere itself; it is an ever-changing structure compounded of the data accruing from human research directed by human curiosity. Biosphere is phenomenon; biology is noumenon.

And so the teacher must save time for Section Six.

CHAPTER 17

Genetic Adaptation: Evolution

MAJOR IDEAS

1. The idea of change in the earth and its inhabitants is very old; even the idea of change in a particular direction (evolution) is old, though it long lacked formulation into theory.

2. In his theory of natural selection, Darwin provided a plausible explanation for the mechanism of organic evolution. After a partial eclipse in the late nineteenth century, Darwin's theory received firm support through twentieth-century studies in genetics, behavior, and population dynamics.

3. Evolution is a "directed" change in one or more characteristics of a population. Essentially it is a statistical concept involving such a shift in the means of a series of frequency distributions that a plot of the means has a consistent direction.

4. The mechanisms of heredity maintain a basic stability in the characteristics of populations. If this were not so, it would be impossible to recognize species; and, therefore, it would be impossible to recognize change in species—evolution.

5. Mutations are the basic source of change, but where recombinations of genes are possible—as they are in sexual reproduction—the chance of change is greatly multiplied.

6. The theory of natural selection provides an explanation for the directionality of evolution. Basically it rests upon differential reproduction among populations: Those that produce more offspring capable of living to maturity tend to survive; those that produce fewer offspring capable of living to maturity tend to die out.

7. The theory of natural selection is an adaptational explanation of evolution. It requires both a genetic constitution and an environment, with which the genetic constitution interacts.

8. In small, isolated populations, chance alone may bring about a shift in the genetic constitution of a population, thus bringing about evolution without natural selection.

9. In widespread species, distance prevents completely random mating throughout the population; speaking figuratively, eddies develop in the species gene pool. As a result, recognizable discontinuities may occur; subspecies may be described.

10. A new species originates when a population (whether originally recognizable as a subspecies or not) becomes reproductively isolated from other populations. In most cases, reproductive isolation develops when genetic changes accumulate in populations that have become separated by a geographic barrier.

11. In some cases (mostly in angiosperms) new species are known to have originated suddenly through the mechanism of polyploidy. Of course, the continued existence of the necessarily small original population of such new species is dependent upon interaction with the environment—natural selection.

TEACHING SUGGESTIONS

Guidelines

Three different avenues of approach are available for Chapter 17; each has its merits, and the choice depends upon local conditions and teacher preference. One approach emphasizes the relation of Section Five to Section Three. In the caption to textbook Figure 8.8, the student was asked to explain the seasonal change in the plumage of ptarmigan and to file his explanation for consideration during work on Chapter 17. A discussion centering around these resurrected explanations can set the stage for considering the theory of natural selection.

If the teacher prefers to hold this discussion after (rather than before) the students have encountered the theory, an approach through Exercise 17.1 is good. The exercise emphasizes the inherent genetic stability of species and the critical role of the environment in the evolutionary process; thus it ties Chapter 17 to Chapter 16 and at the same time recalls the ecological background necessary for understanding evolution.

In some cases, however, the teacher may feel that the mathematics in Exercise 17.1—slight as it is—is more discouraging than enticing. Then an approach through the Darwin narrative in the textbook (pages 573-581) may be best.

Whether it comes first or later, the Darwin narrative is a logical entity within the textbook chapter. It is a variation on the historical motif that has been used to introduce a number of previous chapters. In the previous instances the intention has been to illustrate the dependence of scientific progress on technological advances, the piecemeal development of scientific concepts, and the international character of the scientific enterprise. Here, however, the intention is to illustrate the growth of an idea in the mind of a scientist and to "humanize" (a detestable but perhaps indispensable word) him. Few biologists fit the purpose so well. From his youth a man of many faults, leading (after his one great adventure) an outwardly dull and prosaic life, neither an amateur nor a professional by today's standards, ignorant of mathematics and remote from the universities, a turgid writer— what a wonderful antidote to the popular vision of the scientist as the man in the white laboratory coat! No matter that there can be no Darwin in the milieu of twentieth-century science; the uniqueness of every genius-environment complex provides an ancillary lesson.

The remainder of the textbook chapter can be conveniently divided into two assignments: pages 581-593 and pages 593-606.

A review of Chapter 10 is in order during the study of Chapter 17. The fossil record was one of the roots of Darwin's thinking; it remains today an impressive argument for the theory of evolution. And even though the mechanisms of evolution can perhaps now be most fruitfully studied with living organisms in the laboratory and the field, the history of organisms, as deduced from fossils, offers many clues to the way in which evolutionary mechanisms operate.

Chapter 11 is clearly related to the portion of Chapter 17 that deals with the origin of species. If Chapter 11 had to be omitted previously, it might be picked up here—at least as a reading assignment.

Some Notes

Page 573: Darwin was nearing his twenty-seventh birthday when he encountered the Galápagos. He was born February 12, 1809— a fateful day in both Shropshire and Kentucky.

Figure 17.1: In the lower picture the vegetation consists of tree cacti.

Figure 17.2: A more recent but less readable account of Darwin's finches is "Morphological Differentiation and Adaptation in the Galápagos Finches," by R. I. Bowman (University of California Publications in Zoology, Vol. 58, 1961).

Page 575: For the term "niche," refer to textbook page 71. This chapter constantly harks back to the first three sections of the textbook.

Figure 17.4: During the 1920's the National Geographic magazine published excellently illustrated accounts of the various breeds of horses, cattle, pigeons, and domestic fowl. These are now difficult to obtain. The U. S. Department of Agriculture publishes bulletins on the breeds of domestic animals, but these are likely to emphasize commercially important breeds rather than ones that illustrate the greatest diversity.

Pages 585-588: Review meiosis, mutation, the action of multiple alleles, and the role of genes in continuously varying traits before discussing this part of the chapter.

Page 593: The reference to the modern-species concept (textbook pages 44-46) is so important that the teacher might well make it a class review assignment.

Figures 17.11 and 17.12: The fossil history of the Equidae is interestingly summarized in Horses, by G. G. Simpson (New York: Oxford University Press, 1951; also in paperback— New York: Doubleday & Co., Inc., 1951).

Figure 17.13: Full-color pictures of the Drepaniidae are to be found in Field Guide to Western Birds, 2nd ed., by R. T. Peterson (Boston: Houghton Mifflin Co., 1961).

Figures 17.16 and 17.17: These figures and the discussion of Coluber constrictor are derived from the work of Dr. Walter Auffenberg. When Figure 17.16 was constructed, the samples from Florida were analyzed according to the separate localities from which they were taken; all other samples were lumped by states.

Figure 17.18: The figure is based on the work of Dr. Ernst Mayr (see references on guide page 271).

Figure 17.19: In pre-settlement days trees lined the larger rivers, such as the Platte and the Arkansas, all the way to the Rocky Mountains. But apparently these were not sufficient to maintain populations of large woodpeckers, such as flickers.

EXERCISES

17.1 Population Genetics and Evolution . . . . BASIC
17.2 A Study of Population Genetics . . . . BASIC
17.3 Effect of Population Size— A Study in Human Evolution . . . . Highly Recommended
17.4 Sickle Cells and Evolution . . . Highly Recommended

It might be presumptuous to state that experimental study of evolution is impossible in the high school laboratory, but it is certain that such study—even with rapidly reproducing microorganisms—is extremely difficult. Therefore the exercises for this chapter are mostly of the "read and think" type. This obviously poses a difficulty for teachers who have students with poor reading ability. However, both Exercise 17.2 and Exercise 17.3 involve some doing as well as reading. If reading problems are a factor, it may be well to emphasize these exercises, treat Exercise 17.1 lightly, and omit Exercise 17.4.

Exercise 17.1
Population Genetics and Evolution

In this exercise the intent is to lead the student to a "discovery" of natural selection. Some students may not be able to follow the reasoning. But all can benefit from the exercise by enlarging their understanding of the relation between genes in populations and the action of natural selection.

If a class has a good background in mathematical reasoning, the exercise may be assigned for home study and then discussed in class. In most cases, however, it will be advisable for the teacher to work directly with the class through Part A of the "Procedure," leaving only Part B for homework.

If the exercise is used as an approach to Chapter 17, Items 28 and 29 may be omitted until the students have become acquainted with Darwin's chronological position in the history of biology.

Answers to some items in Parts A and B of the "Procedure":

Item 1 - black ♂ X black ♀ ; black ♂ X speckled white ♀ ;
speckled white ♂ X black ♀ ; speckled white ♂ X speckled
white ♀

Items 2 and 3 - BB X BB ⟶ BB; BB X bb ⟶ Bb; bb X BB ⟶ bB;
bb X bb ⟶ bb

Item 5 - 3 black to 1 speckled white

Item 7 - 0.5 B and 0.5 b

Item 8 - Since the probabilities for the four kinds of matings are
equal and each produces but one genotype (Items 1, 2, and 3),
simply count the gene symbols in the four equally frequent
offspring genotypes (BB, Bb, bB, bb). There are 4 B's and
4 b's; therefore the frequencies are 0.5 B and 0.5 b.

Item 10 - (0.5 B + 0.5 b) X (0.5 B + 0.5 b) = 0.25 BB + 0.5 Bb + 0.25 bb

Item 11 - Suppose the third generation consists of 1000 individuals.
Then 250 are BB (500 B genes) and 500 are Bb (500 B genes),
totaling 1000 B genes. Also, 500 are Bb (500 b genes) and
250 are bb (500 b genes), totaling 1000 b genes. Therefore the
frequencies are 0.5 B and 0.5 b.

Item 14 - 200 male black beetles = 400 B genes; 300 male white
beetles = 600 b genes; the frequencies are 0.4 B and 0.6 b.

Item 16 - (0.4 B + 0.6 b) X (0.4 B + 0.6 b) = 0.16 BB + 0.48 Bb + 0.36 bb

Item 17 - Suppose the third generation consists of 1000 individuals.
Then 160 are BB (320 B genes) and 480 are Bb (480 B genes),
totaling 800 B genes. Also, 480 are Bb (480 b genes) and
360 are bb (720 b genes), totaling 1200 b genes. Therefore the
frequencies are 0.4 B and 0.6 b.

Item 18 - The calculations by the gene-pool method are the same
as in Item 16.

Item 23 - The evidence comes from the middle panel in the bottom
row of Figure 17.1-1. Whether eggs were laid on pine or on
birch, the larvae and adults develop according to the parentage,
not according to the nature of the environment.

Exercise 17.2
A Study of Population Genetics

This exercise is simple in procedure but involves mathematical thinking. It should be emphasized that the calculations
and interpretations are simpler than many expected in first-year
algebra. All students should at least take part in gathering and
analyzing the data.

Tongue-rolling is thought to be inherited as a simple dominant
trait (a trait controlled by genes at one locus). Let the students
discover the basis for this belief by studying the family data col-

lected by the class. A single family in which both parents are tongue-rollers but one or more of the children are not is sufficient to prove that tongue-rolling is not recessive. A family of two tongue-roller parents with only tongue-roller children does not prove anything: this <u>must</u> be the result if tongue-rolling is recessive; but it <u>could</u> happen if tongue-rolling is dominant, for, if either parent has the tongue-rolling ability because of a homozygous genotype, then nonrolling would never show up in the children. In families where one parent is a tongue-roller and the other is not and where the offspring show both phenotypes, the expectation for the offspring is 1/2 rollers, 1/2 nonrollers. But such crosses do not determine whether the trait is dominant or recessive.

In <u>the population</u> the ratio of dominant-type persons to recessive-type persons has, of course, <u>no relation to the 3:1 Mendelian expectation</u>, which applies only to a particular kind of mating. This is perhaps the most important principle of population genetics to recognize.

In any discussion of human genetics, the possibility of turning up some embarrassing cases must be anticipated. A common example—a brown-eyed child states that both of his parents are blue-eyed. Among the causes of such cases are:

1. Adoption
2. Mutation. (Cases in which one eye is blue and the other brown, or in which a sector of the iris is different from the remainder, are good examples of somatic mutations that are easily detected. Others are more difficult to establish as mutations.)
3. Illegitimacy
4. Oversimplification of the mode of inheritance. (The case of eye color is a good example of this. Some eyes are neither brown nor blue, and furthermore there are various shades of brown and blue. There is more than one locus— and perhaps many alleles at each—that accounts for the various eye colors in man.)

The teacher should be prepared to explain away any difficulties. It may even be desirable to stress the last cause (oversimplification) <u>before</u> taking up a particular trait in class.

Exercise 17.3
Effect of Population Size—A Study in Human Evolution

This exercise is an opportunity to explore randomness on an experimental basis. It may provide the repetition needed to drive home (after a period of incubation) some of the ideas of Exercise 16.2. It also provides the teacher with an opportunity to revert to the idea of a model, introduced in Exercise 2.1.

To some teachers the purpose of the exercise may seem worthwhile but the experimental procedure not worth the time. In this case, if the students have the necessary power of abstraction, the mathematical relationship given in Exercise 17.2 (p_2 : 2pq : q_2) can be used to calculate the expected proportion of each kind of individual.

It is important that all the beans be the same size. If they are not, smaller beans will tend to go to the bottom of the container, biasing the results. It is possible to begin with white beans of a single kind and then to dye some. The color, of course, is not important. If beads or marbles are obtainable in sufficient quantities, they may be substituted for beans.

Exercise 17.4
Sickle Cells and Evolution

Even if Exercise 14.5 has been done, it would be well to preface this exercise with a review of capillary circulation and the shape of normal human red blood cells.

The exercise uses a Socratic technique and therefore involves some use of yes-and-no questions. In such a technique it is inevitable that the answers to some questions are given or implied at a later point in the development. Therefore, to obtain the most value from the exercise, it is necessary to work through it point by point. The aim is not to get correct, neatly written answers to all the questions; the aim is to see how the reasoning proceeds.

If most of the students in the class have some facility in reasoning and can word their thoughts easily, they might be asked to work through the exercise independently. Class discussion could then center on points of controversy or confusion. In most cases, however, it is recommended that the teacher work through the exercises step by step with the class. If this procedure is followed, the work should be broken off at Items 13, 14, and 15—the call for formulation of hypotheses—and resumed the following day. This provides the students with an opportunity to formulate their hypotheses. Even if they read on and find out which way the hypotheses should point, they will have some experience in wording hypotheses.

Answers to some items in the exercise:

Item 2 - Note that the pedigree eliminates the possibility of sex linkage. Under conditions of the question, only nondominance is possible.

Item 9 - Since offspring with sickle-cell anemia die in childhood, they can leave no descendants. Therefore parents who can produce children with sickle-cell anemia have a reduced chance of descendants unless, on the average, they have more children than normal parents.

Item 12 - Darwin, of course, would have said nothing about gene frequencies but would have stated the matter in terms of natural selection of individuals.

Item 16 - Any hypothesis for Item 13 must depend upon a mutation rate toward sickling that equals the rate of elimination by natural selection. Therefore the hypothesis is weakened.

Item 17 - The information neither supports nor weakens a hypothesis based on differential fertility: It is negative evidence. But the tendency is to assume a "normal" situation in the absence of contrary evidence.

Item 18 - Since the malaria parasite lives within red blood cells at one point in its cycle (textbook Figure 7.12), it has a close association with them and with hemoglobin. Hookworms are not discussed specifically in the text; but from knowledge of the roundworm group, students should suspect that their connection with hemoglobin is less intimate than that of Plasmodium. Nevertheless, hookworms are blood feeders, so this is merely a matter of differential probability.

Item 21 - When the chi-square test is applied, the expected frequencies of sicklers with malaria and without malaria are the frequencies in the sickler population that would correspond to the frequencies in the normal population.

Item 26 - The frequency of the sickle-cell trait in the present American population designated Negro is about 9 percent.

Item 28 - The main point here is the change in gene frequency in the American population of African descent (see definition of evolution in Chapter 17).

Item 30 - With respect to oxygen supply, the sickling gene certainly is harmful. But when malaria is a factor in the environment, the sickling gene is an advantage to survival in the heterozygous state. When malaria is not a factor in the environment, the gene is a detriment to survival. Thus "harmful" and the other terms are relative (to the environment) rather than absolute terms. The terms also vary between homozygous and heterozygous states. The hybrid has an advantage that neither homozygote has.

SAINT MARY'S COLLEGE, CALIF.

SUPPLEMENTARY MATERIALS

Invitations to Enquiry

Invitation 13 (pp. 87-89 of the Handbook): Attempting to explain the development of resistance to DDT in a fly population provides practice in the making of hypotheses. Can arouse interest if used before the theory of natural selection has been encountered.

Audiovisual Materials

Phonograph record: "The Scientists Speak: Biology." (Harcourt, Brace and Co.). Julian Huxley speaks on his reasons for supporting the theory of natural selection. Huxley's voice is a link to Darwin; his grandfather was chief spokesman for the publicity-shunning Darwin.

Filmstrips: "Darwin Discovers Nature's Plan." ("Darwin's World of Nature," Part 1). LIFE Filmstrips, 1959. Helps to to vivify the story of Darwin's life.

"The Enchanted Isles: The Galápagos." ("Darwin's World of Nature," Part 2). Color. LIFE Filmstrips, 1959. Excellent series of striking pictures that supplement the textbook description of the Galápagos; gives special attention to the finches and their influence on Darwin's thinking.

"Evolution Today." ("Darwin's World of Nature," Part 9). Color. LIFE Filmstrips, 1960. Summarizes present views of the history of life, emphasizing the continuing discovery of fossil evidence.

Teacher's References

DARWIN, C. The Voyage of the Beagle. Annotated, with an introduction by L. Engel. New York: Doubleday & Co., Inc., 1962. (One of the best of the many editions of a book that would be a classic of scientific exploration even if it were not the foundation for the Darwinian theories.)

DOBZHANSKY, T. Genetics and the Origin of Species, 3rd ed.
New York: Columbia University Press, 1951. (A milestone
in the application of genetics to evolution.)

EISELEY, L. Darwin's Century. New York: Doubleday & Co.,
Inc., 1958. (Excellent history of the impact of Darwin on
Western thought.)

FISHER, SIR R. A. The Genetical Theory of Natural Selection,
2nd rev. ed. New York: Dover Publications, Inc., 1959.
(Reprint of a book that had much to do with the revival of
the natural-selection theory after its eclipse in the early
years of the twentieth century.)

GLASS, B., AND OTHERS (eds.). Forerunners of Darwin:
1745-1859. Baltimore: Johns Hopkins Press, 1959. (An
excellent contribution to intellectual history; because it is
neglected in the Green Version, the material in this book
is important for the teacher's background.)

GRANT, V. The Origin of Adaptations. New York: Columbia
University Press, 1963. (A recent survey by a plant
geneticist of a topic central to understanding of evolutionary process.)

HUXLEY, SIR J., A. C. HARDY, and E. B. FORD (eds.).
Evolution as a Process, 2nd ed. London: George Allen
& Unwin, Ltd., 1958. Also in paperback—New York:
Collier Books, 1963. (Nineteen essays on evolutionary
mechanisms by a wide array of specialists.)

MAYR, E. Animal Species and Evolution. Cambridge, Mass.:
Harvard University Press, 1963. (A basic reference for
Chapter 17; a thorough and critical survey of the process
of speciation in animals by a foremost authority.)

METTLER, L. Population Genetics and Evolution. Englewood
Cliffs, N. J.: Prentice-Hall, Inc. To be published in 1964.
(One of a series of short books summarizing current work
in genetics.)

STEBBINS, G. L. Variation and Evolution in Plants. New York:
Columbia University Press, 1950. (An excellent summary of
speciation in plants, with emphasis on genetic mechanisms.)·

TAX, S. (ed.). Evolution after Darwin, 3 vols. Chicago:
University of Chicago Press, 1960. (Papers and discussions
from an impressive meeting that celebrated the centennial of
the Origin of Species; excellent material on all phases of
evolution.)

WEST, G. Charles Darwin: A Portrait. New Haven, Conn.:
Yale University Press, 1938. (Perhaps the best of the
biographies of Darwin.)

CHAPTER 18

Individual Adaptation: Behavior

MAJOR IDEAS

1.   The ability to detect and respond to stimuli from the environment (irritability) is a basic characteristic of living things.

2.   Irritability undoubtedly involves complex biochemical and biophysical actions at the molecular level—indeed, it must involve the whole physiology of the individual. But as a matter of convenience, behavior is usually understood to consist of responses that are visible. In this view plants and protists exhibit behavior, but it is debatable whether much clarity is gained by separating behavior from the rest of the physiology of these organisms.

3.   The scientist's observing and reporting are themselves examples of animal behavior; hence complete objectivity in the study of behavior is extremely difficult to achieve. Furthermore, since different animals perceive different environmental stimuli, only the most painstaking analysis can determine to which of myriad possible environmental stimuli (some may be completely unknown to the observer) an organism is responding.

4.   There is no completely satisfactory classification of animal behaviors, but two approaches are common in behavior research. In one, attention is principally directed to the mechanism of behavior; in the other, attention is principally directed to the way in which behavior affects the life of the individual.

5.   From the viewpoint of mechanism, behaviors can be conveniently divided into two classes: innate and learned. While some behaviors are undoubtedly determined genetically, the way in which genes bring them about—especially the complex ones

called instincts—is not clear.   Learned behavior has been in-
tensively investigated in conditioning experiments, but much
remains unexplained—from the problem of defining it to the
phenomenon of insight (which is almost, but not quite, a monopoly
of Homo sapiens).

6.   From the viewpoint of function in the life of the individual,
behaviors are difficult to classify, because any act may have
various consequences.   Classifications are, therefore, likely to be
protean, and investigators adopt the classification that is most
convenient for the purposes of the investigation at hand.

TEACHING SUGGESTIONS

Guidelines

The student comes to biology with certain ideas about the
word "behavior."   Whatever those ideas may be, they probably
do not coincide with the concept of "behavior" that is encountered
in Chapter 18.   For the most part they are likely to be too narrow.
Broadening the student's viewpoint must be one of the principal
aims of the teacher.   On the whole this is easier than narrowing a
definition (as in the case of "food"), but it requires constant
attention.

No doubt most of the student's ideas of behavior have human
implications, and certainly his major interest lies in human
behavior.   But here the authors' views are similar to their views
on sex education: the social science teachers can better handle
the details of acceptable human behavior in contemporary civili-
zation; the biology teacher can best contribute to the student's
development by providing a broad biological perspective, which
has value in itself and also provides a basis for a rational grasp
of psyche and mores.

Undoubtedly every specialist feels that his field is slighted
in high school textbooks—but none with more justification than the
behavioral scientists.   The authors of the Green Version have
attempted to alleviate this feeling somewhat.   But it must be kept
in mind that Chapter 18 is not the chapter on behavior, just as
Chapter 17 is not the chapter on evolution.   Behavior is treated,
at least implicitly, throughout Sections One and Three, and in
Chapters 13 and 14 the misty border between physiology (sensu
stricto) and behavior is transgressed several times.

Work may begin either with Exercise 18.1 or with the textbook. As usual, beginning with an exercise is likely to arouse interest, but in this case the interest may be somewhat misdirected at first. Therefore, beginning with the textbook probably provides a better initial orientation. If Exercise 18.2 was started in connection with Chapter 13, it may be far enough advanced so that the class can draw some conclusions when Chapter 18 is begun; these conclusions will provide illustrative material for discussion of "Behavior Without a Nervous System" (textbook pages 611-613). Or Exercise 18.3 may be used as the first laboratory work for the chapter.

A wholly satisfactory division of the textbook chapter is probably impossible. Logic calls for a first assignment of pages 610-613, but this is inconveniently short. Two assignments for the chapter— with a division point at page 626—are probably not unreasonable. But near the end of the course, it should be possible with most classes to assign the whole chapter at once and interweave discussion of the chapter with work on the exercises.

In the past investigators of both human and nonhuman behavior have often been hampered by inadequate knowledge of neurology and endocrinology, while investigators of nerve and gland function have suffered from a laboratory myopia that restricted the meaning of their researches. With their increasing attention to interdisciplinary research, this old dichotomy is disappearing. Unfortunately it has not been possible to reflect the new trend adequately in the textbook. It is hoped that during class discussions the teacher will refer the student frequently to Chapter 14. For this task a careful reading of the little book by Dethier and Stellar (see textbook page 645) will be of assistance.

Some Notes

In the photograph at the head of the chapter, a neotropical monkey uses its prehensile tail as an anchor while reaching for a floating object. Specific modes of behavior are dependent upon anatomical equipment.

Pages 611-612: A common household ornamental, the prayer plant (Maranta) can be used to demonstrate nastic movement; its leaves fold in at night and spread out in the daytime. Mimosa pudica is fairly easy to grow; seeds may be obtained from the biological supply companies.

Pages 612-613: Not all biologists distinguish clearly between tropisms and taxes. "Tropism" is properly restricted to nonmotile organisms, principally plants. "Taxis" applies to motile organisms and is not restricted to organisms that lack nervous systems (see "Levels of Animal Behavior," textbook page 617).

Figure 18.7: The construction of nests in a characteristic form by each bird species is often regarded as an example of instinct in birds. Yet carefully controlled observations on the role of heredity in this process have been few. Modern procedure in such study is presented in an article by E. C. and N. E. Collias in The Auk 81 : 42-52, January, 1964. They found that, in a weaverbird, "practice, channelized by specific response tendencies, but not necessarily tuition by example, is needed for development of the ability to build a normal nest."

Pages 622-623: Teachers may wish to point out here the role of fashion in scientific investigation. For thirty years Drosophila and maize have been (not without good reason) the "type" organisms of genetics. For an even longer period, experimental knowledge of learning in animals has been basically a knowledge of learning in the white rat. Only recently have biologists begun to assess the probable bias by employing other animals—especially individuals from wild populations—in their researches (see J. L. Kavanau, Science 143 : 490, January 31, 1964).

Figure 18.12: The data are from E. C. Tolman and C. H. Honzik, University of California Publications in Psychology 4 : 257-275, 1930.

Figure 18.18: The kind of behavior shown here is quite different from that of the young shown in Figure 18.7. Since the offspring of the parasites never see their parents, it seems quite probable that the behavior is innate.

Figure 18.26: The question in the caption appears to be a simple one. But during the southward flight of the Canadian population, young and adults usually migrate in separate flocks that are often several weeks apart.

Pages 633-638: A very large percentage of studies of functional behavior center on reproductive behavior. Some of the more perspicacious students may be able to link this statistical fact with the importance of reproductive behavior for two other burgeoning areas of biological investigation: population dynamics and evolution by natural selection.

EXERCISES

As noted on guide page 273, behavior has frequently been in
the background during the work on previous chapters. Among
previous exercises that involve behavior are 4.4 (part), 9.3,
11.1, 14.1 (part), 14.4, 14.7. Appropriate reference to these
exercises will help make the student aware of the pervading
nature of behavior. Some of them, if not done before, may be
used now. Especially recommended are 9.3 and 14.7.

Exercise 18.1
Social Behavior in Fishes

To emphasize that behavior tends to be diverse even under
apparently identical conditions, two setups and two teams per
class are desirable. But the materials for this exercise occupy
considerable space and must remain in position for a considerable
time; therefore it may be necessary to use the whole class as a
"team." In this case it may be possible to exchange observations
between different classes.

Avoid round jars if possible. Battery jars with straight
rather than rounded sides can be obtained. Some commercial
materials are packed in "square" jars.

The best water to use is, of course, that in which the fish
have been living. However, tap water can be "conditioned" by
allowing it to stand about a week. Be sure the temperature of
the water in the jars is the same as that of the water from which
the fish are transferred.

Betta (Siamese fighting fish) and Corydoras (a catfish) can
be obtained from fish dealers that supply hobbyists. They are
not usually carried in the catalogues of biological supply
companies.

In Experiment F, do not allow students to spend too much
time on preparation of the models; the coloration need only be
approximate.

A little more than two weeks is needed to complete the
experiments in this exercise. If the jars are set up on a
Monday, Experiments A through F can be completed during
the first week. Then the transfer of the three Corydoras to
the large jar would occur on the following Monday. Removal

of one Corydoras would occur on Monday a week later, and the last experiment would occur the next day. Taken together, Experiments A through E will require a whole period; each of the other experiments requires only part of a period.

This exercise gives students a greater opportunity to organize ideas than did most of the preceding ones. After many months of experience in drawing conclusions through rather closely guided steps, most students should be able to see the plan involved in this series of experiments. But do not allow a written report to be the end of the exercise   There should be differences in interpretation—and (if more than one setup is involved) differences in observation. These should be fully aired in class discussion.

Exercise 18.2
Photoperiodic Control of Plant Behavior

This exercise will require six to eight weeks, even though the chosen species develop more rapidly than most. Therefore it should be set up some weeks before work on Chapter 18 is begun.

Planting will require most of a period. While the plants are growing, light treatment, watering, and observations will take only a few minutes each day. Of course observation need not be started until seedlings appear; thereafter, observation every other day may be sufficient. Discussion of the results will probably require a full period.

Materials. In this exercise plants are to be grown to maturity, so considerable care is required in the selection of containers and soil. If clay flowerpots are not available, cans (rather than paper cartons) should be substituted. Be sure there is at least one good drainage hole in the bottom of each container. The saucers made for clay pots are preferable, but kitchenware saucers may be substituted; they should be deep enough to hold sufficient water for a day's use. A good soil is essential for quick growth. Use a loam garden soil mixed with a little sand. Water occasionally with Hyponex solution or some other concentrated plant "food."

The radish variety is not particularly important, but one of the red-globe sorts is recommended. In picking a third kind of plant, students should be guided away from plants that require a long time to reach maturity. Good choices are dwarf zinnia, dwarf marigold, or buckwheat. Weeds such as Mollugo, Galinsoga, and Stellaria are also good if the seeds can be obtained.

Unless the exercise is done in the winter, natural daylight will supply the 10-hour period. If artificial light must be supplied for this period, at least two 40-watt fluorescent tubes at a distance of 0.5 m should be provided. As indicated in the student's directions, the light for the 24-hour period does not need to be as intense.

Some teamwork will be required to make sure that the light treatments are properly applied. It is important to stress the necessity of a strict adherence to the schedule. The dark period is more important than the light period. If for any reason a day's treatment must be missed, it is better to leave the 10-hr plants in the dark for 24 hours than to leave them in the light longer than 10 hours.

Discussion. The botanical terms "short-day plants" and "long-day plants" are useful.

Scarlett O'Hara morning-glories are decidedly short-day plants. The first flower usually appears in the axil of the first true leaf. Plants grown under the long photoperiod are not likely to flower at all. Under the long photoperiod, the stems lengthen and twine around anything at hand, whereas the plants under short photoperiod usually remain shorter and bushier. Several big, red flowers on a short, bushy plant are a spectacular sight!

Radishes are long-day plants. When the photoperiod is long, the stems lengthen rapidly, terminating with an inflorescence of flowers. When the photoperiod is short, a rosette of leaves is formed and almost no stem is visible. Under the short photoperiod, the plants store food in the roots. When the experiment is being brought to a conclusion, the plants may be pulled and the difference in the roots observed.

The third species may be either long-day, short-day, or neutral. Buckwheat is a neutral species.

The teacher may wish to correlate the flowering behavior of plants with the world regimen of light and dark (see pages 135-142 in this guide). Another subject for discussion is the methods by which florists produce flowers on chrysanthemums (short-day plants) at all times of the year.

Exercise 18.3
Tropisms

It is not necessary to have each team set up each part of this exercise. If a class is divided into six teams, each part may be set up by two teams; each team then has another to check on it.

Part A. Corn grains should be soaked about three days
before the exercise is set up.

The larger the petri dishes, the better. Use nonabsorbent
cotton to pack the grains. Paper toweling can be used instead
of blotting paper, but the grade of paper in desk blotters forms
a better support for seeds and cotton. Colored blotters sometimes contain dyes that are harmful to the corn grains.

If taping the dish to a table seems unsatisfactory, try
mounting the edge of the dish in a wad of modeling clay.

Part B. Various substitutes for flowerpots can be used.
Milk cartons with holes punched in the bottoms, for drainage,
are good. Any kind of small cardboard box lined with sheet
plastic or aluminum foil, to keep the moisture from softening
the cardboard, will serve.

The radish seedlings should be allowed to grow for only two
or three days after they break through the soil. Since radish
seeds germinate quickly, not more than a week is needed to
obtain results. Unless you plan to grow the seedlings further,
for some other purpose, the soil may be plain sand or fine
vermiculite. Avoid a clay soil.

Part C. The preferred material for this procedure is
Zebrina (wandering Jew), but coleus may be substituted.

Exercise 18.4
Perceptual Worlds

Exercise 14.8 was relatively unstructured; Exercise 18.4
is even more so. Although, on a class-wide scale, there are
serious difficulties involved in such exercises, and although the
values to be derived from experience in developing hypotheses
and devising appropriate experiments can probably best be
achieved through individual and small-group work, something
can be gained by occasionally setting up an open situation before
an entire class.

After the students have grasped the nature of the exercise,
the teacher should present a list of suitable organisms. This
might be supplemented with student suggestions, passed upon
by the teacher. A day should be allowed for consideration
before choices are made. To avoid duplication, obtain first and
second choices. Of course, all teams might use the same organism, but variety seems desirable. After the specimens have
been obtained, each team should be allowed at least ten minutes
to become generally acquainted with the behavior of the species

it chose.   If the organism is a quite unfamiliar one, time should
be increased.   The remainder of the period may be used for
team planning.   The teacher will then need several days to review
the plans and the equipment lists.   Several more days will be
required for gathering the materials and equipment before a
laboratory period can be scheduled.   Whether one or two periods
are needed will, of course, depend upon the plans.   However,
elaborate plans requiring more time should be avoided.   Encourage simplicity and ingenuity.

Animals already living in the laboratory and somewhat
familiar to the students are perhaps best—for example, Daphnia,
brine shrimp, mealworms, planaria, frogs.   Easily obtained
organisms come next—for example, earthworms, crayfish,
pond snails, crickets.   But there is some gain in interest when
less familiar animals are used—for example, silkworms, cockroaches, salamanders, the lizard Anolis, budgerigars.
(NOTE: It is essential that the teacher guide students away
from all inhumane procedures, even—if necessary—employing
his veto power.)

SUPPLEMENTARY MATERIALS

Because behavior—especially behavior viewed in broad
perspective—has not customarily been a topic in high school
biology, few attempts have been made to prepare instructional
materials.   The situation is similar to that noted for Chapters
2 and 3 (guide pages 69-70 and 80): An excellent opportunity
exists for the development of visual aids.

On the other hand, books for filling in the teacher's background are numerous.   Therefore, the "Teacher's References"
for this chapter are unusually full.   Some of the books listed
can be used quite successfully as references for the abler students.

BSCS Pamphlets

CARR, A. Guideposts of Animal Navigation. Boston: D. C. Heath
& Co., 1962. (Excellent discussion of orientation in
animal migrations.)
MEYERRIECKS, A. J. Courtship in Animals. Boston: D. C.
Heath & Co., 1962. (Courtship has been a focal point in the
investigation of behavior among free-living vertebrates; a
good introduction to ethology.)

Audiovisual Materials

Filmstrip: "Behavior of Living Things." ("Principles of
Biology," Part 6). McGraw-Hill Book Co., Inc., 1955. Employs
a terminology somewhat different from that used in the Green
Version (and confuses tropism and taxis). Of some use for a
review.
Motion-picture films: "Behavior." (AIBS Film Series).
16 mm. Color. 28 minutes. McGraw-Hill Book Co., Inc.
Good for introducing the topic.
"Rhythmic Motions in Growing Plants." 16 mm. Color.
11 minutes. Dr. William Harlow, Syracuse 10, N. Y. Excellent
on plant movements—both those that are responses to environmental
stimuli and intrinsic ones. May be used to arouse discussion on
the meaning of the term "behavior."
"The Senses." (See Chapter 14, guide page 219). Good review
of some physiological mechanisms involved in behavior of "higher"
animals.
"Social Insects: The Honeybee." 16 mm. Color. 24 minutes.
Encyclopaedia Britannica Films. Rather long for the amount of
information it contains, but the subject has a fascination for
students.

Teacher's References

NOTE: Starred items (*) are especially suitable for
students with better-than-average reading ability.

*BROADHURST, P. L. The Science of Animal Behaviour. Baltimore:
    Penguin Books, Inc. , 1963. (Small, but provides an excellent
    survey of the field. The teacher who lacks background in
    animal behavior might very well begin with this book.)
CARTHY, J. D. An Introduction to the Behaviour of Invertebrates.
    New York: The Macmillan Co. , Publishers, 1958. (A standard
    reference for its specialized field.)
*DETHIER, V. To Know a Fly. San Francisco: Holden-Day,
    Inc. , 1962. (Not for information, but a highly amusing
    account by a perceptive biologist of his efforts to understand
    the behavior of a common invertebrate.)
FOLLANSBEE, H. A Laboratory Block on Animal Behavior.
    Boulder, Colo. : Biological Sciences Curriculum Study,
    1961. (Contains much information on methods of studying
    behavior in the high school laboratory.)
*FRISCH, K. VON. Bees: Their Vision, Chemical Senses, and
    Language. Ithaca, N. Y. : Cornell University Press, 1956.
    (Not only a fine account of behavior, but also a record of
    ingenious experimentation.)
*GRIFFIN, D. R. Listening in the Dark. New Haven, Conn. :
    Yale University Press, 1958. (An account of the sonar
    system of bats, with excellent examples of methods involved
    in such research.)
HASKINS, C. P. Of Societies and Men. New York: W. W. Norton
    & Co. , Inc. , 1951. (A biological view of societies—human
    and insect.)
KLOPFER, P. H. Behavioral Aspects of Ecology. Englewood
    Cliffs, N. J. : Prentice-Hall, Inc. , 1962. (Will help the
    teacher relate the subject matter of Chapters 2 and 3 to that
    of Chapter 18.)
MILNE, L. , and M. MILNE. The Senses of Animals and Men.
    New York: Atheneum Publishers, 1962. (Good for developing
    ideas of perceptual worlds.)
RHEINGOLD, H. (ed.). Maternal Behavior in Mammals.
    New York: John Wiley & Sons, Inc. , 1963. (Includes papers
    by biologists who use diverse approaches to the subject;
    studies on both confined and wild species of five different
    orders.)
ROE, A. , and G. G. SIMPSON (eds.). Behavior and Evolution.
    New Haven, Conn. : Yale University Press, 1958.
    (A symposium volume that should do much to relate
    Chapters 17 and 18.)

SOUTHWICK, C. H.   Primate Social Behavior.   Princeton, N. J. :
    D. Van Nostrand Co. , Inc. , 1963.   (Good reference for
    Chapter 18, and background for Chapter 19.)
THORPE, W. H.   Learning and Instinct in Animals.   London:
    Methuen & Co. , Ltd. , 1956.   (Summary of studies up to the
    date of publication.   Much additional material has accumulated
    in the journal literature since.)
*TINBERGEN, N.   The Herring Gull's World.   London:
    William Collins Sons & Co. , 1953.   (A nontechnical book,
    but one that illustrates the kind of results that emerge
    from studies by ethologists.)
_____ .   The Study of Instinct.   New York: Oxford University
    Press, 1951.   (A book that did much to rehabilitate the
    term "instinct. ")
WYNNE-EDWARDS, V. C.   Animal Dispersion in Relation to
    Social Behaviour.   London: Oliver & Boyd, Ltd. , 1962.
    (Elaborates a theory of population homeostasis through the
    development of social behavior.   The theory leaves much
    to be desired, but the material used in explanation is most
    informative.)

section Six

MAN AND THE BIOSPHERE

Anyone who has followed this guide through the preceding sections should need no further orientation for Section Six. The humanistic bias of the Green Version has been frequently implied; it is explicitly stated on guide pages 8-10, 19, and 260. It should be clear that Section Six is not an afterthought but the goal toward which the course has been moving from the start.

From the teaching viewpoint, it follows that Section Six must not be pushed aside in the year-end rush. Too many courses fizzle out in the June heat. If this is allowed to happen with the Green Version, much of the effort of preceding months will have been in vain. With a little forethought, such a debacle can be avoided.

Not more than three weeks are needed for Section Six, and much that is worthwhile can be accomplished in half that time. Only one exercise (19.2) involves extensive laboratory preparations; when it is completed, materials can be put away and equipment can be cleaned and stored for the summer. Then, viewing the course in retrospect and their lives in prospect, students and teacher together can look at biology as a whole—and at its impact on the lives of men.

CHAPTER 19

The Human Animal

MAJOR IDEAS

    1.   Anatomically, man is a vertebrate animal, a mammal of the order Primates; on the family level he is distinguishable from other primates by a number of structural features. These peculiarities lie not in unique structures but, rather, in the degree of development of basic primate structures.

    2.   Man's anatomical equipment allows him no single outstanding physical accomplishment, but it provides him with unparalleled versatility.

    3.   The physiological peculiarities of man are mostly temporal, centering upon his slow development to maturity. They are important primarily because they provide a foundation for the evolution of behavioral characteristics—on the basis of which man's unique culture has arisen.

    4.   During the past few decades paleontologists have uncovered an unlikely (but still meager) amount of fossil evidence for the evolution of hominids. Efforts to elucidate the pongid-hominid divergence have not been as successful; the great apes and man have apparently evolved along separate lines since the Miocene.

    5.   On the basis of the "biological definition" of species, all living hominids undoubtedly belong to one species. As in other wide-ranging species, partial geographic isolation has resulted in the development of varieties; the most significant distinctions between these are cultural rather than physical.

6.   The line between human biology and human sociology is shadowy at best—if, indeed, the latter is not wholly subsumed by the former. But in the high school biology course it is convenient to extend inquiry no further than the earliest stages of human technology.

7.   Man's domestication of other organisms has greatly modified their characteristics, has preserved some from extinction (maize and gingko, for example), and has given rise to a whole community that is dependent upon human artifice.

TEACHING SUGGESTIONS

Guidelines

"Man is an animal" is a statement of biological fact. Obviously this statement does not preclude other viewpoints, some of which may not even belong to other branches of science. Science is not the whole of man's experience; the teacher should remember the third BSCS objective (guide page 5). An even sharper difference than that discussed in the third paragraph of the textbook chapter is afforded by the idea of human spirit, or soul. But the authors believe that it is appropriate for the biology teacher to mark clearly the limits of his competency and his subject.

Again the teacher has a choice of beginning with the laboratory (Exercise 19.1) or with the textbook, the advantage probably lying with the former. The textbook material can be easily encompassed in one assignment.

The search for evidences of man's past is one form of "pure" science that captures the interest of almost everyone. The best indication of this is the space that newspapers are willing to devote to the subject. Certainly it has a high degree of interest for high school students. Therefore the teacher may wish to give special attention to textbook pages 655-660.

On the other hand, "Development of Human Culture" (pages 662 ff.) pushes into the realm of the social sciences. Many students will have encountered such material in history courses; giving it merely cursory treatment should be sufficient— especially if time is pressing. But note that the final part of Chapter 19 leads directly into Chapter 20: Primitive man ends the one and begins the other; also, the concept of the biotic community comes in for treatment in both chapters—in "The Community of the Domesticated" (page 667), and throughout the final chapter, where man's relationship to the world community, the biosphere, is the central theme. Therefore, study of Chapter 20 can proceed without introduction.

Some Notes

Page 651: For a "motion picture" of the running action of the cheetah (and of the horse) see the BSCS Laboratory Block by A. G. Richards, The Complementarity of Structure and Function (Boston: D. C. Heath & Co., 1963).

Figure 19.3: This pair of pictures clearly illustrates some of the characteristics of man's head. In addition to the points made on page 650, note position of the ear on the skull (size of the external ear varies greatly in man), the bony brow ridge, and size of the mouth.

Page 653: The menstrual cycle of the female is sometimes emphasized as a human peculiarity, but it seems to be only a slight extension of a primate variation on the mammalian pattern. To what degree it has contributed to the evolution of human societal organization is an interesting question, but one to be recommended for debate in the social studies, rather than the science, classroom.

Figure 19.6: The vertical scale in this diagram is neither arithmetic nor logarithmic, but a somewhat unfortunate compromise.

Page 658: Good popular accounts of Leakey's discoveries in Olduvai Gorge have appeared in the National Geographic magazine.

Page 661: The marginal note beginning "You know of such cases..." refers to the examples of discontinuous distribution in the previous paragraph.

Figures 19.14 and 19.17: The areas in which domesticated plants and animals originated may be correlated with the biogeographic realms of Chapter 11. Note that the number of animals domesticated in the New World is small compared with the number of plants domesticated there. (Of course the maps do not show all domesticated animals and plants.)

EXERCISES

Exercise 19.1
The Skeletal Basis of Upright Posture

Skeletons of other quadruped mammals may be used in place
of the cat skeleton. Rat skeletons are too small for good observation by groups. Human skeletons are expensive, but full-size
replicas difficult to distinguish from the real item are now available. The small plastic models are not satisfactory for this
exercise.

If only one skeleton of each species is available—as will
usually be the case—the observational part of the exercise can
be done in shifts. The skeletons are large enough to be seen
easily, so the observing group may be rather large. At least
two groups can make all the observations in a single period.
The "Discussion" can be done by students outside of class time;
or, if space and time permit, one group may discuss its observations while another is working with the skeletons.

The exercise should conclude with a general class discussion, because much interpretation is left up to the teacher.

Any study of skeletons can become quite loaded with terminology. The terms used in the exercise are those that will
be found useful for carrying on a discussion. The teacher may
add to them as he sees fit.

The teacher may wish to refer to Exercises 4.2 and 14.1,
in which man and other animals were compared with respect
to other characteristics.

Exercise 19.2
Human Blood Groups

This exercise is interesting to students, but it must be
planned with particular care by the teacher. First, written
permission from parents of participating students is recommended; second, arrangements must be made to take care of
cases of fainting that occasionally occur; third, only sterile,

disposable lancets (Hemolettes) should be used, and each
lancet must be discarded after <u>one</u> use. Some teachers arrange
for the school nurse to carry out the procedure for obtaining
blood. Under extremely unfavorable conditions, it might be
well merely to demonstrate the blood-typing procedure and
omit the consideration of blood-type percentages.

The "Background Information" should suffice for establishing the rationale of the procedure. For most students,
the antigen-antibody explanation of blood-type incompatibility
probably involves more difficulties than it clears up. The
reference to textbook page 199 is intended only to dispel the
notion that incompatibility of blood types is an isolated and
peculiarly human phenomenon.

The exposition of the Rh factor is left to the teacher—if
he and the students are interested. A remarkable number of
students have picked up the medical story of Rh—even though
they may have only a vague idea of the theory. Some teachers
may wish to do Rh typing with the ABO, but the serums
are expensive.

Be sure that students differentiate between <u>clumping</u> of
red cells and <u>clotting</u> of blood.

Concerning materials and equipment (manual page 365),
Items 2, 3, 4, 7, and 10 are required for each student; Items 1,
6, and 11 are needed for each pair or quartet of students; Items 5,
8, and 9 can be shared by rather large groups.

If serums are old or have not been kept under refrigeration,
many errors may occur. These are likely to be systematic rather
than random errors, and of course they will affect the percentages.

In early printings of the manual, the second sentence under
"Summary" (page 367) is in error. It should read as follows:
"Large numbers of 'foreign' red blood cells are introduced in
blood transfusions, but the introduced plasma is quickly diluted
in the plasma of the recipient. "

When checking Items 5 to 12, the teacher may be assisted
by the following tables:

GROUP	PLASMA	RED CELLS
O	anti-a and anti-b	neither
A	anti-b	A
B	anti-a	B
AB	neither	A and B

		RECIPIENT			
		O	A	B	AB
DONOR	O	−	−	−	−
	A	+	−	+	−
	B	+	+	−	−
	AB	+	+	+	−

Exercise 19.3
Biological Distance

In many situations this exercise can be assigned as homework. Not all students, however, will be able to work their way
successfully through it; therefore some class discussion should
follow the work at home. In classes where slow students predominate, the exercise is best done entirely in class, the teacher
leading step by step.

The advantages of blood types over other characteristics
that have been used as bases for racial classification are brought
out clearly in W. C. Boyd's Genetics and the Races of Man
(Boston: D. C. Heath & Co., 1950). A later and smaller book
by Boyd and I. Asimov, Races and People (New York: Abelard-
Schuman, Ltd., 1955), covers some of the same ground and is
more readable for high school students.

Notes. The data for British Columbia are derived from
various tribal groups; those for New Mexico are confined to
the Navaho. The data, of course, are obtained as blood types—
A, B, AB, or O—and the gene frequencies are calculated from
the phenotype frequencies.

Some students may argue that the slight differences between
the British Columbia and Navaho populations represent nothing
more than sampling errors.

Without knowing the number of persons in the sample, it is
not possible to test for the significance of the difference. However, the difference between the British Columbia and Navaho
populations, on the one hand, and the Eskimo population, on the
other, are so great that the matter of testing for significance
can scarcely be raised. And for the purposes of the exercise,
these latter differences are the only significant ones.

Item 6: Most students will probably answer no. And many
will react to the series of items (4-6) with "Why bother to investigate racial frequencies of blood types?" Or "Why bother to
distinguish racially between Eskimos and Indians?" Or, phrased
in the most likely form, "Why bother?" There is, of course, no
rational answer to such questions. They are in the same category
as "Why climb a mountain?" With the course coming to an end,

it is worthwhile to point out (again) that science is not necessarily concerned with "practical" questions. Yet, as stated in the "Introduction" to the student's manual, it brings about improvements in the circumstances of human life more frequently than any other enterprise.

Item 14: Likeness in one characteristic is not sufficient basis for grouping populations into one race.

Item 15: If the teacher wishes to go into the practical consequences of Rh^+—Rh^- incompatibility, here is a good opportunity to do so. Often students bring the matter up, since it is now rather well known. But such a discussion is not necessary for the continued argument of the exercise.

Item 17: This method of calculation may seem faulty, since mixing must involve both populations. But under American conditions, all persons of mixed Negroid and Caucasoid ancestry are classified as Negroid, so that introgression of the Rh^o gene into the Caucasoid population is negligible.

Item 19: The answer to this question is a biological fact. If the class climate is suitable, the teacher may wish to project the situation into the future. Such a projection is still a matter of science, but it may be so obscured by sociological implications that the teacher will not wish to pursue it. However, if the matter is gone into, it should be kept in mind that the answer to Item 19 assumes a constant rate of mixture. And this is highly unlikely. It is much more likely that the rate curve would show some of the characteristics of a growth curve. The Rh^o gene would never disappear from a large population (in the absence of natural selection), but its frequency would reach an asymptote at a level somewhat above that of the European Caucasoid population. It should also be kept in mind that the point in time at which the Negroid and Caucasoid populations become indistinguishable with respect to frequency of the Rh^o gene would not necessarily be a point at which the populations would be indistinguishable with respect to visible characteristics.

SUPPLEMENTARY MATERIALS

Audiovisual Materials

Motion-picture films: "Blood Groups, Skin Color, and Gene Pools." (AIBS Film Series). 16 mm. Color. 28 minutes. McGraw-Hill Text-Film Division. Will serve as a review of

some genetic principles important in human racial differentiation
and as background to Exercise 19.2.

"Evolution of Man." (AIBS Film Series). 16 mm. Color.
28 minutes. McGraw-Hill Text-Film Division. Dr. Marshall
Newman, eminent anthropologist of the Smithsonian Institution,
discusses the evidence for man during the Pleistocene.

Teacher's References

CLARK, SIR W. E. L. History of the Primates. Chicago:
University of Chicago Press, 1957. (A good summary by
an authority.)

COON, C. S. The Origin of Races. New York: Alfred A. Knopf,
Inc., 1962. (Has been a center of controversy because of
its interpretations of evidence, but Coon's grasp of his
material is undoubted.)

_____. The Story of Man, 2nd ed. New York: Alfred A.
Knopf, Inc., 1962. (Narrative account of human origins
and prehistory.)

DART, R. A. Adventures with the Missing Link. New York:
Harper & Brothers, 1959. ("Popular" account of the
australopithecines.)

HULSE, F. S. The Human Species. New York: Random House,
Inc., 1963. (Introduction to physical anthropology, placing
emphasis on genetics. Strong on the developments of the
last twenty years and weak on the historical development
of anthropology.)

LA BARRE, W. The Human Animal. Chicago: University of
Chicago Press, 1954. (The evolution of man and of his
culture from the viewpoints of anthropology and psychology.)

SAUER, C. O. Land and Life; a Selection from [His] Writings,
ed. JOHN LEIGHLY. Berkeley: University of California
Press, 1963. (The fourth part of this volume, "The Farther
Reaches of Human Time," contains materials from Sauer's
contributions to the human ecology of the past.)

TAX, S. (ed.). The Evolution of Man: Man, Culture and Society,
Vol. 2 of "Evolution after Darwin." Chicago: University of
Chicago Press, 1960. (Addresses delivered at a convocation
honoring the centennial of the Origin of Species.)

WASHBURN, S. L. (ed.). Social Life of Early Man. Chicago:
Aldine Pub. Co., 1961.

CHAPTER 20

Man in the Web of Life

MAJOR IDEAS

1. Gradually, as his technology has improved, man's position in the biosphere has shifted. Primitive man was a member of a biotic community, important but not dominant; modern man overrides all natural community boundaries, fabricates new communities, and overbalances meteorological and geological forces in reshaping the earth.

2. Throughout his history, improvement of man's understanding has resulted in improvement in his technology, and improvement in his technology has resulted in improvement of his understanding. The problems of modern man lie as much in the proper application of understanding and technology as they do in the further improvement of either. And most of these problems are basically biological.

3. The roots of most major biological problems—from malnutrition to floods, from traffic to smog—lie in the rapidly increasing world density of human population. As in all other populations, this density involves the four determiners natality, mortality, immigration, and emigration, of which the last two have (at present) zero values.

4. For man the living world is not only an entity that demands study, yielding understanding; it is also an experience that demands appreciation, yielding esthetic pleasure. But scientific study is itself fraught with esthetic qualities. Thus biology is doubly a humanistic enterprise.

TEACHING SUGGESTIONS

Guidelines

Field and laboratory equipment has been inventoried and stored. But—hopefully—impressions of a year's contact with living things remain. These impressions are the "materials" for work on Chapter 20.

It is expected that only a period or two will be available for this epilogue to the course. In the final days of the school year, nothing more than a reading assignment may be possible— but this much is essential. And if opportunity permits, some discussion of the biological problems that face man in the latter half of the twentieth century is appropriate. The form that such discussion takes will depend upon the teacher's sagacity and the students' insight. The areas considered in the chapter should by no means limit the discussion. And wherever possible, the information and insights gained during the year's study of biology should be woven into the prospect of the future. Above all, endeavor to make each student feel his personal responsibility for applying whatever knowledge of science he possesses to the decisions that will need to be made by his generation.

Some Notes

Figures 20.1 and 20.2: Just as extant species that have retained primitive characteristics help us to visualize organisms of the past, so primitive human cultures surviving in remote parts of the modern world show us the conditions of life in ancient human cultures. But study of such surviving primitive cultures must proceed rapidly, for modern culture is penetrating everywhere.

Page 676: "Complexity" is, of course, a relative term. A cell may be called "simple" in contrast to an oak tree or an elephant, though the cytologist finds in the cell plenty to challenge his understanding. In the cotton plant, in invading pathogens, in field weeds, and in soil biota, the agronomist likewise finds more than sufficient complexity to test his scientific understanding and technological skill.

Figure 20.7: The figures in this table are derived primarily from Statistical Abstract of the United States.

Figures 20.9 and 20.10: The development of hybrid corn, perhaps the first "practical" result from the science of genetics, is discussed in most genetics textbooks (see "Teacher's References" for Chapter 16, guide page 258).

Figure 20.11: The scene is in Los Angeles, but smog conditions develop at times in almost every large city.

Pages 685-689: Wildlife and forests seem to have an intrinsic appeal for the fifteen- or sixteen-year-old male. This is as pronounced in urban as in rural areas. A majority of students majoring in forestry and wildlife management now come from urban areas; and agricultural research, if not agricultural practice, increasingly draws its recruits from the cities.

Figure 20.15: See J. C. Greenway, Extinct and Vanishing Birds of the World (1958); G. M. Allen, Extinct and Vanishing Mammals of the Western Hemisphere with the Marine Species of All the Oceans (1942); and F. Harper, Extinct and Vanishing Mammals of the Old World (1945)—all published by the American Committee for International Wildlife Protection, New York.

Figure 20.18: Of course the form of the graph bears a striking resemblance to the one drawn in Exercise 2.1, but students should be cautioned concerning the dangers of extrapolation.

Page 695: A summary for Chapter 20—a chapter that looks both backward and forward—seems inappropriate. Instead, the authors felt that a fitting close to the textbook would be the words with which Charles Darwin, rising above his customary pedestrian style, grandly concluded the Origin of Species.

SUPPLEMENTARY MATERIALS

Teacher's References

ANDERSON, E. Plants, Man and Life. Boston: Little, Brown & Co., 1952. (A botanist, addressing a nontechnical readership, discusses the effects of man upon vegetation, especially with respect to "weeds" and cultivated plants.)
BROWN, H. The Challenge of Man's Future. New York: The Viking Press, Inc., 1954. (More recent surveys of the problems of human populations and resources exist, but this is still one of the most scholarly, balanced, and inclusive.)
CLEPPER, H. (ed.). Careers in Conservation. New York: The Ronald Press Co., 1963. (Useful information for counseling students with an interest in natural resources.)
DUBOS, RENÉ. Mirage of Health. New York: Harper & Brothers, 1959. (A thoughtful essay on the world health problem by a distinguished member of the Rockefeller Institute.)

FROMAN, R. Wanted: Amateur Scientists. New York: David
McKay Co., Inc., 1963. ("This book is not a compilation
of science fair projects but ... will give him [the student]
incentive and encouragement and it may win him for science
after the fairs are over."—From a review in Science)

LANDSBERG, H. H., L. L. FISCHMAN, and J. L. FISHER.
Resources in America's Future. Baltimore: Johns Hopkins
Press, 1963. (A recent authoritative survey.)

LORD, R. The Care of the Earth: a History of Husbandry.
Camden, N. J.: Thomas Nelson & Sons, 1962. Also in
paperback—New York: The New American Library of
World Literature, Inc., 1963. (Although this book begins
with prehistory and ranges throughout the world, the main
theme is the relatively brief career of Anglo-American
agriculture and the ecological basis for any continuing
cultivation of the soil.)

MAY, J. M. (ed.). Studies in Disease Ecology. New York:
Hafner Publishing Co., Inc., 1961. (Emphasizes infectious diseases that are still serious morbidity and
mortality factors, especially in tropical countries.)

MOOREHEAD, A. No Room in the Ark. New York: Harper
& Brothers, 1959. (Not science, but the work of an intelligent and perspicacious journalist; a survey of conditions in
an area—Africa—where human populations are pressing
dramatically upon a wildlife still reminiscent of the great
Age of Mammals.)

THOMAS, W. L. (ed.). Man's Role in Changing the Face of the
Earth. Chicago: University of Chicago Press, 1956. (A
survey by many experts of the activities of man—past and
present—in modifying ecosystems.)

TURNBULL, C. M. The Forest People. New York: Doubleday
& Co., Inc., 1962. (An excellent account of primitive man
in modern times—the pygmies of the Congo—and of their
close ecological relationships with their environment.)

UDALL, S. L. The Quiet Crisis. New York: Holt, Rinehart
& Winston, Inc., 1963. ("An attempt to outline the land-
and-people story of our continent," this book adopts a
historical approach to resource conservation and proceeds
to view the future with a deep ecological understanding.)

WINSLOW, C.-E. The Conquest of Epidemic Disease.
Princeton, N. J.: Princeton University Press, 1953. (A
historical treatment.)

APPENDIX **A**

REFERENCES RECOMMENDED IN THE TEXTBOOK

In the textbook an effort has been made to limit the number of titles listed as "Suggested Readings" at the end of each chapter. Further, some preference has been given to books available in paperback editions. The intention is to encourage the formation of classroom libraries where books may be constantly available to students, leaving the school library as a place for more extensive research. There many of the books listed in the previous pages of this guide should be shelved.

In this appendix all of the books in the "Suggested Readings" are brought together. Following each title is a listing of the Green Version text chapters in which the title is cited. Begin your classroom library with the titles that are recommended for use with two or more chapters.

The following information has been added after the chapter listings for your information:

1. If the title has been issued only as a paperback by the publisher listed, P has been added.

2. If the title has been produced in both hardbound and paperback editions by the publisher listed, H & P has been added.

In cases where a hardbound edition has been issued by one publisher and reprinted as a paperback edition by another, you are so informed within the entry.

ANDREWARTHA, H. G. Introduction to the Study of Animal Populations. Chicago: University of Chicago Press, 1961. (For use with text Chapters 2, 11.)

ASIMOV, I. Chemicals of Life: Enzymes, Vitamins, Hormones. New York: Abelard-Schuman, Ltd., 1954. (For use with text Chapter 12.)

BARNETT, L., and Life Editorial Staff. The World We Live In. New York: Time, Inc., 1955. (For use with text Chapter 8.)

BATES, M. The Forest and the Sea. New York: Random House, Inc., 1960. Also available in paperback—New York: New American Library of World Literature, Inc., 1961. (For use with text Chapters 1, 3, 7, 8, 9, 18, 19.)

_____. Man in Nature. Englewood Cliffs, N.J.: Prentice-Hall, Inc., 1961. (For use with text Chapter 20.) H & P

_____. The Prevalence of People. New York: Charles Scribner's Sons, 1956. (For use with text Chapter 20.) H & P

BENTON, A. H., and W. E. WERNER. Principles of Field Biology and Ecology. New York: McGraw-Hill Book Co., Inc., 1958. (For use with text Chapters 2, 5.)

BONNER, D. M. Heredity. Englewood Cliffs, N.J.: Prentice-Hall, Inc., 1961. (For use with text Chapter 16.) H & P

BUCHSBAUM, R. M. Animals without Backbones. Rev. ed. Chicago: University of Chicago Press, 1948. (For use with text Chapter 4.)

_____, and M. BUCHSBAUM. Basic Ecology. Pittsburgh: The Boxwood Press, 1957. (For use with text Chapters 1, 3.) H & P

_____, AND OTHERS. The Lower Animals. New York: Doubleday & Co., Inc., 1960. (For use with text Chapter 4.)

BURNET, F. M. Viruses and Man. Baltimore: Penguin Books, Inc., 1953. (For use with text Chapter 6.) P

CARSON, R. The Sea around Us. New York: Simon and Schuster, Inc., 1958. Also available in paperback—New York: New American Library of World Literature, Inc. (For use with text Chapter 9.)

_____. Silent Spring. Boston: Houghton Mifflin Co., 1962. (For use with text Chapter 20.)

CHRISTENSEN, C. M. Molds and Man; an Introduction to the Fungi. Minneapolis: University of Minnesota Press, 1951. (For use with text Chapter 5.)

COCHRAN, D. M. Living Amphibians of the World. New York: Doubleday and Co., Inc., 1961. (For use with text Chapter 4.)

COKER, R. E. Streams, Lakes, Ponds. Chapel Hill, N.C.: University of North Carolina Press, 1954. (For use with text Chapter 9.)

COLBERT, E. H. Dinosaurs: Their Discovery and Their World. New York: E. P. Dutton & Co., Inc., 1961. (For use with text Chapter 10.)

D'AMOUR, F. E. Basic Physiology. Chicago: University of Chicago Press, 1961. (For use with text Chapter 14.)

DARWIN, C. The Origin of Species. New York: New American Library of World Literature, Inc., 1958. (For use with text Chapter 17.) P

DE KRUIF, P. Microbe Hunters. New York: Pocket Books Inc., 1926. (For use with text Chapter 6.) P

DETHIER, V. G., and E. STELLAR. Animal Behavior, Its Evolutionary and Neurological Basis. Englewood Cliffs, N.J.: Prentice-Hall, Inc., 1961. (For use with text Chapter 18.) H & P

DOBELL, C. (ed.). Antony van Leeuwenhoek and His Little Animals. New York: Dover Publications, Inc., 1960. (For use with text Chapter 6.) P

DOBZHANSKY, T. Evolution, Genetics, and Man. New York: John Wiley & Sons, Inc., 1955. (For use with text Chapter 17.)

_____. Mankind Evolving: The Evolution of the Human Species. New Haven, Conn.: Yale University Press, 1962. (For use with text Chapter 20.)

DREW, J. Man, Microbe, and Malady. Baltimore: Penguin Books, Inc., 1954. (For use with text Chapter 7.) P

ELTON, C. S. The Ecology of Invasions by Animals and Plants.
New York: John Wiley & Sons, Inc., 1958. (For use with
text Chapter 11.)

FARB, P. Living Earth. New York: Harper & Brothers, 1959.
Also available in paperback—New York: Worlds of Science,
Pyramid Publications, Inc., 1962. (For use with text
Chapter 7.)

FOGG, G. E. The Growth of Plants. Baltimore: Penguin Books,
Inc., 1963. (For use with text Chapter 13.) P

FROBISHER, M. Fundamentals of Microbiology. 7th ed. Philadelphia: W. B. Saunders Co., 1962. (For use with text
Chapter 7.)

GABRIEL, M. L., and S. FOGEL (eds.). Great Experiments in
Biology. Englewood Cliffs, N.J.: Prentice-Hall, Inc., 1955.
(For use with text Chapters 7, 13, 15.) P

GALE, A. H. Epidemic Diseases. Baltimore: Penguin Books,
Inc., 1959. (For use with text Chapter 7.) P

GALSTON, A. W. The Life of the Green Plant. Englewood
Cliffs, N. J.: Prentice-Hall, Inc., 1961. (For use with
text Chapter 13.) H & P

GERARD, R. Unresting Cells. New York: Harper & Brothers,
1961. (For use with text Chapter 12.) H & P

GILLIARD, E. T. Living Birds of the World. New York:
Doubleday & Co., Inc., 1958. (For use with text
Chapter 4.)

GOLDSTEIN, P. Genetics Is Easy. New York: The Viking
Press, Inc., 1961. (For use with text Chapter 16.)

GRAY. J. How Animals Move. New York: Cambridge University
Press, 1953. (For use with text Chapter 14.)

GREULACH. V. A., and J. E. ADAMS. Plants: An Introduction
to Modern Botany. New York: John Wiley & Sons, Inc.,
1962. (For use with text Chapters 13, 15.)

HARRISON, R. J. Man, the Peculiar Animal. Baltimore:
Penguin Books, Inc., 1958. (For use with text
Chapter 19.) P

HERALD, E. S. Living Fishes of the World. New York:
Doubleday & Co., Inc., 1961. (For use with text Chapter 4.)

HOGARTH, P., and J-J. SALOMON. Prehistory. New York:
Dell Publishing Co., Inc., 1962. (For use with text
Chapter 19.) P

HONEGGER, W., H. BURLA, and M. SCHNITTER. Genetics,
Heredity, Environment, and Personality. New York: Dell
Publishing Co., 1962. (For use with text Chapter 16.) P

HYLANDER, C. J. World of Plant Life. 2nd ed. New York:
The Macmillan Co., Publishers, 1956. (For use with
text Chapter 5.)

JAHN, T. L., and F. F. JAHN. How to Know the Protozoa. Dubuque, Iowa: William C. Brown Co., 1950. (For use with text Chapter 6.) H & P

KENDEIGH, S. C. Animal Ecology. Englewood Cliffs, N. J.: Prentice-Hall, Inc., 1961. (For use with text Chapters 2, 8, 9, 11.)

KLOTS, A. B., and E. B. KLOTS. Living Insects of the World. New York: Doubleday & Co., Inc., 1959. (For use with text Chapter 4.)

LORENZ, K. Z. King Solomon's Ring. New York: The Thomas Y. Crowell Co., 1952. (For use with text Chapter 18.) H & P

MC ELROY, W. D. Cellular Physiology and Biochemistry. Englewood Cliffs, N. J.: Prentice-Hall, Inc., 1961. (For use with text Chapter 12.) H & P

MALTHUS, T., J. HUXLEY, and F. OSBORN. On Population: Three Essays. New York: New American Library of World Literature, Inc., 1960. (For use with text Chapter 20.) P

MAVOR, J. W. General Biology. 5th ed. New York: The Macmillan Co., Publishers, 1959. (For use with text Chapter 3.)

MERCER, E. H. Cells: Their Structure and Function. New York: Doubleday & Co., Inc., 1962. (For use with text Chapter 12.) P

MOMENT, G. B. General Zoology. Boston: Houghton Mifflin Co., 1958. (For use with text Chapters 4, 6, 15, 18.)

MONTAGU, A. Man: His First Million Years. New York: New American Library of World Literature, Inc., 1958. (For use with text Chapter 19.) P

ODUM, E. P. In Collaboration with HOWARD T. ODUM. Fundamentals of Ecology. Philadelphia: W. B. Saunders Co., 1959. (For use with text Chapters 1, 2, 3, 8, 9.)

OOSTING, H. J. The Study of Plant Communities. San Francisco: W. H. Freeman & Co., Publishers, 1956. (For use with text Chapters 3, 7, 8, 11.)

PEATTIE, D. C. Natural History of Trees of Eastern and Central North America. Boston: Houghton Mifflin Co., 1950. (For use with text Chapter 5.)

_____. Natural History of Western Trees. Boston: Houghton Mifflin Co., 1953. (For use with text Chapter 5.)

PETERS, J. A. Classic Papers in Genetics. Englewood Cliffs, N. J.: Prentice-Hall, Inc., 1959. (For use with text Chapter 16.) P

RAHN, O. Microbes of Merit. New York: The Ronald Press Co., 1945. (For use with text Chapter 6.)

REED, W. M. The Earth for Sam, ed. P. F. BRANDWEIN. Rev. ed. New York: Harcourt, Brace and Co., 1960. (For use with text Chapter 10.)

_____, and W. S. BRONSON. The Sea for Sam, ed.
P. F. BRANDWEIN. Rev. ed. New York: Harcourt,
Brace and Co. , 1960. (For use with text Chapter 9.)

SANDERSON, I. T. Living Mammals of the World. New York:
Doubleday & Co. , Inc. , 1955. (For use with text Chapter 4.)

SCHMIDT, K. P. , and R. F. INGER. Living Reptiles of the
World. New York: Doubleday & Co. , Inc. , 1957. (For
use with text Chapter 4.)

SCHMIDT-NIELSEN, K. Animal Physiology. Englewood Cliffs,
N. J. : Prentice-Hall, Inc. , 1960. (For use with text
Chapter 14.) H & P

SCHWARTZ, G. , and P. BISHOP (eds.). Moments of Discovery.
2 vols. New York: Basic Books, Inc. , 1958. (For use
with text Chapter 12.)

SCOTT, J. P. Animal Behavior. Chicago: University of Chicago
Press, 1958. Also available in paperback—New York:
Doubleday & Co. , Inc. , 1963. (For use with text Chapter 18.)

SEARS, P. B. Where There Is Life. New York: Dell Publishing
Co. , Inc. , 1962. (For use with text Chapter 20.) P

SIMPSON, G. G. Life of the Past. New Haven, Conn. : Yale
University Press, 1953. (For use with text
Chapter 10.) H & P

_____, C. S. PITTENDRIGH, and L. H. TIFFANY. Life:
An Introduction to Biology. New York: Harcourt, Brace
and Co. , 1957. (For use with text Chapters 1, 2, 3, 8, 10,
11, 12, 14, 15, 16, 17, 18.)

SINGER, C. A History of Biology. Rev. ed. New York: Henry
Schuman, Inc. , 1950. (For use with text Chapter 20.)

SMITH, J. M. The Theory of Evolution. Baltimore: Penguin
Books, Inc. , 1958. (For use with text Chapter 17.) P

SPRUNT, A. , and H. S. ZIM. Gamebirds. New York: Simon
and Schuster, Inc. , 1961. (For use with text Chapter 4.) P

STORER, J. H. The Web of Life (A First Book of Ecology).
New York: The Devin-Adair Co. , 1953. Also available in
paperback—New York: New American Library of World
Literature, Inc. , 1956. (For use with text Chapter 1.)

SUSSMAN, M. Animal Growth and Development. Englewood
Cliffs, N. J. : Prentice-Hall, Inc. , 1960. (For use with
text Chapter 15.) H & P

SWANSON, C. P. The Cell. Englewood Cliffs, N. J. : Prentice-
Hall, Inc. , 1960. (For use with text Chapter 12.) H & P

TIFFANY, L. H. Algae: The Grass of Many Waters. 2nd ed.
Springfield, Ill. : Charles C. Thomas, Publishers, 1958.
(For use with text Chapter 5.)

VILLEE, C. A. Biology. 4th ed. Philadelphia: W. B. Saunders
Co. , 1962. (For use with text Chapters 2, 7, 10, 12, 13,
14, 16, 19.)

WALKER, K. Human Physiology. Baltimore: Penguin Books, Inc. , 1956. (For use with text Chapter 14.) P

WALLACE, B. , and A. M. SRB. Adaptation. Englewood Cliffs, N.J.: Prentice-Hall, Inc. , 1961. (For use with text Chapter 17.) H & P

WATTS, M. T. Reading the Landscape. New York: The Macmillan Co. , Publishers, 1957. (For use with text Chapter 8.)

WILSON, C. L. , and W. E. LOOMIS. Botany. 3rd ed. New York: Holt, Rinehart, & Winston, Inc. , 1962. (For use with text Chapters 6, 10, 13.)

ZIM, H. S. Plants: A Guide to Plant Hobbies. New York: Harcourt, Brace & Co. , Inc. , 1947. (For use with text Chapter 5.)

_____, and C. COTTAM. Insects. Rev. ed. New York: Simon and Schuster, Inc. , 1956. (For use with text Chapter 4.) P

_____, and I. N. GABRIELSON. Birds. New York: Simon and Schuster, Inc. , 1956. (For use with text Chapter 4.) P

_____, and D. F. HOFFMEISTER. Mammals. New York: Simon and Schuster, Inc. , 1955. (For use with text Chapter 4.) P

_____, and H. H. SHOEMAKER. Fishes. New York: Simon and Schuster, Inc. , 1957. (For use with text Chapter 4.) P

_____, and H. M. SMITH. Reptiles and Amphibians. Rev. ed. New York: Simon and Schuster, Inc. , 1956. (For use with text Chapter 4.) P

APPENDIX **B**

SUMMARY OF
MATERIALS AND EQUIPMENT

The consolidated lists of materials and equipment on the following pages may prove helpful for teachers or supervisors who are planning to use the <u>Green</u> <u>Version</u> exercises for the first time. They may also serve as a yearly checklist in school systems that must order supplies six months to a year in advance. In using the lists, keep these points in mind:

1. The lists cover "BASIC" exercises only; they include only materials and equipment <u>required</u> for implementing the course.[1] Undoubtedly teachers will want to use some of the "Highly Recommended" and "Optional" exercises—at least as individual or team projects. Moreover, most teachers will devise exercises of their own. For such additions ordering can best be done by dealing with each exercise separately. However, if the teacher wants an inclusive list—one that covers all the exercises in the manual—he can find one in BSCS Newsletter #21 (April, 1964).

2. Some items are omitted from the lists. These are items easily obtained from students (e.g., cardboard boxes, food samples) and organisms that are a matter of choice (e.g., those in Exercises 1.1, 5.1, 5.2, and 8.1).

3. Substitutes are feasible for some of the listed items. For suggestions check the guide notes on each exercise.

4. Quantities for one class are specified on the basis of thirty pupils, usually working as six teams. In calculating the quantities needed for four classes, the authors have allowed for the possibility of reusing equipment. This is not always a simple matter; it often depends upon the opportunities for cleanup between periods or the possibilities of staggering exercises among classes. An experienced teacher and a supervisor have coöperated in making the decisions.

5. If a school has more than one biology teacher, the quantities needed are not necessarily obtained by multiplying the quantities required for one teacher by the number of teachers. Again this is not a simple matter; each school must consider the physical feasibility of sharing equipment, the possibilities of staggering topics and exercises, and even the temperaments of the teachers involved.

6. For the most part, estimates are close to minimal, with only a small allowance for loss and breakage. However, customary dealers' units have been used; therefore, 4 ounces of a chemical may be listed for one class when 4 ounces is also a sufficient quantity for four classes.

---

[1] Materials and equipment for "Alternate BASIC" Exercises 15.4 and 15.5 are not included.

MATERIALS

Item	1 Class	4 Classes	Exercises
Acetic acid, glacial	1 lb	1 lb	12.4, 14.4
Acetone	1 lb	3 lb	13.1
Agar, granulated	1 lb	1 lb	7.2, 7.3, 16.3
Agrobacterium tumefaciens (See Bacteria cultures.)			
Alcohol:			
ethyl, 95%	1 gal	1 gal	12.4
isopropyl, 70%	1 gal	1 gal	19.2
Aluminum foil	2 rolls	4 rolls	2.2
Bacteria cultures:			
Agrobacterium			
tumefaciens	1	4	7.3
Sarcina lutea	1	4	7.2
Serratia marcescens	1	4	7.2
Beans, dried	1 lb	2 lb	6.1
Beef extract	4 oz	8 oz	7.2, 7.3
Benedict's solution (or			
Fehling's solution—			
A and B)	1 lb	3 lb	12.2
Betta (See Fish.)			
Bile salts	4 oz	4 oz	14.2
Bleach (See Fungicide.)			
Bouillon cubes	1 jar	2 jars	6.2
Bromthymol blue solu-			
tion, aqueous	1 oz	2 oz	1.3
Carnoy's fluid, with			
chloroform	150 ml	500 ml	12.4
Cellulose tubing	50 ft	50 ft	12.3
Chalk, 3 colors	2 sticks per color	8 sticks per color	14.4
Cheesecloth	1 yd^2	4 yd^2	13.1
Chloroform	1 lb	1 lb	3.1
Cleansing tissue	1 box	2 boxes	13.1
Clinitest tablets (See Tes-tape.)			
Collodion	1 lb	1 lb	13.2
Copper sulfate,			
anhydrous	1 lb	1 lb	12.4
Cord, cotton	1 ball	1 ball	7.1, 14.1
Cornmeal	1 lb	3 lb	16.3
Cornstarch	1 lb	1 lb	6.1
Corydoras (See Fish.)			

Item	1 Class	4 Classes	Exercises
Cotton:			
absorbent	1 lb	3 lb	6.2, 13.4, 14.4, 19.2
nonabsorbent	1 lb	4 lb	7.2
Crayons, glass-marking	3 doz	6 doz	general use
Crystal-violet solution	1 oz	2 oz	7.3
Daphnia (living)	1 culture	3 cultures	14.3
Dextrose, C. P.			
(glucose)	5 lb	5 lb	2.2, 7.3, 12.2, 12.3, 16.3
Distilled water	10 gal	40 gal	2.2, 7.2, 7.3, 14.1
Drosophila (See Fruit flies.)			
Egg albumen	4 oz	4 oz	12.2
Eggs, chicken, fer-			
tilized, unincu-			
bated	36	144	15.3
Elodea (Anacharis)	2 bunches	8 bunches	1.3, 12.1
Ethyl ether	1 lb	2 lb	16.3
Fehling's solution (See Benedict's solution.)			
Filter paper (100-mm			
diameter)	5 pkg. (500 sheets)	10 pkg. (1000 sheets)	1.2, 6.1, 6.2, 8.1, 13.1, 15.3
Fish (living):			
Betta (male)	4*	16*	18.1
Corydoras (male)	8*	32*	18.1
Formalin	4 pints	2 gal	3.1
Formalin-acetic alcohol			
(FAA)	1 gal	1 gal	13.3
Frogs (living)	12	48	12.1, 14.1
Fruit flies (living):			
mutant (e.g.,			
"ebony")	1 culture	1 culture	16.3
wild-type	1 culture	1 culture	16.3
Fungicide (sodium			
hypochlorite or			
commercial bleach)	1 quart	1 quart	1.2, 7.3, 8.1
Garlic cloves (or onion			
bulbs)	6	6	12.4
Glucose (See Dextrose.)			

*Quantities based on two teams per class.

Item	1 Class	4 Classes	Exercises
Graph paper:			
semilogarithmic	60 sheets	240 sheets	2.1
square coördinates	500 sheets	2000 sheets	2.1, 2.2, 2.3, 8.2, 13.2, 14.3
Hydrochloric acid	1 lb	5 lb	12.4
Indoleacetic acid in lanolin	1 oz	4 oz	13.4
Iodine—potassium-iodide solution (I_2KI)	8 oz	24 oz	1.5, 12.1, 12.2, 12.3, 13.3
Iron-acetocarmin solution	1 oz	2 oz	12.4
Lens paper	4 books	8 books	1.4, 1.5, and general use
Litmus solution	1 oz	2 oz	14.2
Mealworms (living)	1 culture	2 cultures	14.1
Methylene blue solution	1 oz	3 oz	12.1
Microorganisms (mixed)	1 culture	3 cultures	1.1, 1.5
Millon's reagent	150 ml	500 ml	12.2
Molasses	1 pint	1 pint	1.5
Oats, rolled	1 box	3 boxes	7.1, 16.3
Oil, motor (light)	1 pint	1 pint	16.3
Onion bulbs (<u>See</u> Garlic cloves.)			
Pancreatin	4 oz	4 oz	14.2
Paper clips	1 box	1 box	13.1
Paper cups (small)	200	500	14.4
Paper toweling	12 rolls	48 rolls	general use
Paraffin	1 lb	1 lb	1.3, 6.2
Peppercorns	1 oz	1 oz	6.1
Peptone	4 oz	8 oz	2.2, 7.2, 7.3
Petroleum ether	1 lb	2 lb	13.1
Pins ("bank," or "florist's")	2 boxes	2 boxes	14.1
Pipe cleaners	4 doz	16 doz	15.2
Planarians (living)	24	100	15.1
Plastic bags (sandwich size)	240	500	1.2, 3.1, 8.1, 14.1
Potassium phosphate, monobasic	1 lb	1 lb	2.2
Potatoes, white	6	12	1.5

Item	1 Class	4 Classes	Exercises
Pot labels, wooden	100	200	7.3, 13.4, 18.2
Proprionic acid	4 oz	4 oz	16.3
Quinine sulfate	4 oz	4 oz	14.4
Ringer's solution (amphibian)	1 quart	1 gal	12.1
Rubber bands (assorted)	1 box	2 boxes	general use
Sand:			
coarse	20 lb	50 lb	18.2
fine (washed)	20 lb	50 lb	7.1, 13.1
Sarcina lutea (See Bacteria cultures.)			
Seeds:			
bean	1 lb	2 lb	7.3, 13.4
corn (field-type)	1 lb	2 lb	13.3
lettuce	1 pkg.	2 pkg.	1.2, 8.1
morning-glory (Scarlett O'Hara)	2 pkg.	4 pkg.	18.2
radish	3 pkg.	8 pkg.	1.2, 8.1, 18.2
sunflower	2 pkg.	4 pkg.	1.2, 8.1
tobacco (75% albino, 25% green)	1 pkg.	4 pkg.	16.1
tomato	3 pkg.	8 pkg.	1.2, 8.1
vetch	4 oz	1 lb	1.2, 8.1
Serratia marcescens (See Bacteria cultures.)			
Serums, blood-testing, anti-a and anti-b	1 set	2 sets	19.2
Snails (living)	12	48	1.3
Sodium chloride	1 lb	5 lb	14.1, 14.4, 15.3
Sodium hydroxide	1 lb	1 lb	1.5
Sodium hypochlorite (See Fungicide.)			
Soil, garden	1 bu	4 bu	6.1, 7.1
Spinach	1 lb	4 lb	13.1
Stakes, wooden	48	48	3.1
Starch, soluble	4 oz	1 lb	12.2, 12.3
String (See Cord.)			
Sucrose	1 lb	5 lb	14.1, 14.4
Sudan IV solution	1 oz	2 oz	12.2
Tempera paints (assorted colors)	1 set	2 sets	18.1
Tes-tape (or Clinitest tablets)	1 roll	2 rolls	12.3, 13.3

Item	1 Class	4 Classes	Exercises
Toothpicks:			
flat	1 box (500)	1 box	13.4, 14.2, 14.4
round	1 box (500)	2 boxes	12.1, 12.4, 19.2
Tradescantia flowers	6	24	12.1
Vegetable oil, cottonseed			
or peanut	4 oz	1 pint	12.2
Wrapping paper	1 roll	2 rolls	15.2
Yeast:			
brewers'	4 oz	8 oz	16.3
dried	3 pkg.	12 pkg.	1.5, 2.2, 16.3
Yeast extract	4 oz	4 oz	2.2

EQUIPMENT

Item	1 Class	4 Classes	Exercises
Aquariums	2	2	14.1
Autoclave (or pressure			
cooker)	1	1	2.2, 6.2, 7.2
Balance	1	2	2.2, 7.2
Battery jars, large	2	4	13.2
Beads, poppit, 2 colors	216 each color	216 each color	15.2
Beakers, Griffin, low-form:			
50-ml	24	24	8.1, 12.4, 14.3
100-ml	12	12	12.4
250-ml	36	36	1.2, 6.2, 7.3, 13.3, 14.4, 16.1
600-ml	12	12	7.2, 12.3, 14.2, 14.3
1000-ml	6	6	6.2, 7.2
Berlese apparatus	3	3	3.1
Bottles, wide-mouth,			
screw-cap:			
2-oz, round	30	120	3.1
4-oz, round	24	96	3.1
4-oz, square	30	60	3.1
8-oz, round	18	64	3.1

Item	1 Class	4 Classes	Exercises
Brushes, water-color, small	6	6	15.1, 16.3, 18.1
Bunsen burners	6	6	general use
Clamps:			
burette	6	24	13.2
pinch or spring	3	3	7.2
Clothesline, plastic (50-ft lengths)	6	6	3.1
Corks:			
assorted sizes	1 pkg. (100)	1 pkg.	13.2
No. 6 size	1 pkg. (100)	2 pkg.	13.1
Cover slips	2 oz	4 oz	1.4, 1.5, 2.2, 6.1, 12.1, 12.4
Culture bottles (glass vials, 25 X 95 mm)	30	120	16.3
Culture tubes, screw-cap, 20 X 150 mm	24	96	1.3
Dishes, deep	24	96	7.1
Dissecting needles (straight)	60	60	5.2, 6.1, 7.3, 12.1
Dissecting pans	6	12	14.1
Etherizers (funnel and shot glass)	6	6	16.3
Files, triangular	6	6	6.2, 18.2
Finger bowls, glass or clear plastic, 250-ml (4-inch diameter)	60	240	1.4, 1.5, 6.1, 15.3
Flasks, Erlenmeyer:			
250-ml	7	28	6.2
500-ml	6	24	13.2
2000-ml	1	2	2.2
Flowerpots:			
3-inch diameter	12	48	7.3
4-inch diameter	24	96	7.1
6-inch diameter, shallow form (or No. 3 tin cans)	36	144	18.2

Item	1 Class	4 Classes	Exercises
Flowerpot saucers (to fit 6-inch pots)	36	144	18.2
Forceps:			
fine-pointed	30	36	12.1, 12.4, 14.1, 15.3, 16.1
student-grade	30	36	1.2, 1.4, 3.1, 6.1, 6.2, 7.3, 8.1, 13.3, 19.2
Funnels, glass, 75-mm diameter	6	6	6.2, 7.2, 13.1
Funnel supports	6	6	13.1
Glass covers, 5-inch squares	24	96	6.1
Glass rods	1/2 lb	1/2 lb	6.2, 7.2, 12.2, 13.2
Glass slides:			
"micro-culture" (with center depression)	6	12	14.3
regular	1/2 gross	1 gross	1.4, 1.5, 2.2, 6.1, 7.3, 12.1, 12.4, 14.1, 15.1, 19.2
Glass tubing, 7- to 8-mm diameter	5 lb	10 lb	6.2, 13.2
Graduated cylinders:			
25-ml	6	12	14.2
100-ml	10	10	2.2, 6.2
500-ml	2	2	7.2
Hammers (or small mallets)	3	3	3.1
Hand lenses	30	48	1.1, 4.1, 5.1, 5.2, 14.1, 15.3, 16.1
Incubator, 50-egg capacity	1	3	8.1, 15.3
Inoculating loops	6	12	7.2, 7.3
Jars, glass:			
1-liter	10*	40*	18.1
4-liter	2*	8*	18.1

*Quantities based on two teams per class.

Item	1 Class	4 Classes	Exercises
Lamps, gooseneck (with 40- to 60-w bulbs)	6	12	2.4, 3.1, 18.2
Lancets, sterile, disposable	30	120	19.2
Medicine droppers	40	80	general use
Microscopes:			
monocular	15-20	15-20	1.1, 1.4, 1.5, 2.2, 5.1, 6.1, 7.3, 12.1, 12.4, 14.1, 15.3, 19.2
stereo	6-10	6-10	1.1, 4.1, 5.1, 6.1, 14.3, 15.1, 15.3, 16.3
Mirrors, plane, 4 X 4 inches or 2 X 6 inches	6	6	18.1
Mortar and pestle	6	6	13.1
Petri dishes, pyrex, 100 X 15 mm	30	120	1.2, 7.1, 7.2, 7.3, 8.1, 13.3, 14.1, 15.1, 16.1
Pipettes:			
1-ml or 5-ml	6	12	13.2, 14.1
10-ml	6	12	7.2
Razor blades	12	24	7.3, 15.1
Refrigerator, 9 to 11 ft^3	1	1	8.1, 14.1
Ring stands	6	12	6.2, 7.2, 13.2, 14.2
Rubber tubing:			
to fit funnel tubes	10 ft	20 ft	7.2
to fit 7- to 8-mm glass tubing	10 ft	20 ft	13.2
Rulers, millimeter, transparent	15	24	1.4
Scalpels	12	12	7.3, 12.1, 12.2, 12.4, 13.2, 13.3, 14.1
Scissors:			
fine-pointed	6	12	15.3
regular	12	12	1.4, 12.4, 13.1, 13.4, 14.1, 15.2, 16.1, 18.1

Item	1 Class	4 Classes	Exercises
Skeletons, mounted:			
cat	1	1	19.1
human	1	1	19.1
Spatulas, stainless-steel,			
4-inch blade	6	6	2.2
Stereomicroscopes (See Microscopes.)			
Stoppers, rubber:			
No. 6, solid	12	48	6.2
No. 6, 1-hole	24	96	6.2
No. 7, 2-hole	6	12	13.2
Test tubes			
16 X 125 mm	120	240	12.2
18 X 150 mm	140	280	2.2, 7.2, 13.1, 14.2
Test-tube holders	12	12	12.2
Test-tube racks	6	12	1.3, 7.2, 12.2, 13.1
Thermometers, -10° to			
+110°C	16	16	7.2, 8.1, 14.2, 14.3, 15.3
Tile, plastic, white	6 squares	6 squares	16.3
Trowels	6	6	3.1
Waste jars	6	6	14.4
Watches (with second			
hand)	6	6	13.2, 14.1, 14.3, 15.3
Watch glasses,			
Syracuse	15	30	14.4, 15.3
Wire basket, 50-tube			
capacity	1	4	7.2

APPENDIX **C**

SOURCES OF SUPPLY

MATERIALS AND EQUIPMENT

The companies listed below have indicated their desire to provide materials and equipment for schools using the BSCS courses. This is not an "official list"—there is none; undoubtedly, other good suppliers are available.

BALTIMORE BIOLOGICAL LABORATORY, INC., 1640 Gorsuch
    Ave., Baltimore, Md. 21218
CALBIOCHEM, 3625 Medford St., Los Angeles 63, Calif.
    161 W. 231 St., New York 63, N. Y.
    4930 Cordell Ave., Bethesda 14, Md.
CAMBOSCO SCIENTIFIC CO., 37 Antwerp St., Brighton 35, Mass.
CAROLINA BIOLOGICAL SUPPLY CO., Burlington, N. C. 27216,
    and POWELL LABORATORIES, Gladstone, Ore. 97027
CENTRAL SCIENTIFIC CO., 1700 N. Irving Park Rd., Chicago 13,
    Ill.
    3232 Eleventh Ave., N., Birmingham 4, Ala.
    160 Washington St., Somerville, Mass.
    6446 Telegraph Rd., Los Angeles, Calif.
    1040 Martin Ave., Santa Clara, Calif.
    237 Sheffield St., Mountainside, N. J.
    6610 Stillwell, Houston 32, Tex.
    6901 E. 12th St., Tulsa 12, Okla.
CLAY-ADAMS, INC., 141 E. 25th St., New York 10, N. Y.
CLINTON MISCO CORP., P. O. Box 1005, Ann Arbor, Mich.
DALE SCIENTIFIC CO., P. O. Box 1721, Ann Arbor, Mich.
FAUST SCIENTIFIC SUPPLY, LTD., 5407 Schlueter Rd.,
    Madison 4, Wis.
GENERAL BIOLOGICAL SUPPLY HOUSE, INC. (Turtox), 8200
    S. Hoyne Ave., Chicago, Ill. 60620
HARVARD APPARATUS CO., INC., Dover, Mass.
THE LEMBERGER CO., P. O. Box 482, Oshkosh, Wis.
MACALESTER SCIENTIFIC CORP., Educational Division,
    253 Norfolk St., Cambridge 39, Mass.
NORTHERN BIOLOGICAL SUPPLY, P. O. Box 222,
    New Richmond, Wis.
POWELL LABORATORIES (See Carolina Biological Supply Co.)
SCIENCE EDUCATION PRODUCTS, Division of B-D Laboratories,
    Inc., San Carlos, Calif.
SCIENTIFIC PRODUCTS, Division of American Hospital Supply
    Corp., 4700 W. Chase St., Lincolnwood, Ill.
    5056 Peachtree Rd., Chamblee, Ga.
    101 Third Ave., Waltham 54, Mass.
    3713 N. Davidson St., Charlotte 5, N. C.
    1586 Frebis Lane, Columbus 6, Ohio
    2505 Butler St., Dallas 35, Tex.
    17150 Southfield Rd., Allen Park, Mich.
    12th Ave. and Gentry St., N. Kansas City 16, Mo.

3815 Valhalia Drive, Burbank, Calif.

1951 Delaware Parkway, Miami 35, Fla.

3846 Washington Ave. , N. Minneapolis 12, Minn.

4408 Catherine Ave. , Metairie, La.

40-05 168 St. , Flushing 48, Long Island, N. Y.

150 Jefferson Drive, Menlo Park, Calif.

14850 N. E. 36 St. , Bellevue, Wash.

3175 V. St. , N. E. , Washington 18, D. C.

SHERWIN SCIENTIFIC CO. , 1112 Ruby St. , Spokane 2, Wash.

TRAVEL-LAB SCIENCE CO. , P. O. Drawer M, Manor 1, Tex.

VAN WATERS & ROGERS, INC. , P. O. Box 5287, Denver, Colo.

BKH Division:

P. O. Box 3200, San Francisco 19, Calif.

850 S. River Rd. , W. , Sacramento, Calif.

650 W. 8 St. , S. , Salt Lake City 4, Utah

313 Kamakee St. , Honolulu 14, Hawaii

Scientific Supplies Co. Division:

600 S. Spokane St. , Seattle 4, Wash.

3950 N. W. Yeon Ave. , Portland 10, Ore.

Braun Division:

1363 S. Bonnie Beach Place, Los Angeles 54, Calif.

P. O. Box 1391, San Diego 12, Calif.

P. O. Box 1431, Phoenix, Ariz.

2030 E. Broadway, Tucson, Ariz.

324 Industrial Ave. , N. E. , Albuquerque, N. M.

6980 Market Ave. , El Paso, Tex.

WARD'S NATURAL SCIENCE ESTABLISHMENT, INC. ,

P. O. Box 1712, Rochester 3, N. Y.

P. O. Box 1749, Monterey, Calif.

WELCH SCIENTIFIC CO. , 1515 Sedgwick, Chicago 10, Ill.

331 E. 38th St. , New York 16, N. Y.

AUDIOVISUAL MATERIALS

This list is restricted to sources cited in the body of this guide.

AIBS Films (See McGraw-Hill.)

COLUMBIA RECORDS, Educational Department, 799 Seventh Ave. , New York, N. Y. 10019

CONTEMPORARY FILMS, 614 Davis St. , Evanston, Ill.

267 W. 25th St. , New York 1, N. Y.

1211 Polk St. , San Francisco 9, Calif.

CORONET FILMS, Coronet Building, 65 E. South Water St. , Chicago 1, Ill.

ENCYCLOPAEDIA BRITANNICA FILMS, INC. , 1150 Wilmette Ave. , Wilmette, Ill.

FILM ASSOCIATES OF CALIFORNIA, 11014 Santa Monica Blvd. ,
    Los Angeles 25, Calif.
FOLKWAYS RECORDS AND SERVICE CORP. , 165 W. 46th St. ,
    New York, N. Y. 10036
HARCOURT, BRACE AND WORLD, 757 Third Ave. , New York 17,
    N. Y.
WILLIAM HARLOW, Syracuse 10, N. Y.
INDIANA UNIVERSITY FILMS, Indiana University Audiovisual
    Center, Bloomington, Ind.
INTERNATIONAL FILM BUREAU, INC. , 332 S. Michigan Ave. ,
    Chicago, Ill. 60604
LIFE FILMSTRIPS, Time and Life Building, 9 Rockefeller Plaza,
    New York 20, N. Y.
McGRAW-HILL BOOK CO. , INC. , Text-Film Division,
    330 W. 42nd St. , New York 36, N. Y.
METROPOLITAN LIFE INSURANCE CO. , 1 Madison Ave. ,
    New York 10, N. Y.
NATIONAL FILM BOARD OF CANADA, Canada House, 680 Fifth
    Ave. , New York 19, N. Y.
A. J. NYSTROM AND CO. , 3333 Elston Ave. , Chicago,
    Ill. 60618
SHELL OIL CO. , 50 W. 50th St. , New York 20, N. Y.
SOCIETY FOR VISUAL EDUCATION, INC. , 1345 W. Diversey
    Parkway, Chicago 14, Ill.
THORNE FILMS, INC. , 1229 University Ave. , Boulder, Colo.
UNITED WORLD FILMS, INC. , 1445 Park Ave. , New York 29,
    N. Y.
UNIVERSITY OF CALIFORNIA, Department of Visual Education,
    Berkeley, Calif.
WARD'S NATURAL SCIENCE ESTABLISHMENT, INC. ,
    P. O. Box 1712, Rochester 3, N. Y.
    P. O. Box 1749, Monterey, Calif.